ENGINEERING ECONOMY

PRENTICE-HALL INTERNATIONAL, INC., *London*
PRENTICE-HALL OF AUSTRALIA, PTY., LTD., *Sydney*
PRENTICE-HALL OF CANADA, LTD., *Toronto*
PRENTICE-HALL OF INDIA (PRIVATE) LTD., *New Delhi*
PRENTICE-HALL OF JAPAN, INC., *Tokyo*
PRENTICE-HALL DE MEXICO, S.A., *Mexico City*

ENGINEERING ECONOMY

THIRD EDITION

H. G. Thuesen

Head Emeritus

W. J. Fabrycky

Assistant Professor

School of Industrial Engineering and Management

Oklahoma State University

Prentice-Hall, Inc., *Englewood Cliffs, N.J.*

© 1950, 1957, and 1964 by
PRENTICE-HALL, INC.
Englewood Cliffs, N.J.

Library of Congress Catalog Card Number 64-10139
Printed in the United States of America
73029C

PREFACE TO THE THIRD EDITION

The aim of this Third Edition of *Engineering Economy*, as with previous editions, is to extend the engineer's quantitative thinking to situations involving both engineering and economic factors. Throughout the text, we emphasize that the essential prerequisite of successful engineering application is economic feasibility. Our objective is to help the reader grasp the significance of the economic aspects of engineering, and to become proficient in the evaluation of engineering proposals in terms of worth and cost.

The engineering approach to problem solution has advanced and broadened to the extent that success, as an engineer, often depends upon both the ability to deal with economic aspects and physical aspects of the environment. Down through history, the limiting factor has been predominantly physical, but with the development of science, goods and services have become physically possible that may not have utility. Fortunately, the engineer can readily extend his inherent ability of analysis to embrace economic factors. To aid him in so doing is a primary aim of this book.

The subject matter has been completely reorganized and extensively rewritten to accommodate new concepts, principles, and methods of analysis. A six-section classification has been adopted which serves to consolidate similar topics and to assist in the logical development and presentation of the material.

Interest formulas have been extended beyond the annual compounding assumption to include the frequently used cases of continuous compounding and the funds-flow process. The method of designating interest factors for the annual compounding case has been expanded to include these developments. Additional sets of tables have been added to facilitate their application.

A tabular approach to the derivation and explanation of depreciation models is included with special emphasis on the fact that capital

v

recovery plus return is equivalent for all models. The development of interest formulas, the concept of equivalence, and depreciation calculation comprise one section providing prerequisite material for subsequent sections.

Economy analysis applicable to the comparison of engineering alternatives, break-even and minimum cost analysis, the evaluation of replacements, the utilization of personnel, and the evaluation of public activities are grouped into one section. In this section, the reader will find numerous examples of the fruitful application of engineering economy analysis.

Accounting, cost accounting, and income taxes follow as areas to be explored after fundamental skills in economy analysis are gained. Although accounting and tax considerations are mentioned whenever appropriate, this special treatment is justified to provide a more complete understanding.

The last section concerns itself with analysis procedures applicable to the evaluation of operational alternatives and is presented under the title of Operations Economy. The many similarities of engineering economy and operations research become evident from a study of this section.

Throughout the text, numerous illustrations and examples are employed to assist in fixing concepts, principles, and methods in the reader's mind. A completely revised set of problems is presented at the end of each chapter to illustrate the application of concepts and to provide practice in analysis.

It is our pleasure to acknowledge the stimulation provided by the many students who have consented to the testing and use of this material in the classroom. Specific thanks are due Mr. P. F. Ostwald and Mr. D. A. Pierce for their willingness to use portions of the new material in their classes. Without this testing opportunity, the value of the material for instruction would be questionable.

Indebtedness is acknowledged to Mr. P. M. Ghare who provided valuable assistance in the preparation of many key sections and to Dr. R. W. Gibson for reading the manuscript and making suggestions for improvement. Miss Velda D. Davis deserves special credit for competent assistance in the preparation of the manuscript.

H. G. Thuesen
W. J. Fabrycky

CONTENTS

Part I

INTRODUCTION TO ENGINEERING ECONOMY

Part III

PLANNING ENGINEERING ECONOMY ANALYSIS

9 TREATMENT OF ESTIMATES IN ECONOMY ANALYSIS   193

Part IV

ENGINEERING ECONOMY ANALYSIS

10 BASES FOR COMPARSION OF ALTERNATIVES   213

11 BREAK-EVEN AND MINIMUM COST ANALYSIS   239

Part V

ACCOUNTING, COST ACCOUNTING, AND INCOME TAXES

Part VI

OPERATIONS ECONOMY

18 EVALUATION OF PROPOSED OPERATIONS 437

APPENDICES

INDEX 519

ENGINEERING
ECONOMY

PART I

INTRODUCTION TO ENGINEERING ECONOMY

CHAPTER 1

ENGINEERING ECONOMY
AND THE ENGINEERING PROCESS

The engineer is confronted with two environments, the physical and the economic. His success in manipulating or altering the physical environment to produce products or services depends upon his knowledge of physical laws. However, the worth of these products and services lies in their utility measured in economic terms. There are numerous examples of structures, machines, and processes that exhibit excellent physical design but possess little economic merit. For this reason, it is essential that engineering proposals be evaluated in terms of worth and cost before they are undertaken. Therefore, in this chapter and throughout the text, we emphasize that the essential prerequisite of successful engineering application is economic feasibility.

1.1. ENGINEERING AND SCIENCE

Engineering is not a science but is rather an application of science. It is an art composed of the skill and ingenuity in adapting knowledge to the uses of the human race. As expressed in a definition adopted by the Engineers' Council for Professional Development: "Engineering is the profession in which a knowledge of the mathematical and natural sciences gained by study, experience, and practice is applied with judgment to develop ways to utilize, economically, the materials and forces of nature for the benefit of mankind." In this, as in most other accepted definitions, the applied nature of engineering activity is emphasized.

The purpose of the scientist is to add to mankind's inventory of systematic knowledge and to discover universal laws of behavior. The purpose of the engineer is to *apply* this knowledge to particular situations to produce products and services. To the engineer, knowledge is not an end in itself but is the raw material from which he fashions structures, machines, and processes. Thus, engineering involves the determination of the combination of materials, forces, and human factors that will yield a desired result with a reasonable degree of accuracy. Engineering activities are rarely carried out for the satisfaction that may be derived from them directly. With few exceptions, its use is confined to helping people to satisfy their wants.

Modern civilization rests to a large degree upon engineering. Most products used to facilitate work, communication, and transportation and to furnish sustenance, shelter, and even health are directly or indirectly a result of engineering activity. Engineering has also been instrumental in providing leisure time for pursuing and enjoying culture. Through the development of the printing process, television, and rapid transportation, engineering has provided the means for both cultural and economic improvement of the human race. In addition, engineering has become an essential ingredient in national survival as is evident from the considerable portion of engineering talent that is employed in national defense.

The scientist and engineer form a team that paces modern technology. In science lies the foundation upon which the engineer builds toward the advancement of mankind. With the continued development of science and the widespread application of engineering, the standard of living may be expected to improve and further increase the demand for those things that minister to man's love for the comfortable and beautiful. The fact that these human wants may be expected to engage the attention of engineers to an increasing extent is, in part, the basis for the movement to broaden the humanistic and social content of engineering curricula. A knowledge of economics, sociology, psychology, and the fine arts is now recognized to be useful or essential in most fields of modern engineering.

1.2. THE BI-ENVIRONMENTAL NATURE OF ENGINEERING

The usual function of engineering is to manipulate the elements of one environment, the physical, to create utility in a second environment, the economic. However, engineers are sometimes handicapped by a tendency to disregard economic feasibility and are often appalled in practice by the necessity for meeting situations in which action must be based on estimates and judgment. Yet the modern engineering graduate is increasingly finding himself in positions in which his responsibility is extended to embrace economic factors.

The engineer's approach to the solution of problems has broadened to such an extent that his success may depend as much upon his ability to cope with economic aspects as it does on the physical aspects of the total environment. The engineer can readily extend his inherent ability of analysis to become proficient in the analysis of the economic aspect of engineering application. Furthermore, the engineer who aspires to a creative position in engineering will find proficiency in economic analysis helpful. The large percentage of engineers who will eventually be engaged in managerial activities will find such proficiency a necessity.

Initiative for the use of engineering rests, for the most part, upon those who will concern themselves with social and economic consequences. Therefore, to maintain the initiative, engineers must operate successfully in both the physical and economic segments of the total environment. It is the objective of *engineering economy* to prepare engineers to cope effectively with the bi-environmental requirements of successful engineering application.

1.3. PHYSICAL AND ECONOMIC EFFICIENCY

The objective of engineering application is to get the greatest end result per unit of resource input. This statement is essentially an expression of efficiency which may be stated mathematically as

$$\text{efficiency (physical)} = \frac{\text{output}}{\text{input}}.$$

If interpreted broadly enough, this statement measures the success of engineering activity in the physical environment. However, the engineer must be concerned with two levels of efficiency. On the first level is physical efficiency expressed as outputs divided by inputs of such physical units as Btu's, kilowatts, and foot pounds. When such physical units are involved, efficiency will always be less than unity or less than 100 per cent.

On the second level are economic efficiencies. These are expressed in terms of economic units of output divided by economic units of input, each expressed in terms of an economic medium of equivalence such as money. Economic efficiency may be stated mathematically as

$$\text{efficiency (economic)} = \frac{\text{worth}}{\text{cost}}.$$

It is well known that physical efficiencies over 100 per cent are not possible. However, economic efficiencies can exceed 100 per cent and must do so for economic undertakings to be successful.

Physical efficiency is only indirectly related to economic efficiency. For example, a power plant may be profitable in economic terms even though its physical efficiency in converting units of energy in natural gas to electrical energy may be relatively low. As an example, in the conversion of energy in a certain plant, assume that the physical efficiency is only 14 per cent. Assuming that output Btu's in the form of electrical energy have an economic value of $8 per million and that input Btu's in the form of natural gas have an economic value of $0.70 per million, then

$$\text{efficiency (economic)} = \frac{\text{Btu output} \times \text{value of electricity}}{\text{Btu input} \times \text{value of natural gas}}$$

$$= 0.14 \times \frac{\$8}{\$0.70} = 160 \text{ per cent.}$$

Since physical processes are of necessity carried out at efficiencies of less than 100 per cent and economic ventures are feasible only if they attain efficiencies of greater than 100 per cent, it is clear that the economic worth per unit of physical output must always be greater than the economic cost per unit of physical input in feasible economic ventures. Consequently, economic efficiency must depend more upon the worth and cost per unit of physical outputs and inputs than upon mechanical efficiency. Physical efficiency is always significant, but only to the extent that it contributes to economic efficiency.

In the final evaluation of most ventures, even in those in which engineering plays a leading role, economic efficiencies must take precedence over physical efficiencies. This is because the function of engineering is to create utility in the economic environment by means of altering the elements of the physical environment.

1.4. RESPONSIVE AND CREATIVE ENGINEERING

There are those, and some are engineers, who feel that the engineer should restrict himself to the consideration of the physical and leave the economic and humanistic aspects of engineering to others; some would not even consider these aspects as coming under engineering. This viewpoint may arise in part because those who take pleasure in discovering and applying the well-ordered certainties of the physical environment find it difficult to adjust their thinking to consider the complexities of the economic environment.

Since economic factors are the strategic consideration in most engineering activities, engineering practice may be either responsive or creative. If the engineer takes the attitude that he should restrict himself to the physical he is likely to find that the initiative for the application of engineering has passed on to those who will consider economic and social factors.

The engineer who acts in a responsive manner acts on the initiative of others. The end product of his work has been envisioned by another. Although this position leaves him relatively free from criticism, he gains this freedom at the expense of professional recognition and prestige. In many ways, he is more of a technician than a professional man. Responsive engineering is, therefore, a direct hindrance to the development of the engineering profession.

The creative engineer, on the other hand, not only seeks to overcome physical limitations, but also initiates, proposes, and accepts responsibility for the success of projects involving human and economic factors. General acceptance of this viewpoint of creative engineering will enhance the prestige and profession of engineering since it will bring about the active search by engineers for more efficient utilization of the materials and forces of nature for the benefit of mankind.

Engineers in any capacity have the opportunity to be creative by considering human and economic factors in their work. The machine designer may design tools or machines that will require a minimum of maintenance and that can be operated with less fatigue and greater safety. The highway designer may consider durability, cost, and safety. Engineers in any capacity can see to it that both private and public projects are planned, built, and operated in accordance with good engineering practice. Engineering is an expanding profession.

People have great confidence in the integrity and ability of engineers. Perhaps nothing will enhance the image of the individual engineer and the profession of engineering more than the acceptance of the creative role.

1.5. ENGINEERING ECONOMY DEFINED

The complex equations used in the design and operation of engineering works are not an end in themselves, but are a means for satisfying human wants. Engineering has two aspects. One aspect concerns itself with the materials and physical forces of nature; the other is concerned with the satisfaction of human wants. Thus, engineering is closely associated with economics.

The term *engineering economy* may be defined as a body of knowledge, techniques, and practices of analysis and synthesis involving an attitude toward human factors useful in evaluating the worth of physical products and services in relation to their cost. The noun *economy* means management with thrift. This meaning, coupled with the term *engineering*, embodies the idea of maximum service per unit of cost, through engineering.

The primary function of engineering economy analysis is the quantitative evaluation of engineering proposals in terms of worth and cost before they are undertaken. In this function, engineering economy is analogous to engineering design, whose function is to predict the material, size, and combination of structural elements needed in a structure before the structure is built.

An economy study may be considered to embrace two aspects. One is the collection of data and the other is the mathematical treatment of data so their affects may become more apparent. Neither of these aspects should become an end in itself. Economy studies must have as their ultimate objective the improvement of the want satisfying power of engineering activity. In keeping with the defined objective of engineering economy, the cost of economy studies is only justified when the result is an output of benefits that exceeds cost.

1.6. THE ENGINEERING PROCESS

Man is continually seeking to satisfy his wants. In so doing, he surrenders certain utilities in order to gain others that he values more.

This is essentially an economic process in which the objective is the maximization of economic efficiency.

Engineering is primarily a producer activity that comes into being to satisfy human wants. Its objective is to get the greatest end result per unit of resource expenditure. This is essentially a physical process with the objective being the maximization of physical efficiency.

Want satisfaction in the economic environment and engineering proposals in the physical environment are linked by the production process. Figure 1.1 is a schematic illustration of the relationship that exists between engineering proposals, producer goods, consumer goods, and want satisfaction. Each of these elements fall within the

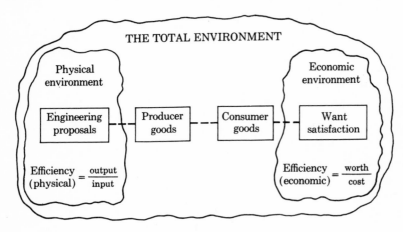

Figure 1.1. The essential steps in want satisfaction.

total environment and exist as a part of organized activity. As essential steps in the process of want satisfaction, these elements exist as a result of the demand created by the basic needs of mankind.

The engineering process employed from the time a particular human need is recognized until the time when the need is satisfied may be divided into a number of activities. These activities will be discussed under the headings which follow and will be related to the essential steps in want satisfaction.

Determination of objectives. One important facet of the engineering process involves the search for new objectives for engineering application — to learn what people want that can be supplied by engineering. In the field of invention, success is not a direct result of the construction of a new device; rather, it is dependent on the capability of the invention to satisfy human wants. Thus, market surveys seek to learn what the desires of people are. Automobile manufacturers make surveys to learn what mechanical, comfort, and style features people want in transportation. Highway commissions make traffic counts to learn what construction programs will be of greatest use. Considerations of technical feasibility and cost come only after what is wanted has been determined. Engineers have done extensive research to learn what people want in a great many products in which the user's taste is of paramount importance in their acceptance or rejection.

The things that people want may be the result of logical considerations, but more often are the result of emotional drives. There appears to be no logical reason why one prefers a certain make of car, a certain type of work, or a certain style of clothes. The bare necessities needed to maintain physical existence, in terms of calories of nourishment, clothing, and shelter are limited and may be determined with a fair degree of certainty. But the wants that stem from emotional drives seem to be unlimited.

The facet of the engineering process that seeks to learn of human wants requires not only a knowledge of the limitations of engineering capability but also a general knowledge of sociology, psychology, government, literature, and the fine arts, and other fields related to the understanding of human nature.

Identification of strategic factors. The factors that stand in the way of attaining objectives are known as *limiting factors.* An important element of the engineering process is the identification of the limiting factors restricting accomplishment of a desired objective. Once the limiting factors have been identified they are examined to see which ones may be operated on with success. Thus, each of the limiting factors should be examined in order to locate *strategic factors;* that is those factors which, if altered, will remove limitations restricting the success of an undertaking.

Consider the following example. A shaft will not enter a hole. The limiting factors may be that the shaft is too large or that the hole is too small. The difficulty can be eliminated by reducing the diameter of the shaft or by increasing the diameter of the hole. But if decreasing the diameter of the shaft is not suitable for the total purpose, and increasing the diameter of the hole is suitable, then the diameter of the hole is the strategic factor and should be selected for alteration.

The identification of strategic factors is important, for it makes possible the concentration of effort on those areas in which success is obtainable. This may require inventive ability, or the ability to put known things together in new combinations, and is distinctly creative in character. The means that will achieve the desired objective may consist of a procedure, a technical process, or a mechanical, organizational, or administrative change. Strategic factors limiting success may be circumvented by operating on engineering, human, and economic aspects individually and jointly.

Determination of means. Engineers are remarkably well equipped by way of training and experience to determine means of attainment of an objective. Ordinarily, however, those who limit themselves to the consideration of means alone will find themselves in a subordinate position to those who have the imagination, courage, and ability to gain the acceptance of objectives. As previously defined, the engineer who allows himself to fall into the former category may be conveniently called a responsive engineer. His contribution to the engineering process as envisioned here is of minor importance.

The identification of strategic factors is necessarily subordinate to the determination of objectives. Likewise, the determination of means is subordinate to the identification of strategic and limiting factors. Limiting factors may often be circumvented in many ways. These possibilities must then be evaluated to determine which will be most successful in terms of over-all economy. If the means devised to overcome limiting factors come within the field of engineering, they may conveniently be termed engineering proposals.

Evaluation of engineering proposals. It is usually possible to accomplish a desired result by several methods, each of which is feasible from the physical aspects of engineering application. The most desirable of the several proposals is the one that can be performed at the least expense. The evaluation of engineering proposals in terms of comparative cost is an important facet of the engineering process and an essential ingredient in want satisfaction. Although engineering alternatives are most often evaluated to determine which is most desirable economically, exploratory evaluations are also made to determine if any likely engineering proposal can be formulated to reach a goal profitably.

A wide range of factors may be considered in evaluating the worth of engineering proposals. When investment is required, the time value of money must be considered. Where machinery and plants are employed, capital consumption becomes an important factor. Most proposals involve organized effort, thus making labor costs an important consideration. Material is an important ingredient which may lead to market analyses and a study of procurement policy. Risks of a physical and economic nature may be involved and must be evaluated. Where the accepted engineering proposal is successful a net income will be derived, thus making the consideration of income tax necessary. This text offers specific instruction in methods of analysis pertaining to each of these factors and general instruction regarding the engineering process as a whole.

Assistance in decision making. Engineering is concerned with action to be taken in the future. Therefore, an important facet of the engineering process is to improve the certainty of decision with respect to the want satisfying objective of engineering application. Correct decisions can offset many operating handicaps. On the other hand, incorrect decisions may and often do hamper all subsequent action. No matter how expertly a bad decision is carried out, results will be at best unimpressive and at worst disastrous.

To make a decision is to select a course of action from several. A correct decision is the selection of that course of action which will result in an outcome more desirable than would have resulted from any other selection. Decision rests upon the possibility of choice; that is, on the fact that there are alternatives from which to choose. The engineer acting in a creative capacity proceeds on the thought that there is a most desirable solution if he can find it.

The logical determination and evaluation of alternatives in tangible terms have long been recognized as an integral facet of the engineering process. The success of engineers in dealing with this element of application is responsible, in part, for the large percentage of engineers that are either directly or indirectly employed in the decision-making aspect of organized activity.

1.7. ENGINEERING ECONOMY AND THE ENGINEER

Economy, the attainment of an objective at low cost in terms of resource input, has always been associated with engineering. During much of history the limiting factor has been predominantly physical. Thus, a great innovation, the wheel, awaited invention, not because it was useless or costly, but because the mind of man could not synthesize it earlier. But, with the development of science, things have become physically possible that people are interested in only slightly or not at all. Thus, a new type of heating system may be perfectly feasible from the physical standpoint but may enjoy limited use because of its first cost or cost of operation.

Engineers are becoming increasingly aware of the fact that many sound proposals fail because those who might have benefited from them did not understand their significance. A prospective user of a good or service is primarily interested in its worth and cost. The person who lacks an understanding of engineering technology may find it difficult or even impossible to grasp the technical aspects of a proposal sufficiently to arrive at a measure of its economic desirability. The uncertainty so engendered may easily cause loss of confidence and a decision to discontinue consideration of the proposal.

Being accustomed to the use of facts and being proficient in computation, the engineer should accept the responsibility for making an economic interpretation of his work. It is much easier for the engineer to master the fundamental concepts of economic analysis necessary to bridge the gap between physical and economic aspects of engineering application than it is for the person who is not technically trained to acquire the necessary technical background.

The general acceptance by engineers of the responsibility for seeing that engineering proposals are both technically and economically sound, and for interpreting proposals in terms of worth and cost, may be expected to promote confidence in engineering endeavor and enhance the worth of engineering service. In assuming this responsibility, the engineer also assumes greater control of the application of engineering. This seems desirable for it is unlikely that the future potential of engineering can be fully utilized unless engineers participate in determining its objectives.

QUESTIONS

1. Contrast the role of the engineer and the scientist.

2. Discuss the place of the engineer in modern civilization.

3. Give several examples of products that would be technically feasible but that would possess little economic merit.

4. Why should the engineer concern himself with both the physical and the economic aspects of the total environment?

5. Explain how physical efficiency below 100 per cent may be converted to economic efficiency above 100 per cent.

6. Why must economic efficiency take precedence over physical efficiency?

7. Describe the responsive engineer; the creative engineer.

8. Why is responsive engineering a direct hindrance to the development of the engineering profession?

9. Define *engineering economy*.

10. Name the essential steps in want satisfaction.

11. Name the essential activities in the engineering process.

12. What is involved in seeking new objectives for engineering application?

13. What is a limiting factor; a strategic factor?

14. Give reasons why engineers are particularly well equipped to determine means for the attainment of an objective.

15. Why is it essential that engineering proposals be evaluated in terms of economy?

16. How may engineers assist in decision making?

17. As compared with the economic aspect of engineering application, give reasons why the physical aspect is decreasing in relative importance.

18. Why should the economic interpretation of engineering proposals be made by engineers?

CHAPTER 2

SOME CONCEPTS USEFUL
IN ECONOMY ANALYSIS

Concepts are crystallized thoughts. They are qualitative in nature and are not necessarily universal in application. However, if carefully related to fact, concepts may be useful in suggesting solutions to problems or in stimulating new ideas and new possibilities for action. Those given in this chapter are by no means exhaustive. Others will be found throughout the text. Those wishing to improve their ability to arrive at sound decisions pertaining to economy analysis will find it helpful to give careful thought to the development of additional concepts to supplement those given here.

2.1. PHYSICAL AND ECONOMIC LAWS

In dealing with the physical environment the engineer has a body of physical laws upon which to base his reasoning. Such laws as Boyle's law, Ohm's law, and Newton's laws of motion were developed primarily by collecting and comparing a multitude of comparable instances and by the use of an inductive process. These laws may then be applied by deduction to specific instances. They are supplemented by many formulas and known facts, all of which enable the engineer to come to conclusions about the physical environment that match the facts within narrow limits. Much is known with certainty about the physical environment.

Much less, particularly of a quantitative nature, is known about the economic environment. Since economics is involved with the actions of people, it is apparent that economic laws must be based upon their behavior. Economic laws, therefore, can be no more exact than the description of the behavior of people acting singly and collectively. But the engineering process is concerned with the economic as well as the physical environment. Therefore, economics and economic laws are important factors in successful engineering application.

2.2. ECONOMICS DEALS WITH THE ACTIONS OF PEOPLE

The engineer is often confused by the lack of certainty associated with the economic aspect of engineering. However, it must be recognized that economic considerations embrace many of the subtleties and complexities characteristic of people. Economics deals with the behavior of people individually and collectively, particularly as their behavior relates to the satisfaction of their wants.

The wants of people are motivated largely by emotional drives and tensions and to a lesser extent by logical reasoning processes. A part of human wants can be satisfied by physical goods and services such as food, clothing, shelter, transportation, communication, entertainment, medical care, educational opportunities, and personal services; but man is rarely satisfied by physical things alone. In food, sufficient calories to meet his physical needs will rarely satisfy. He will want the food he eats to satisfy his energy needs and also his emotional needs. In consequence we find people concerned with the flavor of food, its consistency, the china and silverware with which it is served, the person or persons who serve it, the people in whose company it is eaten, and the "atmosphere" of the room in which it is served. Similarly, there are many desires associated with clothing and shelter, in addition to those required merely to meet physical needs.

Anyone who has a part in satisfying human wants must accept the uncertain action of people as a factor with which he must deal, even though he finds such action unexplainable. Much or little progress has been made in discovering knowledge on which to base predictions of human reactions, depending upon one's viewpoint. The idea that human reactions will someday be well-enough understood to be predictable is accepted by many people; but in spite of the fact that this has been the objective of the thinkers of the world since the beginning of time, it appears that progress in psychology has been meager compared to the rapid progress made in the physical sciences. But, in spite of the fact that human reactions can be neither predicted nor explained, they must be considered by those who are concerned with satisfying human wants.

2.3. CONSUMER AND PRODUCER GOODS

Two classes of goods are recognized by economists; *consumer goods* and *producer goods*. Consumer goods are products and services that directly satisfy human wants. Examples of consumer goods are television sets, houses, shoes, books, orchestras, and health service. Producer goods also satisfy human wants but do so indirectly as a part of the production process. Broadly speaking, the ultimate end of all engineering activity is to supply goods and services that people consume to satisfy their desires and needs.

Some kinds of human wants are much more predictable than others. The demand for food, clothing, and shelter, which are needed for bare physical existence, is much more stable and predictable than the demand for those items that satisfy man's emotional needs. The amount of foodstuffs needed for existence is ascertainable within reasonable limits in terms of calories of energy, and the clothing and shelter requirement may be fairly accurately determined from climate data. But once man is assured of physical existence he reaches out for satisfactions related to his being a person rather than merely to his being a physical organism.

Producer goods are a means to an end. Producer goods are, in the long run, used as a means to an end; namely, that of producing goods and services for human consumption. Examples of this class of goods are lathes, bulldozers, ships, and railroad cars. Producer goods are an intermediate step in man's effort to supply his wants. They are not desired for themselves, but because they may be instrumental in producing something that man can consume.

Once the kind and amount of consumer goods to be produced has been determined, the kinds and amounts of facilities and producer goods necessary to produce them may be approached objectively. In this connection consider the satisfaction of the human want for harmonic sounds as in music. Suppose it has been decided that the desire for music can be met by 100,000 phonographic records.

Then the organization of the artists, the technicians, and the equipment necessary to produce the records becomes predominantly objective in character. The amount of material that must be compounded and processed to form one record is calculable to a high degree of accuracy. If a concern has been making records for some time, it will know the various operations that are to be performed and the unit times for performing them. From these data, the kind and amount of producer service, the amount and kind of labor, and the number of various types of machines are determinable within rather narrow limits. Whereas the determination of the kinds and amounts of consumer goods needed at any one time may depend upon the most subjective of human considerations, the problems associated with their production are quite objective by comparison.

2.4. VALUE AND UTILITY

The term *value*, like most other widely used terms, has a variety of meanings. In economics, value designates the worth that a person attaches to an object or a service. Thus the value of an object is not inherent in the object but is inherent in the regard that a person or people have for it. The subject of engineering valuation, for instance, is directed at assigning values to property in accordance with precepts that will be judged fair by the parties concerned. Value should not be confused with the cost or the price of an object in engineering economy studies. There may be little or no relation between the value a person ascribes to an article and the cost of providing it or the price that is demanded for it.

The general economic meaning of the term *utility* is the power to satisfy human wants. The utility that an object has for an individual is determined by him. Thus the utility of an object, like its value, is not inherent in the object itself but is inherent in the regard that a person has for it.

Utility and value in the sense here used are closely related. The utility that an object has for a person is the satisfaction he derives from it. Value is an appraisal of utility in terms of media of exchange.

In ordinary circumstances a large variety of goods and services are available to an individual. The utility that available items may have in the mind of a prospective user may be expected to be such that his desire for them will range from abhorrence, through indifference, to intense desire. His evaluation of the utility of various items is not ordinarily constant but may be expected to change with time. Each person also possesses either goods or services that he may render. These have the utility for the person himself that he regards them to have. These same goods and possible services may also be desired by others, who may ascribe to them very different utilities. The possibility for exchange exists when each of two persons possesses utilities desired by the other.

Utility of consumer goods. A person will consider two kinds of utility. One kind embraces the utility of goods and services that he intends to consume personally for the satisfaction he gets out of them. Thus, it seems reasonable to believe that the utility a person attaches to goods and services that are consumed directly is in large measure a result of subjective, nonlogical mental processes. That this is so may be inferred from the fact that sellers of consumer goods apparently find emotional appeals more effective than factual information. Early automobile advertising took the form of objective information related to design and performance, but more recent practice stresses such subjective aspects as comfort, beauty, and prestige values.

An analysis of advertising and sales practices used in selling consumer goods will reveal that they appeal primarily to the senses rather than to reason, and perhaps rightly so. If the enjoyment of consumer goods stems almost exclusively from how one feels about them rather than what one reasons about them, it seems logical to make sales presentation on the basis on which customers ascribe utility.

Since the ultimate end of almost all engineering activity is consumer goods and services, the basis on which they are sold and evaluated by the consumer is a subject that might be given greater emphasis by engineers than it usually is.

Utility of producer goods. The second kind of utility that an object or service may have for a person is its utility as a means to an end. Producer goods are not consumed for the satisfaction that can be directly derived from them but as a means of producing consumer goods.

It is inconceivable that a person would acquire such items as coal, steel bars, crude oil, or hay — none of which he has any intention of consuming directly — except as producer items. Although the utility of consumer goods is primarily determined subjectively, the utility of producer goods as a means to an end may be, and usually is, in large measure considered objectively. The value ascribed to producer goods is often quite objective. The energy, ash, and other contents of coal, for instance, can be determined very accurately and are the basis of evaluating the utility of the coal. The extent to which producer utility may be considered by logical processes is limited only by factual knowledge and the ability to reason.

How utilities are created. If the supernatural is excluded from consideration all that has utility is physically manifested. This statement is readily accepted in regard to physical objects that have utility — an automobile, a tractor, a house, or a steak dinner. But this statement is equally true in regard to the more intangible things. Music, which is regarded as pleasing to a person, is manifested to him as air waves which impinge upon his ears. Pictures are manifested as light waves. Even friendship is realized only through the five senses and must, therefore, have its physical aspects. It follows that utilities must be created by changing the physical environment.

For example, the consumer utility of raw steak can be increased by altering its physical condition by an appropriate application of heat. In the area of producer utilities the machining of a bar of steel to produce a shaft for a rolling mill is an example of creating utility by manipulation of the physical environment. The purpose of much engineering effort is to determine how the physical environment may be altered to create the most utility for the least cost in terms of the utilities that must be surrendered.

2.5. THE ECONOMY OF EXCHANGE

Economy of exchange occurs when utilities are exchanged by two or more people. In this connection, a utility means anything that a person may recieve in an exchange that has any value whatsoever to him; for example, a lathe, a dozen pencils, a meal, music, or a friendly gesture.

As an illustration of the economy of exchange consider the following example. Two workmen, upon opening their lunch boxes, discover that one contains a piece of apple pie and the other a piece of cherry pie. Suppose further that Mr. A evaluates his apple pie to have 10 units of utility for him and the cherry pie to have 30 units. Suppose, also that Mr. B evaluates his cherry pie to have 20 units of utility for him and the apple pie 40 units. If Mr. A consumes his apple pie and Mr. B consumes his cherry pie, the utility realized in the system is 10 plus 20, or 30 units. But, if the two workmen exchange pieces of pie, the resulting utility will be increased to 30 plus 40, or 70 units. The utility in the system can be increased by 70 less 30, or 40 units by exchange.

Economy of exchange is possible because consumer utilities are evaluated by the consumer almost entirely, if not entirely, by subjective consideration. Thus, if the workmen in the example believe that the exchange has resulted in a gain of net satisfaction to them, no one can deny it. On the other hand, at the time of exchange, unless each person valued what he had to give less than what he was about to receive, an exchange could not take place. Thus, we conclude that an exchange of consumer utilities results in a gain for both parties because the utilities are subjectively evaluated by the participating parties. The reason that people can be found who will subjectively evaluate consumer utilities so that an exchange will permit each to gain is that people have different needs by virtue of their history and their environment.

Assuming that each party to an exchange of producer utilities correctly evaluates the objects of exchange in relation to his situation, what makes it possible for each person to gain? The answer is that the participants are in different economic environments. This fact may be illustrated by an example of a merchant who buys lawn mowers from a manufacturer. For example, at a certain volume of activity the manufacturer finds that he can produce and distribute mowers at a total cost of $70 per unit and that the merchant buys a number of the mowers at a price of $80 each. The merchant then finds that by expending an average of $40 per unit in selling effort, he can sell a number of the mowers to homeowners at $160 each. Both of the participants profit by the exchange. The reason that the manufacturer profits is that his environment is such that he can sell to the merchant for $80 a number of mowers that he cannot sell elsewhere at a higher price, and that he can manufacture lawn mowers for $70 each. The reason that the merchant profits is that his environment is such that he can sell mowers at $160 each by applying $40 of selling effort upon a mower of certain characteristics which he can buy for $80 each from the manufacturer in question, but not for less elsewhere.

The questions may be asked, why doesn't the manufacturer enter the merchandising field and thus increase his profit or why doesn't the merchant enter the manufacturing field? The answer to these questions is that neither the manufacturer nor the merchant can do so unless each changes his environment. The merchant, for example, lacks physical plant equipment and an organization of engineers and workmen competent to build lawn mowers. Also, he may be unable to secure credit necessary to engage in manufacturing, although he may easily secure credit in greater amounts for merchandising activities. It is quite possible that he cannot alter his environment so that he can build mowers for less than $80. Similar reasoning applies to the manufacturer. Exchange consists essentially of physical activity designed to transfer the control of things from one person to another. Thus, even in exchange, utility is created by altering the physical environment.

Each party in an exchange should seek to give something that has little utility for him but that will have great utility for the receiver. In this manner each exchange can result in the greatest gain for each party. Nearly everyone has been a party to such a favorable exchange. When a car becomes stuck in snow, only a slight push may be required to dislodge it. The slight effort involved in the dislodging push may have very little utility for the person giving it, so little that he expects no more compensation than a friendly nod. On the other hand it might have very great utility for the person whose car was dislodged, so great that he may offer a substantial tip. The aim of much sales and other research is to find products that not only will have great utility for the buyer but that can be supplied at a low cost — that is, have low utility for the seller. The difference between the utility that a specific service has for the buyer and the utility it has for the seller represents the profit or net benefit that is available for division between buyer and seller.

The point has been made that exchanges are not consummated unless at the time of exchange each party believes he will gain thereby. However, after an exchange many things may take place to cause a party to an exchange to wish he had not done so. After a lapse of time new information may become available; change in needs and change in the economic environment may take place that will alter the relative worth, in the eyes of a participant, of the utilities exchanged.

Persuasion in exchange. It is not uncommon for an equipment salesman to call on a prospective customer, describe and explain a piece of equipment, state its price, offer it for sale, and have his offer rejected. This is concrete evidence that the machine does not possess sufficient utility at the moment to induce the prospective customer to buy it. In such a situation, the salesman may be able to induce the prospect to listen to further sales talk, during which the prospect may decide to buy on the basis of the original offer. This is concrete evidence that the machine now possesses sufficient utility to induce the prospective customer to buy. Since there was no change in the machine or the price at which it was offered, there must have been a change in the customer's attitude or regard for the machine. The pertinent fact to grasp is that a proposition at first undesirable now has become desirable as a result of a change in the customer, not in the proposition.

What brought about the change? A number of reasons could be advanced. Usually it would be said that the salesman persuaded the customer to buy, in other words that the salesman induced the customer to believe something, namely that the machine had sufficient utility to warrant its purchase. There are many aspects to persuasion. It may amount only to calling attention to the availability of an item. A person cannot purchase an item he does not know exists. A part of a salesman's function is to call attention to the things he has to sell.

It is observable that persuasive ability is much in demand, is often of inestimable beneficial consequences to all concerned, and is usually richly rewarded. Persuasion as it applies to the sale of goods is of economic importance to industry. A manufacturer must dispose of the goods he produces. He can increase the salability of his products by building into them greater customer appeal in terms of greater usefulness, greater durability, or greater beauty, or he may elect to accompany his products to market with greater persuasive effort in the form of advertising and sales promotion. Either plan will require expenditure and both are subject to the law of diminishing returns. It is a study in economy to determine what levels of perfection of product and sales effort will be most profitable.

It is interesting to note, in this connection, that the costs of some things that increase the sale of a product may be more than outweighed by the economies that result. Thus qualities that make a product more desired, or sales promotion, may have two beneficial effects. One of these is that it may be feasible to increase the price asked for the product and the other is that the volume of product sold may increase to the extent that a lower manufacturing cost per unit may result.

Whatever the approach, factual or emotional, persuasion consists of taking a person on an excursion into the future in an attempt to show and convince him what will happen if he acts in accordance with a proposal. The purpose of engineering economy analyses is to estimate, on as factual a basis as possible, what the economic consequences of a decision will be. It is therefore a useful technique in persuasion. With its wide use by both sellers and buyers many foolish decisions might be avoided.

The range of mutual benefit in exchange. A buyer will purchase an article when he has money available and when he believes that the article has equal or greater utility for him than the amount required to purchase it. Conversely, a seller will sell an article when he believes that the amount of money to be received for the article has greater utility than the article has for him. Thus, an exchange will not be effected unless at the time of exchange both parties believe that they will benefit. Exchanges are made when they are thought to result in mutual benefit. This is possible because the objects of exchange are not valued equally by the parties to the exchange.

Suppose that A has a house he values at $10,000 and that B has $14,000, which he values equal to A's house. Then A may be expected to sell his house if he can receive $10,000 or more for it and B may be expected to buy the house if he can buy it for $14,000 or less. This situation is illustrated by Figure 2.1.

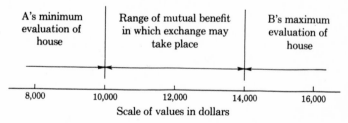

Figure 2.1. The range of mutual benefit in exchange.

The price at which exchange in the above situation will take place is dependent upon many factors. For instance, if prices have risen very rapidly and A is ignorant of the current values of property and timid, he may have found it difficult to name a price as high as $10,000. If this amount is offered to him, he is likely to accept. On the other hand, if B is very anxious to get the house, he may "talk when he should be listening" and offer $14,000 and the exchange will take place at this amount.

The factors that may determine a price within the range of mutual benefit at which exchange will take place are infinite in variety. They may be either subjective or objective. A person seeking to sell may be expected to make two evaluations: the minimum amount he will accept and the maximum amount a prospective buyer can be induced to pay by persuasion. The latter estimate may be based upon mere conjecture or upon a detailed analysis of buyers' subjective and objective situations. In bargaining it is usually advantageous to obscure one's situation. Thus, sellers will ordinarily refrain from revealing the costs of the things they are seeking to sell or from referring a buyer to a competitor who is willing to sell at a lower price.

2.6. PRICE IS DETERMINED BY SUPPLY AND DEMAND

In a free enterprise system, the price of goods and services is ultimately determined by supply and demand. Typical demand and supply curves are illustrated in Figure 2.2. The demand curve shows

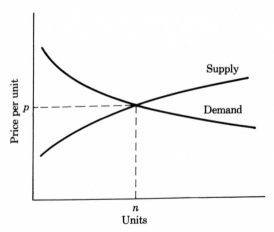

Figure 2.2. Typical supply and demand curves.

the relationship between the quantity of a product that people are willing to buy and the price of the product. The supply curve shows the relationship between the quantity of a product that vendors will offer for sale and the price of the product. Therefore, the intersection of these curves determines the price at which exchange will take place. The quantity exchanged is equal to both quantity of supply and quantity of demand. In the illustration, the number of units that will be exchanged is n and the price at which exchange will take place is p.

As a concept, the law of supply and demand is important in engineering economy analysis since proposed ventures frequently involve action that will increase the supply of a product or influence its demand. The effect of such action upon the price at which the product can be sold is an important factor to be considered in evaluating the desirability of the venture.

The elasticity of demand. Consumer goods and services may be c'assified as being either necessities or luxuries. The classification is relative, for that which is considered to be a necessity by one person may be considered a luxury by others. The classification depends upon the individual's economic and social position.

People will decrease their consumption of luxury goods at a faster rate than their consumption of necessities for a given increase in price. This relationship is illustrated in Figure 2.3.

The extent to which price changes effect demand is measured by

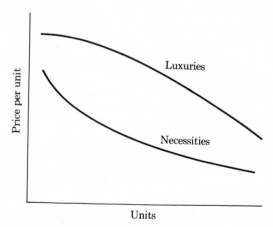

Figure 2.3. Price — demand relationship for luxuries and necessities.

a concept called the *elasticity of demand*. If the product of volume and price is constant, the elasticity of demand is unitary. Under this condition, the total amount which will be spent for the product will be constant regardless of the selling price. A drop in price would cause an increase in demand. Thus, the demand for a product is *elastic* when a decrease in price results in a greater than proportionate increase in sales. On the other hand, if a decrease in selling price produces a less than proportionate increase in sales, the demand is said to be *inelastic*.

Obviously, luxuries have a much greater elasticity of demand than do necessities. A change in demand will have a much greater effect on the price of necessities than on the price of luxuries. This relationship is important in evaluating the probable effect of alternate engineering proposals.

2.7. THE LAW OF DIMINISHING RETURNS

The term *law of diminishing returns* was originally used to designate the relation of input of fertilizers to land and the output of crops. It is a special application of the law of diminishing productivity, which may be stated as follows: *The amount of product obtained in a productive process varies with the way the agents of production are combined. If only one agent is varied, the product per unit of this agent may increase to a maximum amount, after which the product per unit may be expected to diminish but not necessarily proportionately.*

This concept may be illustrated by an example. A certain production line where an assembly operation is performed may be manned by a varying number of men. As the number of men on the line is increased from 15 to 19, production increases from 40.6 units per hour to 53.7 units per hour. The men are paid at the rate of $1.16 per hour. The output relationships are given in Table 2.1.

In Table 2.1 the output is given in terms of units of product and the agent of production is given in terms of man-hour input and dollar input per unit of product. It will be noticed that output per unit of input increases, reaches a maximim, and then diminishes.

The law of diminishing returns is directly applicable in a great number of engineering situations where it manifests itself in terms of providing a service at least cost. In a given situation one element may be increased and for a time costs will be decreased to a minimum point

Table 2.1. AN ILLUSTRATION OF THE LAW OF DIMINISHING RETURNS

Number of men employed on line	Labor input in man hours per hour	Labor input in dollars per hour	Output in number of assemblies per hour	Units of output per man-hour of input	Units of output per dollar of labor input
15	15	$17.40	40.6	2.71	2.33
16	16	18.56	46.7	2.92	2.51
17	17	19.72	52.5	3.09	2.66
18	18	20.88	53.3	2.96	2.55
19	19	22.04	53.7	2.83	2.44

only to rise again if the element is further increased. This may be illustrated by increasing the amount of fuel fed into an engine. Below a certain fuel-air ratio the engine will not start. When fed a little more fuel, it may produce just enough power to run itself. As the fuel fed into the engine is increased, the cost of power delivered will reach a minimum value per unit of power delivered. As the fuel intake is increased, cost of power per unit will increase. The engine will sputter and stop, with the result that no power is delivered as at first.

Most situations have many elements, and where the optimum whole is sought, the optimum of elements must often be compromised. Long bridge spans reduce the cost of piers but will increase the cost of superstructure. Prices can be increased but sales may fall so that profit is less. Managements are continually confronted with finding the balance between supervisory and nonsupervisory workers.

The chief value of the concept of the law of diminishing returns in engineering economy situations is that it produces an awareness that output does not necessarily increase in a straight-line relationship with an increase in input of an agent of production. The solution of many problems in economy centers around adjusting the amounts of agents of productivity to produce maximum output per unit of input. This end is frequently expressed as an effort to find the input ratio that will result in least cost per unit of output. Such expressions as horsepower-hour output per pound of fuel, miles per gallon of fuel, sales per dollar of advertising, units of output per fatal accident, and defects per 100 units of product are associated with analyses in search of a maximum output per unit of input.

2.8. THE RELATION OF OBJECTIVE AND PERFORMANCE TO SUCCESS

Attention may be focused on doing very worth-while things or on doing things very well. Economic success depends to an extent on each and therefore an optimum balance should be sought.

It appears that greater emphasis is usually directed to doing things well than is directed to seeking to do things that have maximum promise. All too often the effort of each is not given consideration separately in contemplating undertakings. Views on this subject may be clarified by consideration of an example.

Let it be assumed that two prospectors are seeking ore veins to mine. After a short period of search Prospector A discovers a vein and immediately begins to remove the ore. Prospector A is both ingenious and industrious in his mining operations. Prospector B diligently continued his prospecting long after A was actively mining because he felt that the discovery of a potentially profitable ore body was paramount to success; his search was finally attended with the discovery of a rich vein after he had uncovered numerous poorer ones, including the one that A was now working. In the operation of his mine, B was only reasonably effective in both method and industry.

Assume that Prospector A's mine was exhausted at the end of five years after the removal of 20 tons of ore. His net return per year of effort may be calculated as follows:

Total gross income, 20 tons ore at $300 per ton..............		$ 6,000
Cost of prospecting to discover mine......	$ 400	
Cost of supplies to operate mine at $30 per ton mined, 20 × $30..................	600	
Total costs...		1,000
Net return to Prospector A for 5 years of effort..............		$ 5,000
Net return per year of effort...............................		$ 1,000

Prospector B's mine was exhausted at the end of five years after the removal of 150 tons of ore. His net return per year of effort is calculated as follows:

Total gross income, 150 tons at $400 per ton.................		$60,000
Cost of prospecting to discover mine......	$2,500	
Cost of supplies to operate mine at $50 per ton, 150 × $50.......................	7,500	
Total costs...		10,000
Net return to Prospector B for 5 years of effort..............		$50,000
Net return per year of effort...............................		$10,000

Under the cost conditions assumed A's mine resulted in an annual income of only $1,000, even though it was efficiently operated whereas B's mine produced an annual income of $10,000 despite its inefficient operation.

On the basis of the above analysis, it appears warranted to draw the conclusion that the outcome of an undertaking is jointly dependent upon the potentialities of the undertaking itself and upon how well it is prosecuted. The potentialities of A's and B's mines in the above example were taken to be a total output of 20 and 150 tons, respectively, of ore of a certain grade located in a certain situation. If it is assumed for convenience that the income per ton could not be increased by action of the operators (which would ordinarily be reasonably true), $6,000 and $60,000 would represent the monetary income potentialities of the two mines, respectively. A decision to select A's mine was a decision to undertake an enterprise that could not result in a total income greater than $6,000 regardless of subsequent action.

It may also be noted that there are costs associated with seeking out and deciding upon undertakings. The cost of seeking out desirable undertakings is a charge that must be deducted from the income potentialities of the undertakings that are decided upon. This limits the outlay that can be justified for search on the basis of economy. The measure of the net success of a venture may be thought of as being the difference between its potentialities for income and the sum of the outlay incurred in finding and deciding to undertake it and the outlay incurred in carrying it to completion.

The total success of an individual or an organization is the summation of the successes of all the ventures that he or it has undertaken. Also, the success of a major undertaking is the summation of the successes of the minor ventures of which it is constituted. In Figure 2.4 each vertical block represents the income potentialities of a venture, the outlay incurred in seeking it, the outlay incurred in prosecuting it, and the net gain of carrying it on. In this conceptual scheme the several quantities are considered to be measured in a single commensurable term, such as money.

From this figure it is apparent that the extent of the success of a venture depends upon its potentialities for income less the sum of the costs of finding it and carrying it on. It is also apparent that the success of an individual or an enterprise is the summation of the net success of the several ventures undertaken during a period of time.

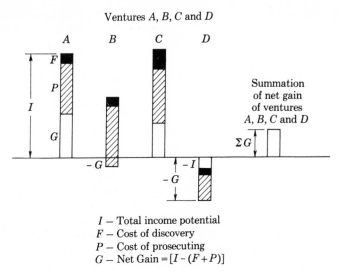

I — Total income potential
F — Cost of discovery
P — Cost of prosecuting
G — Net Gain $= [I - (F + P)]$

Figure 2.4. An illustration of the final outcome of several ventures.

2.9. MAJOR AND SUBORDINATE OBJECTIVES

Any enterprise has a major objective and subordinate objectives. For example, the ultimate aim of a contractor may be to earn a profit through activities associated with earth moving, such as digging pipeline trenches, excavating for buildings, or building earthen dams. Let earning a profit by digging pipeline trenches be considered to be a major objective designated by A. Objective A is an abstract aim that cannot be realized except by digging pipeline trenches in definite ways in definite places. An objective, a_1, subordinate to A, might be to earn a profit by digging a pipeline trench from Welltown to Pipetown via a certain route and in accordance with certain specifications. Realization of objective A depends upon the realization of objectives a_1, a_2, a_3, and so on. Also each subordinate objective, as for instance a_1, has objectives subordinate to it. And each of these subordinate objectives has its subordinate objectives and so on until the final subordinate objective involves activities of very narrow scope.

An economy study may concern itself with the evaluation of contemplated activities associated with any level of objective. In one case a study may be made to decide whether or not a job involving the digging of 100 miles of trench should be undertaken. In another case the thing that is to be decided is whether it will be more profitable to dig a short length of trench where rocks are encountered with a machine or by men with shovels. How the next step may be performed with economy is a concern in any activity performed for a purpose. Therefore, it is apparent that the realization of any major objective is a summation of the realization of its subordinate objectives.

2.10. THE ECONOMY OF INITIATIVE

There are many things that are highly profitable to the person who initiates them and much less profitable to those who follow. The person who initiated the idea of a chocolate coating for a piece of ice cream on a stick is reputed to have made a fortune. The government recognizes the merit of originality and through patent and copyright laws extends special privileges to those who present new ideas.

Air conditioning in theaters has become commonplace. The theater owner who was first in a city to make an installation generally profited handsomely, drawing customers because of the novelty as well as because of the comfort that air conditioning could provide. Increased sales during the first summer frequently were sufficient to more than pay for the installation. Attendance at the favored theater increased largely at the expense of loss of attendance in competing theaters.

As competitors became aware of what was happening, they too installed air conditioning. In many cases these later installations served only to recapture attendance, that is, to offset a loss occasioned by the competing installations. The economy of initiative accrues to the individual with foresight.

2.11. PRE-PLANNING AND ECONOMY

Pre-planning is the formulation, prior to beginning an undertaking, of more or less detailed plans for carrying it out. One important economy of this practice is that it permits specialization. People with unusual ability can be assigned the task of making plans covering a narrow scope of activities. Repeated experience with similar situations may also be expected to improve performance. Not only may people who are specialized in the task of planning be expected to produce plans that can be executed economically, but it is likely that the cost of the plans themselves will be less.

Planning is essentially a form of design and may be defined as being the projection and evaluation of ideas. In planning and designing, ways for accomplishing a contemplated end are literally invented and then evaluated on the basis of strength, fuel consumption, weight, economy, and so forth. The conception of different ways to accomplish a desired end does not appear to be a logical process, but their evaluation is largely a matter of reasoning. One important aspect of planning is that it makes it possible to try out a great many ideas on paper more or less conclusively. The cost of such trials may be negligible in comparison with actual accomplishment.

Consider the case of a manufacturer who has been asked to supply in quantity a certain chemical not now being produced. Where the art and science is well known, it is quite likely that he will be able to determine on paper and within narrow limits what material, labor, equipment, and related requirements will be necessary to make the product in several technically possible ways. Once he has learned the physical requirements, these can readily be converted into expenditures to determine the comparative economy of the several processes. Thus he may know the cost of producing the chemical without making costly trials of all the feasible methods.

2.12. FEEDBACK AND IMPROVED ACTION

Feedback for the purpose of improving future action is an essential of the decision-making process. It is unlikely that future action can be improved without knowledge of the results of action just completed.

A great deal of time and energy is spent in acquiring information about an undertaking that has been completed. Thus motion pictures of last week's football game may be examined with great care. Business firms make quarterly or annual reports purporting to summarize their activities and to show their status at the end of these periods. The economic justification for acquiring knowledge of the past is that it will enable better decisions to be made in the future.

It is a recognized psychological fact that a person cannot improve his skill by practice unless he learns the outcome of his actions. Thus a person could not improve his ability to throw darts if the lights on the target are extinguished from the time a dart leaves his hand until after it is removed from the target.

In a similar way, it is reasonable to believe that skill in making decisions must be dependent upon knowing the result of previous decisions. Since the chief purpose of information of past activity is to aid in performing activities more efficiently in the future, this purpose should be considered in relation to economy. Investigation often reveals that huge sums are spent in business for reports, records, audits and analyses. It often happens that much of such information is of little use. At the same time some items that would be of great value are not available. The benefits to be gained by the availability of information should always be considered in relation to the cost of collecting it.

2.13. QUALITATIVE AND QUANTITATIVE KNOWLEDGE

Qualitative knowledge is knowledge of the attributes of the thing under consideration. It is descriptive and tells how a thing is constituted by naming its distinctive characteristics. In the expression of qualitative knowledge such statements are used as: Repair cost of the truck will be low; Many units of this item will be sold this year; This method was less expensive than that method; The turbine had much power and used little fuel. Such expressions cannot be precisely evaluated and have comparatively little value in economy studies.

Quantitative knowledge is knowledge of the amount or extent of the attributes of a thing in terms that are capable of being counted. It is information that is capable of being expressed in numbers. Representative of quantitative knowledge are such statements as: The repair cost of the truck amounted to $358 per year; this year 6,200,000 units of this item were sold; this method costs $0.07 per piece but that method costs $0.09 per piece; the turbine developed 286 horsepower and used 0.48 pound of fuel per horsepower-hour.

The eminent British scientist Lord Kelvin expressed his regard for quantitative knowledge in the following quotation:

I often say that when you can not measure what you are speaking and express it in numbers your knowledge is of meager and unsatisfactory kind;

it may be the beginning of knowledge, but you have scarcely in your thoughts advanced to the stage of science, whatever the matter may be.

It appears that qualitative knowledge is primarily evaluated by one's feeling for it and one's judgment. Different people are likely to vary widely in their interpretation of the significance of qualitative ideas. Quantitative knowledge, on the other hand, is quite precise and may be evaluated in large measure by the processes of reasoning. Also, most people may be expected to attach about the same significance to quantitative statements pertaining to fields with which they are familiar. This is an important characteristic because it facilitates communication of ideas.

A comparison of the effectiveness of the two kinds of knowledge may be gained from a consideration of two statements: (1) The turbine had much power and used little fuel; and (2) The turbine developed 286 horsepower and used 0.48 pound of fuel per horsepower-hour. Let each statement be considered in conjunction with the knowledge that a machine for which a prime mover is sought will require a torque of 420 foot-pounds at 3,200 revolutions per minute (r.p.m.), that the cost of fuel is $0.02 per pound, and that

$$\text{h.p.} = \frac{\text{torque} \times 2\pi \times \text{r.p.m.}}{33,000}.$$

If the economy of using the turbine as the prime mover for the machine were being considered, two questions would be pertinent. These are: (1) Is the turbine powerful enough? and (2) What will be the fuel cost per hour? It will be noted that qualitative statements cannot be used to arrive at the desired answers. The quantitative information can be used as follows:

$$\text{required h.p.} = \frac{420 \times 2\pi \times 3,200}{33,000} = 256.$$

This answers the first question. The answer to the second question may be developed as follows:

$$\text{fuel cost per hour} = 256 \times 0.48 \times \frac{256}{286} \times 0.02 = \$2.20.$$

One important aspect of quantitative data is that it can often be combined with other quantitative data by logical processes to produce new quantitative knowledge as was illustrated above.

This is a very important characteristic in making economy studies and suggests that quantitative knowledge be exhausted before consideration of qualitative ideas. However, in many situations the need for action demands decision not fully covered by quantitative knowledge. In such cases decision must be based in part on qualitative knowledge.

2.14. ADVANTAGES AND DISADVANTAGES

Any contemplated action has its advantages and disadvantages. In considering alternative automobile routes between two points, nearly every one has said the equivalent of "Route A is shorter but rougher than the Route B," or the reverse, "Route B is longer but smoother than Route A."

A person who has enthusiasm for a proposal, particularly its originator, is likely to give undue favorable weight to its advantages and to minimize its disadvantages. But experience has taught most people to be skeptical of new things. The opposition to a new proposal may tend to stress its disadvantages and disregard its advantages.

Quite often a proposal is presented to replace a present practice that affects the working routine of a number of people. In such a situation the proposed method may encounter a great deal of opposition. Real and fancied disadvantages will be pointed out and the claimed advantages will not be admitted. The personal feelings with which people who will be affected by a proposal regard it may in themselves constitute very important advantages or disadvantages. Many meritorious proposals have been rejected or have failed after adoption because they had the disadvantage of the opposition of those who were affected by them. Enthusiasm for a measure, on the other hand, may be an advantage that results in indifferent proposals being adopted and being carried on with excellent results.

The point to realize is that every proposal has its advantages and disadvantages whether these exist in the proposal itself or in people's regard for it. The sponsor of a proposal should school himself to consider advantages and disadvantages as impersonally as possible, because the economic advantage of a proposal depends upon its advantages and disadvantages in comparison with those of other alternatives.

2.15. THE THRESHOLD IDEA

There are degrees of action in a great many fields below which the effect of the action is insignificant. For example, a small movement of a gear in a gear train will merely take up the back-lash without moving an adjacent gear.

Similarly many economic efforts are unfruitful for the reason that there is not sufficient economic input to pass the threshold of success. The threshold of success varies greatly for different activities. It has been estimated that an initial input of the order of several hundred million dollars would have to be made before success in automobile manufacture could be expected. Failure often attends inability to develop an activity to a level where it can be successful. The threshold idea should be taken into consideration in evaluating engineering alternatives.

QUESTIONS

1. Discuss the difference between a physical and an economic law.

2. Why should engineers be concerned with the actions of people?

3. Describe the two classes of goods recognized by economists.

4. Define value; utility.

5. Contrast the utility of consumer goods with the utility of producer goods.

6. Explain how utilities are created.

7. Explain the economy of exchange.

8. Why is it possible for both parties to profit by an exchange?

9. How may persuasion increase the utility of an item?

10. Explain the relationship between price and supply; price and demand.

11. Explain why luxuries have a greater elasticity of demand than do necessities.

12. Why is the law of diminishing returns a useful concept in economy studies?

13. Give an example of a venture in which success is dependent jointly upon its inherent potential and upon how well it is undertaken.

14. State an over-all objective and list the necessary subordinate objectives for its attainment.

15. How does initiative contribute to the success of an undertaking?

16. How does pre-planning contribute to the potential success of an undertaking?

17. Why is feedback necessary for the improvement of future action?

18. Define qualitative knowledge; quantitative knowledge.

19. Why should the sponsor of a proposal consider both its advantages and disadvantages?

20. Explain the threshold concept.

CHAPTER 3

SELECTIONS
IN PRESENT ECONOMY

The phrase *present economy* means a condition wherein the worth of alternatives can be evaluated on the basis of present or immediate cost. There are many situations in which alternate designs, materials, or methods will provide identical results and will involve expenditures occurring in substantially the same short time period considered to be the present. Since the results of the alternatives will be identical, the immediate cost of each is a measure of its comparative economy. Economic evaluations that fall into this category do not require consideration of the time value of money. Therefore, before beginning a study of interest and interest calculation it seems best that this special case be explored. The selections given in this chapter will illustrate the analysis required in present economy.

3.1. ECONOMY INHERENT IN DESIGN

The results of design effort, as manifested in plans and specifications, crystallize the final form of the product to be produced as to its physical form, material, and manufacturing requirements. For this reason design affords many opportunities for economy. Design, no matter how poorly done, is predicated on the thought that the effort devoted to it will be outweighed by the results.

To design is to project and evaluate ideas for attaining an objective. Suppose that a person employed in a machine design department has been assigned the task of designing a machine for a special purpose. His first step will be to project, literally to invent,

new combinations of materials, machine elements, forces, and kine-
matic motions that it is believed may meet the purposes of the
machine. His next step will be to evaluate these combinations.

There may be many bases of evaluation: certainty of operation,
consequences of failure, operator attention required, safety of operator, rate of operation, power required, maintenance required, floor
space required, and so forth. On the whole, these bases of evaluation
all relate to economy in one way or another. In fact, economy is
inherent in design. Consider a roller bearing in conjunction with a
plain brass bearing. The friction induced by a turning load on a
roller bearing is less than that of a plain bearing, by virtue of the
fact that the rolling friction inherent in the former is less than the
sliding friction of the latter. Where friction is economically undesirable, the roller bearing is inherently more economical than the plain
bearing.

A decision to accept a design is a decision to assume the advantages and disadvantages associated with it, and to discard other
designs that may have been considered. The following examples will
illustrate several aspects of economy as it relates to design.

Elimination of overdesign. In the design of a certain building
it was found that 180 2-inch by 8-inch by 16-foot rafters, 16 inches
center-to-center, are just sufficient to meet the contemplated load.
It was also found that the sheathing to span rafters placed 24 inches
center-to-center was just adequate for strength and stiffness. Consequently, the sheathing will be stronger and stiffer than necessary
for the 16-inch spacing. The excess is called *overdesign* since it has
no functional value and may be disadvantageous because of its
extra weight.

A new design is contemplated using 2-inch by 10-inch cross-
section rafters. On the principle that the bending moment resisted
by a rafter is in accordance with $bd^2/6$, the ratio of the load-carrying
capacity of the 2-inch by 10-inch rafter to the 2-inch by 8-inch rafter
is 1.56 to 1.00

As far as load-carrying capacity is concerned, the 2-inch by 10-
inch rafters may be spaced 16 inches $\times$ 1.56, or 25 inches. In accordance with practical standards, the rafters are spaced 24 inches center-
to-center. The analysis required for 2-inch by 8-inch by 16-foot
rafters, 16 inches center-to-center, is as follows:

Number of rafters required.............................. 180

Overdesign of rafters................................... 0%

Overdesign of sheathing, $\dfrac{24 \text{ in.} - 16 \text{ in.}}{24 \text{ in.}}$ 33%

Cost of rafters @ $0.10 per board foot,

$\dfrac{180 \text{ rafters} \times 2 \text{ in.} \times 8 \text{ in.} \times 16 \text{ ft.}}{12 \text{ in.}} \times \$0.10$............. $384.00

For 2-inch by 10-inch by 16-foot rafters, 24 inches center-to-center, the required calculations are:

Number of rafters required, $\dfrac{180 \times 16 \text{ in.}}{24 \text{ in.}}$.................. 120

Overdesign of rafters, $\dfrac{25 \text{ in.} - 24 \text{ in.}}{24 \text{ in.}}$...................... 4%

Overdesign of sheathing.................................. 0%

Cost of rafters @ $0.10 per board foot,

$\dfrac{120 \text{ rafters} \times 2 \text{ in.} \times 10 \text{ in.} \times 16 \text{ ft.}}{12 \text{ in.}} \times \$0.10$.............. $320.00

In this example, the design with 2-inch by 10-inch rafters is not only adequate, but it is less expensive by $64. In addition, savings will result from having to handle less pieces.

Designing for economy of production. A product may exhibit excellent functional design, but may be poorly designed from the standpoint of producibility. The drawings and specifications establishing the design also establish a minimum manufacturing cost regardless of efforts to reduce labor, material, and overhead costs. The effect of design on production cost is illustrated in Figure 3.1.

The difference in production cost for the most expensive and the least expensive design is $1.15 less $0.31, or $0.84. In addition, choice of the least expensive design will result in a weight saving of 6 pounds less 2.2 pounds, or 3.8 pounds. Under the assumption that each foot pedal will perform equally well, and that each will contribute equally to the salability of the final product, the designer would choose the least expensive design. The saving over the most expensive design would be 73 per cent.

Economy in the design of producer goods. In the design of equipment for carrying on manufacturing, the designer may become too engrossed in the mechanical features and give insufficient attention to over-all economy. As an example, assume that a jig is to be

(a) Traditional construction. Machine foot lever, 10 inches long, weighs 6 pounds. Cost with broached keyway is $1.15.

(b) Simple steel design costs 41% less. Can be built by the shop with only saw and shears. Weighs 2.7 pounds. Costs 68¢ with keyway.

(c) Saves 53%, cast by forming lever arm and pad as integral piece from 10 gauge metal. Weighs 2.5 pounds. Costs 54¢.

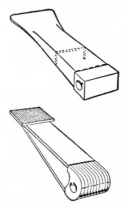

(d) Saves 73%, eliminates broaching. Hub with integral key is produced by stacking stampings in assembly. Arm is 10 gauge, brake-formed and welded to hub. Weighs 2.2 pounds. Costs 31¢.

Figure 3.1. The effect of design on the economy of production is shown by these four designs for a foot pedal. [*Courtesy Lincoln Electric Co.*]

designed for adjusting 100,000 assemblies for a special production order. Two designs are presented and are evaluated as follows:

	Jig A	Jig B
Life, estimated	100,000 pieces	100,000 pieces
Cost	$200	$300
Hourly rate of class of labor required	$1.60	$1.80
Operator hourly output rate	62	54

The cost of adjusting the 100,000 assemblies with Jig A is:

Labor cost, $\dfrac{100{,}000 \text{ pc.} \times \$1.60 \text{ per hr.}}{62 \text{ pc. per hr.}}$ $2,581

Cost of Jig A.   200

$2,781

The cost of adjusting the 100,000 assemblies with Jig B is:

Labor cost, $\dfrac{100{,}000 \text{ pc.} \times \$1.80 \text{ per hr.}}{54 \text{ pc. per hr.}}$ $3,333

Cost of Jig B.   300

$3,633

The net advantage of selecting Jig A over Jig B is $3,633 less $2,781, or $852. This economic advantage is inherent in the design of Jig A. Its characteristics were such that it could be operated more rapidly with less operator skill.

In industrial literature, many examples may be found in which economy of production was effected through design of equipment, equipment layout, and plant. In such cases, it is apparent that the economic advantage resulted from wise choice among alternative designs.

Economy of interchangeable design. Interchangeability in design is an extension of the mathematical axiom that things equal to the same thing are equal to each other. Components of an assembly that are to be interchangeable with components of other assemblies must possess specific tolerance limits.

As an example of the economy inherent in interchangeability, consider an engine re-manufacturing process. If the parts were not originally designed to be interchangeable with like parts of other engines of the same model, it would be necessary to keep all parts of each engine together in the re-manufacturing process. The needed coordination, tagging, and cost of locating stray parts is eliminated through initial design that allows interchangeability.

Design for economy of shipping. The shipping costs of products can often be reduced by proper design. Some products are designed so they can be easily assembled upon receipt by the customer. Others are designed so they may be easily packaged for shipment.

Often it may be advantageous to design so that the product can be nested to save space in shipment. In the shipment of pipe to Saudi Arabia this principle was used. The design called for pipe approximately 30 inches in diameter. To facilitate shipment by water, where bulk freight rates were in effect, half of the pipe was made 30 inches in diameter and the other half was made 31 inches in diameter to make nesting possible. As a result, shipping charges were reduced by several million dollars.

3.2. ECONOMY OF MATERIAL SELECTION

A designer has a choice of specifying either aluminum or grey iron castings for an intricate housing for an instrument to be permanently mounted in a power plant. He has ascertained that either metal will serve equally well. The aluminum casting will weigh 0.8 pound and the grey iron casting 2.2 pounds. His analysis of the cost of providing each type of casting follows:

	Grey Iron	Aluminum
Cost of casting delivered to factory..........	$0.76	$0.92
Cost of machining........................	0.63	0.52
	$1.39	$1.44

On the basis that either material will serve equally well and provide an identical service, the grey iron casting will be selected because its immediate or present cost is the lower of the two.

In the above example, in which it is specified that the instrument is to be mounted on a power plant wall, differences in weight were not considered to be a factor. However, for an instrument for airplane service the difference in weight might be the deciding economic factor. In airplane service the lighter instrument casting would have an economic value in lessened fuel consumption or greater pay load and would thus have greater utility.

In determinations of economy, care must always be exercised to see that alternatives provide identical services. "Sales appeal" of one type of casting over the other may easily render their worths nonidentical. Even for power plant use it might have been recognized that the lighter metal had "sales appeal" over the heavier metal.

If concrete value can be given to a quality, this difference in service can be taken into account to render the services of the two alternatives identical. For instance, the quality of lightness might have service value to the manufacturer in that it would reduce the delivery cost of his product to the consumer. If this had applied in the example of the instrument casting, the two types of castings could have been placed on an identical service basis for comparison as follows:

	Grey Iron	Aluminum
Cost of casting delivered to factory..........	$0.76	$0.92
Cost of machining.......................	0.63	0.52
Average additional cost to deliver grey-iron-casting-equipped instruments to customer...	0.26	0.00
	$1.65	$1.44

Processing rates of material a factor in selection. In cases where two or more materials may serve a purpose equally well from a functional standpoint, the relationship of their cost and the cost of processing them may be the factor that determines which is chosen. Brass, for example, is often found to be less costly for parts than cold rolled steel because it can be machined at a higher rate, in spite of its greater weight per unit volume and greater cost per pound. Aluminum, which is easily machinable and in addition has a low specific weight, is being used in increasing amounts as a replacement for steel, cast iron, and other metals whose cost per pound is considerably less. Because of the ease with which they can be processed, plastics have proved to be an economy in many applications as a replacement for materials of less cost per pound. The same can be said of die castings.

In some cases the decision to substitute one material for another will result in an entirely different sequence of processing. For instance, a change from grey iron to zinc alloy castings will require marked change in equipment. To determine the comparative economic desirability of two materials, it is necessary to make a detailed study of the costs that arise when each is used. In some cases this may involve the economy of disposing of present equipment and acquiring new equipment.

3.3. PERFECTION AND ECONOMY

Perfection is often a false ideal unless perfection is taken to mean that which is most appropriate. To secure a desirable result in even the physical world, compromises from perfection must often be made. For example, increasing the compression ratio of an internal combustion engine, ideally, will increase its efficiency but at the same time necessitate use of fuel of higher anti-knock characteristics. In order to produce a smooth-running engine, a compromise between an ideal compression ratio and characteristics of available fuel will have to be made. If economy of operation is now a factor to be considered, both the compression ratio and the anti-knock characteristics of the fuel may be compromised further on the basis of the cost of fuel of different anti-knock characteristics.

But it usually is not enough that a machine shall function properly as a physical unit; it must also function properly as an economic unit. Thus, compromises of physical perfection may be suggested by cost of the materials and processes which will be needed to produce it. And still further compromises of physical perfection may be dictated by the economic climate in which the engine will be marketed.

Figure 3.2 shows an approximate general relationship between tolerance in inches and the cost of production.

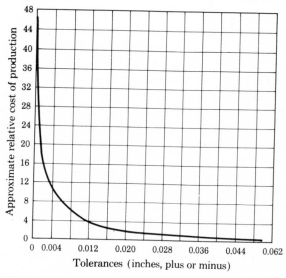

Figure 3.2. Chart of general cost relationship of various degrees of accuracy. [From Roger W. Bolz, *Production Processes — Their Influence on Design* (Cleveland: Penton Publishing Co., 1949)]

According to this figure, the specification of a tolerance of 0.001 inch, when 0.003 inch is adequate, might increase the cost by 32 minus 12 divided by 12, or 167 per cent. The concept that this figure exhibits has many applications. Whenever a product is to be designed or an activity planned, consideration should be given to the determination of the degree of perfection which will lead to the most desirable result in economic terms. In addition, it must be realized that there is a degree of perfection that, if specified, will be beyond the capability of the process to which it applies.

3.4. SIZE AND ECONOMY

The cost of many items varies on the basis of size. Extremely large units and extremely small units may cost relatively more than sizes that come in between. One reason for this variation in unit cost is that the number produced is often greater in the sizes that lie between the extremes. Some products, such as valves, electric motors, lathes, and engines, are essentially identical except for size. Thus the same number of parts will have to be processed. Though larger parts may be expected to require longer time for processing than smaller parts, it is unlikely that a part twice the size of another will require twice the time to process.

Figure 3.3 shows the relationship between the cost per unit and

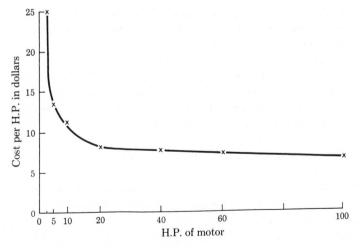

Figure 3.3. Cost of electric motors per horsepower, based on a manufacturer's list price for squirrel-cage induction, 3-phase, 60-cycle, 220-volt, 1800-rpm motors.

the size of a certain make of electric motor. From this figure, it may be seen that a motor capacity of 20 horsepower, which could be provided for approximately $160 with a 20-horsepower motor, would cost approximately $260 with four 5-horsepower units. It is clear that the latter installation could only be justified where it would permit offsetting advantages.

Similarly, there are many activities that cannot be carried on economically above or below a certain scale. Products that require a large variety of heavy equipment for their manufacture such as locomotives, steam turbines, automobiles and steamships cannot be made economically in small scale operations. On the other hand, certain hazardous processes in the manufacture of explosives are carried on in small isolated units as a matter of economy. There are many activities that are best carried on on a small scale. This fact is obscured in many cases because of an extreme regard for size by many people.

3.5. ECONOMY OF VIGILANCE AND ERROR

Some years ago a large manufacturing concern placed on its employee bulletin boards an illustrated poster stating that 14 per cent of its production cost was due to errors. The first reaction that one might have to such a statement is that a reduction in errors would result in reduced production costs. This certainly would be true if the cost of eliminating errors would be less than the cost arising from the errors that could be eliminated. Since the concern in question was recognized for its efficient operation, it is probable that errors would not be reduced substantially unless added vigilance were exercised. It is reasonable to assume that the added vigilance would not be obtained without cost. Thus, if the errors eliminated do not result in a reduction in costs equal to the cost of the added vigilance, the latter is not an economy.

The question of costs arising from errors and the vigilance necessary to keep errors at an economical level in a manufacturing establishment is very complex and is therefore very difficult to analyze in quantitative terms. However, it is possible to deduce that there is a level of error or vigilance which will result in maximum economy. The general relationship involved is shown by Figure 3.4.

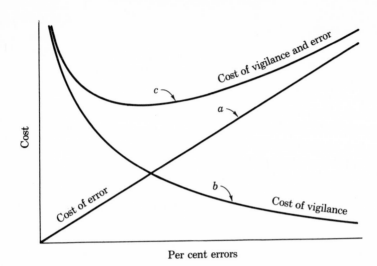

Figure 3.4. An illustration of the economy of vigilance and error.

Curve *a* represents the cost in dollars arising from errors in production. Curve *b* represents cost of vigilance and is given its trend on the basis of the following consideration. It is reasonable to assume that the cost of vigilance necessary to eliminate all errors will approach an infinite amount. On the other hand, it is reasonable to assume that some things would be performed correctly without vigilance, even though only by chance. Thus, it is reasonable to assume that the curve *b* will approach zero cost when production cost due to error approaches 100 per cent.

The optimum relation between errors and vigilance exists when the sum of their costs is at a minimum; this relation may be determined from curve *c*, produced by adding curves *a* and *b*.

Proofreading will serve to illustrate further the concept expressed in Figure 3.4. In the first reading of the copy for a book, for instance, a proofreader may be expected to find a majority of the errors. During each subsequent rereading he may be expected to find fewer and fewer errors. But it is not likely that he will detect all errors in a reasonable number of rereadings.

In some operations the relationship between vigilance and error can be established. One such operation is the percentage inspection of parts, where only a percentage, determined on the basis of economy, of the parts in a lot is inspected. This is done on the premise that the consequences of passing some defective parts will be less than the cost of the additional inspection necessary to inspect all.

Industry seeks to reduce errors in many ways. One way is to reduce the possibility for error; this is done, for example, in equipping machine tools with interlocking controls to make them "foolproof." Another way is to make vigilance easier or less costly. Fewer drivers run out of gasoline since the dash gasoline gauge replaced the rear tank-mounted gauge. Mechanical and electrical inspection devices are being used increasingly to reduce the cost of vigilance and, in turn, the cost of errors.

One aspect of personnel selection is the elimination of the error-prone and the accident-prone. It is common knowledge among safety engineers that a majority of accidents can be eliminated by eliminating a small minority of accident-prone persons. Employment techniques are also used to select persons for all manner of inspection work who have a higher-than-average proficiency in detecting errors.

3.6. ECONOMY OF STANDARDIZATION AND SIMPLIFICATION

A standard is a specification. Products designated as *standardized* conform to a previously accepted specification. Standardization, the conduct of activities in accordance with previously determined specifications, appears to be a modern development, particularly as it relates to the production of goods. Both products and the procedures by which they are made are subject to standardization.

Simplification is a name for the practice of examining a line of products for the purpose of eliminating useless variety in style, color, dimensions, size range, and the like. Its practice results in setting up what might be termed *most useful specifications* for a line of products. Thus simplification is closely related to standardization. Simplification may be thought of as being the practice of eliminating undesirable standards.

There are a number of reasons, related to economy, why standardization has become a widespread practice. One factor is undoubtedly that human actions are characterized by variation and individualism whereas machine action is characterized by repetition of identical patterns. Thus it is relatively easy to build machines that operate and produce goods in accordance with predetermined specifications. As the burden of production has been shifted from human effort and skills to machines, it has been necessary, at least to the extent of machine processes, to standardize.

The chief drive to standardization is probably specialization. It is recognized as characteristic that the skill and speed of performance is increased and the effort of performance is decreased as a person repetitiously performs a specified task. It is also known that persons have greater aptitude for doing some things than others; more people may be found with one skill than several. It is rarity that places triple-threat men in demand in football.

Specialization is not economically practical unless it can be engaged in for some time. It is rarely profitable to build a machine for a total lifetime production of a single part. Nor would it be profitable to set up an assembly line of a number of specialized people to assemble a single unit of product.

Standardization is a method of increasing the number of units of one kind for a given total production. Suppose that a pottery has had an annual output of 1,000 nonstandardized vases made in accordance with 40 different patterns, each in 5 different sizes. Thus the output embraces 200 different specifications and an average annual output of 5 units per specification. If it were decided to standardize on one vase of one size, the annual output per specification would be increased from 5 to 1,000 units. Thus it appears that the economy of standardization lies, in large measure, in the increased opportunity for specialization afforded by increased volume of one kind of product or activity.

Since standards ordinarily have extended usefulness in terms of time and volume, it is often economical to take great pains to perfect them. A standard is in reality a predetermined decision to act in accordance with a certain specification in certain situations. Even though a standard may be developed only after a considerable expenditure, it will probably result in a lower cost per decision than if each specification problem were decided as it arose without benefit of a standard. Suppose that a certain situation necessitating decision arises in a concern 1,000 times per year and that the cost of making each decision individually, owing to confusion, error, and loss of time, amounts to $1. A standard procedure that could reduce this cost to $0.10 per decision, for instance, would justify an expenditure of $900 (or more, if applicable for more than one year).

One valuable feature of standards is that they greatly facilitate communication. Involved directions, for instance, may be given simply by pointing out the standards that should be applied. This is of tremendous value in coordinating the activities of large groups of people as in modern industry.

3.7. ECONOMY OF METHOD

The same end result may often be attained by two or more different methods. For instance, parts made to the same specifications on a machine lathe or an automatic lathe have equal objective or functional value. However, we should not lose sight of the fact that the method by which an article is made often affects people emotionally so that they impute value to an article because of the method by which it was made. Thus, hand-sewn leather goods frequently command a higher price than those which are machine-sewn, although they possess no greater functional value. It is in recognition of this fact that such terms as hand-sewn, hand-polished, and hand-set are used in sales literature.

Comparisons of the economic desirability of methods are significant only when their end results are of equal value. Both functional and intangible values must be considered. Consider the following example:

A builder of homes who is operating in a small town is building a house for a client who specifies a full basement. The basement is to have outside dimensions of 30 feet by 32 feet and will require excavation to a depth of 6 feet below grade. The plans for the basement walls specify 12-inch concrete blocks; and, since the location is high and underdrainage is provided, no waterproofing will be required. Thus, the excavation may be as close to exact size as is practical for the method used.

A survey of equipment and labor available reveals that the contractor can have a local man do the excavating with a tractor and scraper for $24 per eight-hour day; or, he can rent a power shovel from a neighboring town for $120 per day plus a $100 moving charge. In either case some handwork will be necessary to trim corners and to level at the rate of $6 per cubic yard. Either method of excavation will be equally satisfactory to the client, since the end result will have equal functional value regardless of the method used.

The tractor with scraper can remove an average of 3 cubic feet per load and will require approximately 4 minutes per trip to load and unload. To enable the tractor to move in and out, a slope must be maintained which leaves 4 cubic yards to be removed by hand shoveling. Trimming of corners will require removal of an additional 10 cubic yards by hand.

The contractor analyzes the costs associated with the tractor scraper method as follows:

Total cubic yards to be removed, $\dfrac{30 \times 32 \times 6}{27}$................... 214

Cubic yards removable by tractor scraper.................... 200

Tractor method cost,

$\dfrac{200 \text{ cu. yd.} \times 27 \text{ cu. ft. per cu. yd.}}{3 \text{ cu. ft. per load} \times 15 \text{ loads per hr.}} \times \$3 \text{ per hr.}$.............. $360

Hand excavation 14 cu. yd. @ $6............................ 84

$\overline{}$

$444

The power shovel can excavate the basement in 2 days, leaving only 8 yards to be completed by hand. The contractor analyzes the costs associated with the power shovel method as follows:

Moving cost... $100
Rental charge, 2 days @ $120................................ 240
Hand excavation 8 cu. yd. @ $6.............................. 48

$\overline{}$

$388

Based on the calculations above the contractor would hire the power shovel to do the excavation since its use results in the lower net cost to him.

Later on in the construction of the residence, the contractor finds that he is unable to secure the services of a painter to hand-paint the exterior as specified in the contract. He asks the client to accept spray painting in return for a reduction of the contract price by $30. Although agreeing that the functional result of the two methods will be equal, the client refuses to accept the spray painting and the reduction in cost to him. The reason for his refusal is that he is on a bowling team on which there is a painter.

It should be noted that the client was concerned only with the final results in considering methods of excavation, but that while agreeing that either method of painting resulted in equal functional value to him, he held the intangible consideration of offending a teammate to be in excess of the $30 he might have saved.

Many decisions are made on the basis of intangible considerations. It is defensible to make such decisions when they are made knowingly, in full knowledge of the cost and other considerations. It should be the aim of economy studies to assign concrete values to as many of the factors involved as possible, in order to minimize the consideration of intangibles in making a decision.

3.8. ECONOMY AND PREPARATION

Nearly any activity requires some preparation prior to its performance. After the activity has been performed, it is frequently necessary to expend further effort in restoration — cleaning the machine, returning tools to the cabinet, and so forth. These two items are frequently termed *set-up* and *break-up*.

A student about to do an assigned plate in mechanical drawing must assemble his books and instruments, go to the drafting laboratory, arrange his books and instruments upon the drafting table, and study the assignment prior to performing any actual work upon the plate. After he has completed the plate and handed it to his instructor, he will gather up books and instruments and return to his room. It may be noted that set-up and break-up, for convenience lumped together as preparation in the example, may represent a large proportion of the total effort. It may also be noted that the preparation is constant for a considerable range of time devoted to the actual drafting in a single period.

In a certain office where mimeographed sheets were collated, it had been the practice to collate each day. Observation of the collating job revealed that it required an average of 24 minutes of preparation time for the girl employed at this task each time it was performed. The actual collating was done at the average rate of 50 sheets per minute. This situation is presented diagrammatically in Figure 3.5.

Further observation revealed that an average of 500 sheets were collated per day and that this work could as well accumulate and be done weekly. The girl's hourly pay rate was $1.60.

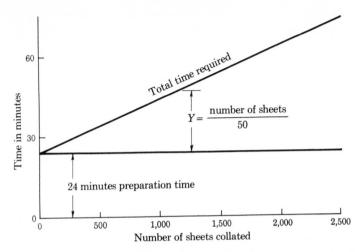

Figure 3.5. Preparation and actual collating time required.

When the collating is done daily, the cost per thousand sheets may be calculated as follows:

$$\frac{24 \text{ min.} + 10 \text{ min.}}{0.5 \text{ M sheets}} \times \frac{\$1.60}{60 \text{ min.}} = \$1.81.$$

When the collating is done weekly (5 days), the cost per thousand sheets is calculated as follows:

$$\frac{24 \text{ min.} + 50 \text{ min.}}{2.5 \text{ M sheets}} \times \frac{\$1.60}{60 \text{ min.}} = \$0.79.$$

The decision to collate weekly would thus result in a cost reduction of

$$\frac{\$1.81 - \$0.79}{\$1.81} = 56 \text{ per cent.}$$

3.9. ECONOMY AND LOCATION

There are many situations in which geographical location is a factor in economy. Situations in which location is important over a short period of time, say a year or less, come properly under the heading of present or immediate economy. Small differences of location, as for example the location of part bins and tools in a work place, may have considerable effect upon economy and are often given very detailed consideration by motion study analysts.

It is not uncommon for concerns to set up temporary service facilities in an area in which they have unusual temporary activities. They are then confronted with determining the economy of setting up such facilities and the economy of various locations within the area.

A firm having a contract to build a dam requiring 300,000 cubic yards of gravel found two feasible sources whose characteristics are summarized as follows:

	Source A	Source B
Distance, pit to dam site	1.8 miles	0.6 mile
Cost of gravel per cubic yard at pit	. . .	$0.08
Purchase price of pit	$7,200	. . .
Road construction necessary	$2,400	None
Overburden to be removed at $0.24 per cu. yd.	. . .	60,000
Hauling cost per cubic yd. per mile as bid by hauling contractor	$0.072	$0.084

In order to make a selection on the basis of economy, the cost of securing the required gravel from either source should be determined. The cost of 300,000 cubic yards of gravel from Source A is calculated as follows:

Purchase price of pit	$ 7,200
Road construction	2,400
Hauling cost, 300,000 cu. yd. × 1.8 miles @ $0.072 per cu. yd. per mile	38,900
	$48,500

The cost of 300,000 cubic yards of gravel from Source B is:

Cost of gravel at pit, 300,000 yd. @ $0.08	$24,000
Removal of overburden, 60,000 yd. @ $0.24	14,400
Hauling cost, 300,000 cu. yd. × 0.6 mile @ $0.084 per cu. yd. per mile	15,100
	$53,500

The cost of making analyses similar to the one covering the situation above is often a small percentage of the saving that may result from a correct decision. A cursory analysis or "hunch" cannot often be defended for decision-making on the basis of its lesser cost.

3.10. ECONOMY AND IDENTIFICATION

Much effort is devoted to ascertaining what things are. After a thing has been identified, further effort is often expended in having the thing carry its identification along with it for subsequent ready reference. Identification refers to the establishment of certain qualities of a thing and may embrace a wide variety of attributes. Some of these that are related to physical qualities are chemical constituents, proportion of ingredients in a mix, history of processing (such as in the case of heat treatment of steel), and dimensions.

Inability to identify an object or a service may greatly impair its value. This may be illustrated by an amusing example. As a prank, a youngster removed the labels from the family's stock of canned goods. The prank proved to be a costly one, for to get a desired item for a meal it often became necessary to open and discard several cans of fruit or vegetables. In military activities, identification is considered of such importance that great precaution is exercised to see that the enemy cannot identify military units, equipment, installations, and roads.

Identification is an important factor in economy; many practices are based upon knowing the attributes of things. The activity of inspection is based upon the value of identification, the knowing that the attributes of the things being inspected come within prescribed limits. A failure to identify industrial stores properly may result in serious losses. It is not uncommon for extensive damage to be caused to elaborate cutting tools through the substitution of a material of inferior machinability in an automatic machining process. Airplanes may be rendered hazardous by inadvertent substitution of inferior fuel. Some chemical processes become dangerous through the inclusion of an undesired ingredient through misidentification. Though welding is far superior in many applications for joining materials, the strategic factor in rejecting it for some applications has been the difficulty of identifying inferior welds. Better methods of identifying the quality of welds have been the object of tremendous effort; welding has been extended as these have been developed. In the manufacture of pharmaceuticals, unusual precautions are taken to insure that each item manufactured is correctly identified by its label. Means for identification may be an object of investigation; more and more technical research is directed to this end.

The economic value of an identification depends upon (1) the cost of identification, (2) the consequences of misidentification, and (3) the cost related to making a decision when identification is lacking. Consider a large lot of castings, all of which are supposed to be annealed, which is suspected of including several unannealed castings.

If the cost of inspecting the lot at the machine or elsewhere is $8, and the consequences of each attempt at machining an unannealed casting is $2 in broken tools, delay, and so forth, it is reasonable to suppose that the lot will be inspected. If the lot is inspected, the lack of identification will add $8 to the cost of the lot. If the lot is not inspected, the lack of identification will add $2 times the number of unannealed castings to the cost of the lot. In either case a decision must be made whether to spend $8 or take a chance that there will be less than four defective castings in the lot. The cost of making this decision also adds to the cost of this lot.

Identification is also important in relation to knowledge about nonphysical things. One of the most important assets that a concern may have is that large numbers of customers and prospective customers identify the concern as being a vendor of good products at reasonable prices. It is not enough that a concern makes a good product, if this fact remains unknown to potential buyers of such a product. Thus huge sums are spent upon establishing brand names as means whereby people can identify products.

Success in engineering consulting practice depends upon being known for sound counsel as well as upon the actual rendering of sound counsel. Most consultants realize this and take definite steps to identify themselves to people as being dependable. This they may do by rendering service that will elicit the favorable comment of those they serve, and by taking part in the activities of technical societies, writing for publication, and in other ways directing the attention of prospective clients to their capabilities.

3.11. ECONOMY IN THE APPROPRIATE COMBINATION OF ELEMENTS

There are many instances in which economy rests on the appropriateness of a combination of several elements. Consider the machining of a metal shaft on a lathe. The job will be accomplished economically if the feed and speed of the tool is appropriate in the light of the metal being machined, the character of the tool, the rigidity of the tool holder, the power available, and the strength of the machine components. Each of these elements must be appropriate for the total purpose if the total purpose is to be pursued economically.

A great many machines can be built from such common machine

elements as levers, cams, columns, beams, ratchets, gears, and pulleys. However, the economic worth of the resulting machines depends largely upon the appropriateness of the combination of the several machine elements, rather than upon the excellence of the individual elements. In a similar manner, the success of any economic venture results from the effectiveness of the combination of elements employed rather than upon the success of the separate elements.

For example, a well-designed office building might be constructed on a well-located site for the purpose of economic gain by lease of office space. But if the building is too small to yield a return sufficient for the purpose as a whole, the income derived might only cover the cost of the building and not the cost of the expensive site. In this case, the building was not matched to the site in a manner that would contribute to the economic success of the entire undertaking.

Much excellent work produces little result because it is directed to perfecting details rather than to perfecting their joint effect. One objective of engineering economy is to prepare the engineer to cope with social and economic elements as well as with physical factors so that his ability will be improved to consider the joint effect of these elements in situations involving engineering application.

PROBLEMS

1. Two alternate designs are under consideration for a tapered fastening pin. Either design will serve equally well and will involve the same material and manufacturing cost except for the lathe and grinder operations.

   Design A will require 16 hours of lathe time and 4.5 hours of grinder time per 1,000 units. Design B will require 7 hours of lathe time and 12 hours of grinder time per 1,000 units. The operating cost of the lathe including labor is $4.60 per hour. The operating cost of the grinder including labor is $3.80 per hour. Which design should be adopted if 80,000 units are required per year and what is the saving over the alternate design?

2. The flooring for an area 12 feet by 15 feet has been designed for a floor joist spacing of 18 inches center-to-center. The joists may span either the 12-foot or the 15-foot dimension. The joists are to support a uniform loading of 120 pounds per square foot including the weight of the flooring. Space restrictions limit the depth of the joists to 10 inches. Joists are to

be selected from standard size lumber; that is, the width is available in increments of 1 inch and the length in increments of 2 feet. The allowable stress in the joist is 1,400 psi and the cost of the lumber is $140 per 1,000 board feet.

The stress in a beam of rectangular cross section is given by the expression $S = 6$ $l^2w/8bd^2$, where $S =$ stress in psi; $l =$ span of joist in inches; $w =$ load on beam in pounds per inch of length; $b =$ width of beam in inches; $d =$ depth of beam in inches. Determine the most economical span for the joists and find the saving over the alternate design.

3. It has been decided by a previous design that 4 by 4-inch rough pine shores will be used to support certain concrete forms. The contractor will need 175 shores, each 10 feet long and each capable of supporting a load of 5,000 pounds induced by the forms and concrete.

The maximum safe load on a shore is given by the expression $P = 1,000$ $(1 - g/80b)bh$, where $P =$ maximum safe load in pounds; $g =$ height of shore in inches; $b =$ width of shore in inches; $h =$ depth of shore in inches. It has been decided that the 4-inch width of the shores will be maintained in any redesign consideration. If rough pine lumber costs $100 per 1,000 board feet, what total amount can be saved by the elimination of overdesign?

4. The chief engineer in charge of refinery operations is not satisfied with the preliminary design for storage tanks to be used as part of a plant expansion program. The engineer who submitted the design was called in and asked to reconsider the over-all dimensions in the light of an article in *The Chemical Engineer*, titled "How to Size Future Process Vessels."

The original design submitted called for 4 tanks 15 feet in diameter and 20 feet high. From a graph in the article, the engineer found that the present ratio of height to diameter of 1.33 is 111 per cent of the minimum cost and that the minimum cost for a tank occurred when the ratio of height to diameter was 4 to 1. The cost for the tank design as originally submitted was estimated to be $15,000. What are the optimum tank dimensions if the volume remains the same as for the original design? What total saving may be expected through redesign?

5. An architectural engineer is considering means for saving design and construction cost for a new suburban development involving 100 new homes. The approach of using a limited number of house designs repeated throughout the area is eliminated because of the resulting reduction in sales appeal produced by an area of "look alike" houses. Individual designs for each house would increase design and construction costs to such an extent that sales would be difficult.

The engineer decides that one means of decreasing costs without making houses look alike is to use interchangeable foundation and floor structure designs. Estimates show that the average cost of design for a foundation is $260 and that floor structure design averages $180 per design; the average cost of construction of a foundation is $2,400 and the average cost of floor structure construction is $1,600. The use of 10 basic designs repeated throughout the housing area will save the total costs of design after the first 10 houses and will save 6 per cent of the costs of construction of foundations and floor structures after the first 10 houses. How much can the sale price of each house be reduced without a loss of profit by using this system of interchangeable design for foundations and floor structure?

6. In the design of buildings to be constructed in Northern Greenland, the designer is considering the type window frame to specify. Either steel or aluminum window frames will satisfy design criteria. Due to the remote location of the building site and the lack of building materials in Greenland, the window frames will be purchased in the United States and transported a distance of 3,500 miles to the site. The price of window frames of the type required is $42 each for steel frames and $56 each for aluminum frames. The weight of steel window frames is 150 pounds each and the weight of aluminum window frames is 50 pounds each. The transportation shipping rate is $0.005 per pound per 100 miles. Which design should be specified and what is the economic advantage of the selection?

7. In the design of an engine part, the designer has a choice of specifying either an aluminum alloy casting or a steel casting. Either material will provide equal service, but the aluminum casting will weigh 1.20 pounds as compared with 1.35 pounds for the steel casting.

The aluminum can be cast for $2.40 per pound and the steel can be cast for $1.30 per pound. The cost of machining per unit is $1.20 for the aluminum and $1.40 for the steel. Every pound of excess weight is assessed a penalty of $20 due to increased fuel consumption. Which material should be specified and what is the economic advantage of the selection per unit?

8. The volume of the raw material required for a metal part is 0.123 cubic inch. Its finished volume is 0.064 cubic inch. The machining time per piece is 0.246 minute for steel and 0.144 minute for brass. The cost of the specified steel is $0.18 per pound and the value of steel scrap is negligible. The cost of the specified brass is $0.46 per pound and the value of brass scrap is $0.08 per pound. The hourly cost of the required machine and operator is $3.20. The weight of brass and steel

is 0.309 and 0.283 pounds per cubic inch, respectively. Determine the comparative costs per piece for steel and brass parts.

9. An engineer in charge of quality control in a production shop finds that the cost of decreased tolerance on a certain shaft is $10 for every increment of 0.005 of an inch. The cost of material per unit is $20. The operation cost of the lathe is $4 per hour and the operator receives $3 per hour.

The time required for turning a shaft with a tolerance limit of 0.030 is 2 hours. For each incremental reduction of 0.005 in tolerance, the machining time may be expected to increase by 30 minutes, 60 minutes, 90 minutes, 120 minutes, and 180 minutes from the 2-hour base time. Find the degree of perfection expressed as a tolerance limit that will result in a minimum total cost per shaft produced.

10. A chemical processing company is currently producing 10,000,000 pounds of Class B sulphuric acid per year at a cost of $1.80 per 100 pounds. At the present time, the process is controlled so that the product is 94.6 per cent pure.

Upon checking the specifications for Class B sulphuric acid, the engineer in charge of the process finds that the purity must fall between 90 and 95 per cent. The decision is made to adjust the process so that the degree of purity obtained drops by 4.2 per cent, thus resulting in a product purity of 90.4 per cent. After one year of operation, cost data indicates that production costs fell to $1.75 per 100 pounds of product. As a result of this reduction in perfection, how much was the company able to save for the year's operation?

11. A 3-phase, 220-volt, squirrel cage induction motor is to be used to drive a pump which will fill a series of storage tanks. It is estimated that 300 horsepower-hours will be required each day for 365 days per year. Motors having the following characteristics may be leased:

Size (h.p.)	Lease Rate (Per Year)	Operating Cost (Per h.p.-hr.)
20	$128	$0.0044
40	$134	$0.0037
75	$142	$0.0031
100	$156	$0.0028
150	$192	$0.0025

Plot the total yearly cost as a function of the size of the motor and select the size that will result in a minimum cost per year.

12. Either aluminum alloy or stainless steel will serve equally well in a certain corrosive environment. Aluminum alloy has a yield strength of

20,000 pounds per square inch and stainless steel has a yield strength of 33,000 pounds per square inch. The aluminum alloy will cost $0.68 per pound and the stainless steel will cost $0.94 per pound. The specific gravities of aluminum alloy and stainless steel are respectively 2.79 and 7.77. If selection is based upon yield strength which material will be more economical?

13. In the manufacture of a line of equipment, a number of metal cylinders 3 inches long and of the following diameters were specified to be used in the indicated quantities:

Diameter in inches...	¼	⅜	½	⅝	¾	⅞	1
Annual quantity.....	12,000	10,000	8,000	5,000	4,000	3,000	2,000

It is estimated that each size eliminated will result in an annual savings of $70 owing to decrease in set-up costs, record keeping, and so forth. It is proposed that the ⅜-inch, ⅝-inch, and ⅞-inch sizes be eliminated and that the next larger size be used in each case. The simplification of sizes will increase material costs. Determine the savings resulting from the elimination of each of the three sizes if the $70 estimate is correct. The metal weighs 0.29 pound per cubic inch and costs $0.11 per pound.

14. A contractor has been awarded the contract to construct an earth fill dam requiring 500,000 cubic yards of fill. Two possible sources of fill have been found: Source A, above the dam site at a distance of 4 miles at which the pit will be operated and maintained by the contractor, and Source B which is below the dam site at a distance of 2.6 miles from which the contractor must purchase the fill by the cubic yard. The haul cost per cubic yard will be different because in one instance the loaded trucks will travel down slope, in the other they will travel up slope. The following estimates are available:

	A	B
Purchase price of pit.....................	$10,000	....
Cost of fill per cu. yd. at pit..............	....	$0.12
Construction of haul road................	$ 3,500	....
Maintenance of haul road................	$ 1,800	....
Hauling cost per cu. yd. per mile..........	$ 0.095	$0.13

Which source should the contractor choose? What savings will result from choosing this source?

15. A ditching machine that averages 40 feet per hour is to be used for a ditch 5,280 feet long. Allowing 30 minutes for servicing the machine per day, how many days will it take to complete the ditch if a total of 6, 8, 10 hours per day is devoted to the job?

16. In a steel fabrication shop, various size rivet holes must be made in structural members. This may be done by laying out the position of the holes on the members and using a drill press. For this method, a machinist's wage rate is $2.25 per hour and he can drill 27 holes per hour. An alternate method is the use of the multiple punch machine. For this process, the machinist's wage rate is $2 per hour and he can complete 8 holes per minute. This method requires $0.05 per hole to set the multiple punch machine and installation cost is $2,000.

(a) If all other costs of the two methods are assumed equal, what is the comparative costs for 3,000 holes?

(b) For what number of rivet holes will the multiple punch machine pay for itself?

17. A manufacturer makes 7,000,000 radio tubes per year. An assembly operation is performed on each tube for which a standard piece rate of $1.02 per hundred pieces is paid. The standard cycle time per piece is 0.624 minute. Overhead costs associated with the operation are estimated at $0.36 per operator hour.

If the standard cycle time can be reduced by 0.01 of a minute and if one-half of the overhead cost per operator hour is saved for each hour by which total operator hours are reduced, what will be the maximum amount that can be spent to bring about the 0.01 of a minute reduction in cycle time? Assume that the improvement will be in effect for one year, that piece rates will be reduced in proportion to the reduction in cycle time, and that the average operator's time per piece is equal to the standard time per piece in either case.

18. An automobile parts manufacturer located in City A dispatches a shipment of finished parts to its warehouse in City B each day. The distance is 200 miles and the cost per mile is estimated to be $0.15 plus $2.50 per hour for the driver. The truck makes the return trip without payload. A trucking company located in City B has a contract to haul finished castings to City A and has established its cost per mile to be $0.18 plus $2 per hour for the driver. The return trip is made without payload. The round-trip time for the trucking company and the manufacturer is 9 hours.

The parts manufacturer has offered to subcontract the hauling of the machined castings. It is estimated that the task will cause an increase in expenses equivalent to an additional 20 miles and an increased round-trip time of 1 hour and 45 minutes.

(a) What is the minimum that the manufacturing company can charge for the casting haul?

(b) What is the maximum that the trucking company can pay for sub-contracting the haul?

19. The cost of manufacturing a certain tool is $2.75 per unit of which $0.85 arises from material cost and the balance is processing cost. A new design is under consideration which will require an initial cost of $19,500. If the new design is adopted, the cost of material will be reduced by 6 per cent and the cost of processing will be reduced by 3.5 per cent. If 800,000 units are to be manufactured per year, and if the benefits from the improved design are to be considered for one year only, what amount can be spent for the new design if a return of $3 is required for each $1 spent?

20. A product that costs $2 to manufacture is being made at the rate of 500,000 per year. Manufacturing cost is divided as follows: $1.25 for processing and $0.75 for materials. A new design is being considered as a replacement for the old. It is estimated that the processing cost and the material cost can be reduced 5 per cent and 10 per cent, respectively. It is also estimated that it will cost $20,000 to change production facilities so that the new design can be implemented. The benefits of the new design are not to be considered for more than one year. For every $10 of savings produced by the design, the company is willing to spend $3 How much may the company spend on the new design?

PART II

INTEREST, EQUIVALENCE, AND DEPRECIATION

CHAPTER 4

INTEREST
AND INTEREST FORMULAS

The term *interest* is used to designate a rental for the use of money. Fundamentally, the rental paid for the use of equipment is essentially the same as interest paid for the use of capital. Charging a rental for the use of money is a practice dating back to the time of man's earliest recorded history. The ethics and economics of interest have been a subject of discussion for philosophers, theologians, statesmen, and economists throughout the ages. The individual interested in these aspects of interest will find extensive literature for study, but the charging of interest for the use of money is a practical fact that must be considered by those who make engineering economy studies.

Unlike the examples of present economy analysis given in the previous chapter, many engineering proposals will involve receipts and disbursements over an extended period of time. In such cases the time value of money in the form of an interest rate becomes an important consideration. This chapter will be devoted to the task of developing interest formulas needed in the equitable comparison of these alternative engineering proposals.

4.1. INTEREST RATE AND INTEREST

An *interest rate* is the ratio of the gain received from an investment and the investment over a period of time, usually one year. Also, an interest rate may be expressed as a ratio between the amount paid for the use of funds and the amount of funds used.

In one aspect, interest is an amount of money *received* as a result of investing funds, either by loaning it or by using it in the purchase of materials, labor, or facilities. Interest received in this connection is gain or profit. In another aspect, interest is an amount of money *paid out* as a result of borrowing funds. Interest paid in this connection is a *cost*.

In many engineering economy studies only small elements of a whole enterprise are considered. For example, studies are often made to evaluate the consequences of the purchase of a single tool or machine in a complex of many facilities. In such cases it would be desirable to isolate the element from the whole by some means analogous to the "free body" diagram in mechanics. To do this, for example, with respect to a machine being considered for purchase, it would be necessary to learn all the receipts and all the disbursements that would arise from the machine. If this could be done, the disbursements could be subtracted from the receipts. This difference would represent profit or gain, from which a rate of return could be calculated.

It is usually difficult and often impossible to learn what receipts result from a small part of a much larger whole. Therefore, numerous engineering economy studies are made on the basis of costs. For example, it may be assumed that two machines will perform a necessary service, i.e., result in equal income for the enterprise as a whole. Then the two machines can be compared on the basis of a summation of their costs.

In a cost analysis of an element, the element is isolated from the whole, even to the point of considering that the funds necessary to put it into effect are borrowed by the element. The interest on the funds assumed to be borrowed will then become a charge against the element and thus a cost. This is merely a method of taking cognizance of the amount of funds required to put into effect alternatives to be compared.

4.2. INTEREST RATE FROM THE LENDER'S VIEWPOINT

A person who has a sum of money is faced with several alternatives regarding its use:

1. He may exchange the money for goods and services that will satisfy his personal wants. Such an exchange would involve the purchase of consumer goods.

2. He may exchange the money for productive goods or instruments. Such an exchange would involve the purchase of producer goods.

3. He may hoard the money, either for the satisfaction of gloating over it, or in awaiting an opportunity for its subsequent use.

4. He may lend the money asking only that the original sum be returned at some future date.

5. He may lend the money on the condition that the borrower will repay the initial sum plus interest at some future date.

If the decision is to lend the money with the expectation of its return plus interest, the lender must consider a number of factors in deciding on the interest rate. The following are perhaps the most important:

1. What is the probability that the borrower will not repay the loan? The answer to this question may be derived from the integrity of the borrower, his wealth, his potential earnings, and the value of any security granted the lender. If the chances are one in fifty that the loan will not be repaid, the lender is justified in charging 2 per cent of the sum to compensate him for the risk of loss.

2. What expense will be incurred in investigating the borrower, drawing up the loan agreement, transferring the funds to the borrower, and collecting the loan? If the sum of the loan is $1,000 for a period of one year and the lender values his efforts at $10, then he is justified in charging 1 per cent of the sum to compensate for the expense involved.

3. What net amount will compensate for being deprived of electing other alternatives for disposing of the money? Assume that $3 per hundred or 3 per cent is considered adequate.

On the basis of the reasoning above, the interest rate arrived at will be 2 per cent plus 1 per cent plus 3 per cent, or 6 per cent. Therefore, an interest rate may be thought of, for convenience, as being made up of percentages for (1) risk of loss, (2) administrative expenses, and (3) pure gain or interest.

4.3. INTEREST RATE FROM THE BORROWER'S VIEWPOINT

In many, if not most, cases the alternatives open to the borrower for the use of borrowed funds are limited by the lender, who may grant the loan only on condition that it be used for a specific purpose. Except as limited by the conditions of a loan, the borrower has open to him essentially the same alternatives for the use of money as a person who has ownership of money, but the borrower is faced with the necessity of repaying the amount borrowed and the interest on it in accordance with the conditions of the loan agreement or suffering the consequences. The consequences may be loss of reputation, seizure of property or of other moneys, or the placing of a lien on his future earnings. Organized society provides many pressures, legal and social, to induce a borrower to repay a loan. Default may have serious and even disastrous consequences to the borrower.

The prospective borrower's viewpoint on the rate of interest will be influenced by the use he intends to make of funds he may borrow. If he borrows the funds for personal use, the interest rate he is willing to pay will be a measure of the amount he is willing to pay for the privilege of having satisfactions immediately instead of in the future.

If funds are borrowed to finance operations expected to result in a gain, the interest to be paid must be less than the expected gain. An example of this is the common practice of banks and similar enterprises of borrowing funds to lend to others. In this case it is evident that the amount paid out as interest, plus risks incurred, plus administrative expenses must be less than the interest received on the money reloaned, if the practice is to be profitable. A borrower may be expected to seek to borrow funds at the lowest interest rate possible.

4.4. THE EARNING POWER OF MONEY

Funds borrowed for the prospect of gain are commonly exchanged for goods, services, or instruments of production. This leads us to the consideration of the earning power of money that may make it profitable to borrow money. Consider the following example:

Mr. Digg manually digs ditches for draining land. For this he is paid $0.06 per linear foot and averages 200 linear feet per day. Weather conditions limit this kind of work to 120 days per year. Thus, he has an income of $12 per day worked or $1,440 per year.

An advertisement brings to his attention a power ditcher that can be purchased for $1,200. He buys the ditcher after borrowing $1,200 at 8 per cent interest. The machine will dig an average of 800 linear feet per day. By reducing the price to $0.05 per linear foot he can get sufficient work to keep the machine busy when the weather will   permit.

At the end of the year the ditching machine is abandoned because it is worn out.   A summary of the venture follows:

Receipts
Amount of loan....................................	$1,200	
Payment for ditches dug, 120 days × 800 lin. ft. × $0.05	$4,800	$6,000

Disbursements
Purchase of ditcher..............................	$1,200	
Fuel and repairs for machine.......................	700	
Interest on loan, $1,200 × 0.08....................	96	
Repayment of loan..............................	1,200	$3,196

Receipts Less Disbursements...............................	$2,804

For Mr. Digg, $2,804 represents an increase in net earnings for the year with the ditcher over the previous year of $2,804 − $1,440 = $1,364. Thus, the borrowed funds have made it possible for Mr. Digg to increase his earnings by $1,364.

The above example is an illustration of what is commonly spoken of as the "earning power of money." It should be noted that the money borrowed was converted into an instrument of production. It was the instrument of production, the ditcher, which enabled Mr. Digg to increase his earnings. If Mr. Digg had held the money throughout the year it could have earned him nothing; also, if he had exchanged it for an instrument of production that turned out to be unprofitable, he might have lost money. Indirectly money has earning power when exchanged for profitable instruments of production.

4.5. SIMPLE INTEREST

The rental rate for a sum of money is usually expressed as the per cent of the sum that is to be paid for the use of the sum for a period of one year. Interest rates are also quoted for periods other than one year, known as interest periods. In order to simplify the following discussion, consideration of interest rates for periods of other than one year will be deferred until later.

In simple interest the interest to be paid on repayment of a loan is proportional to the length of time the principal sum has been borrowed. The interest that will be earned may be found in the following manner. Let P represent the principal, n the interest period, and i the interest rate. Then

$$I = Pni.$$

Suppose that $1,000 is borrowed at simple interest at a rate of 6 per cent per annum. At the end of one year, the interest would be

$$I = \$1,000(1)(0.06) = \$60.$$

The principal plus interest would be $1,060 and would be due at the end of the year.

A simple interest loan may be made for any period of time. Interest and principal become due only at the end of the loan period. When it is necessary to calculate the interest due for a fraction of a year, it is common to consider the year as composed of twelve months of thirty days each, or 360 days. For example, on a loan of $100 at an interest rate of 7 per cent per annum for the period February 1 to April 30, the interest due on April 20 along with the principal sum of $100 would be $0.07(\$100)(80 \div 360) = \$1.55$.

4.6. COMPOUND INTEREST

When a loan is made for a length of time equal to several interest periods, provision is made that the earned interest is *due at the end of each interest period.* For example, the payments on a loan of $1,000 at 6 per cent interest per annum for a period of four years would be calculated as shown in Table 4.1.

Table 4.1. APPLICATION OF COMPOUND INTEREST WHEN INTEREST IS PAID ANNUALLY

Year	Amount owed at beginning of year	Interest to be paid at end of year	Amount owed at end of year	Amount to be paid by borrower at end of year
1	$1,000	$60	$1,060	$ 60
2	1,000	60	1,060	60
3	1,000	60	1,060	60
4	1,000	60	1,060	1,060

If the borrower is allowed to keep the earned interest until the entire loan becomes due, the loan will be increased by an amount equal to the interest due at the end of each year. In this case, no yearly interest payments are required and interest is said to be compounded. On this basis, a loan of $1,000 at 6 per cent interest compounded annually for a period of four years will be as shown in Table 4.2.

Table 4.2. APPLICATION OF COMPOUND INTEREST WHEN INTEREST IS PERMITTED TO COMPOUND

Year	Amount owed at beginning of year (A)	Interest to be added to loan at end of year (B)	Amount owed at end of year (A + B)	Amount to be paid by borrower at end of year
1	$1,000.00	$1,000.00 × 0.06 = $60.00	$1,000 (1.06) = $1,060.00	$00.00
2	1,060.00	1,060.00 × 0.06 = 63.60	1,000 (1.06)² = 1,123.60	00.00
3	1,123.60	1,123.60 × 0.06 = 67.42	1,000 (1.06)³ = 1,191.02	00.00
4	1,191.02	1,191.02 × 0.06 = 71.46	1,000 (1.06)⁴ = 1,262.48	1,262.48

Where the interest earned each year is added to the amount of the loan, as in the example above, it is said to be *compounded annually*. The section which follows will present interest formulas useful in dealing with the case where annual payments and annual compounding interest are incurred.

4.7. INTEREST FORMULAS, ANNUAL COMPOUNDING INTEREST-ANNUAL PAYMENTS

The derivations which follow will explore the common situation of annual compounding interest and annual payments. The following symbols will be used. Let

i = the nominal annual interest rate;

n = the number of annual interest periods;

P = a present principal sum;

R = a single payment, in a series of n equal payments, made at the end of each annual interest period;

S = a future sum, n annual interest periods hence, equal to the compound amount of a present principal sum P, or equal to the sum of the compound amounts of payments, R, in a series.

Single-payment compound-amount factor. When interest is permitted to compound, as in Table 4.2, the interest earned is added to the principal at the end of each annual interest period. By substituting general terms in place of numerical values in Table 4.2, the results shown in Table 4.3 are developed. The resulting factor, $(1 + i)^n$, is known as the *single-payment compound-amount factor*.[1]

Table 4.3. DEVELOPMENT OF SINGLE-PAYMENT COMPOUND-AMOUNT FACTOR

year	Amount at beginning of year	Interest earned during year	Compound amount at end of year	
1	P	Pi	$P + Pi$	$= P(1 + i)$
2	$P(1 + i)$	$P(1 + i)i$	$P(1 + i)\quad + P(1 + i)i$	$= P(1 + i)^2$
3	$P(1 + i)^2$	$P(1 + i)^2 i$	$P(1 + i)^2\quad + P(1 + i)^2 i$	$= P(1 + i)^3$
n	$P(1 + i)^{n-1}$	$P(1 + i)^{n-1}i$	$P(1 + i)^{n-1} + P(1 + i)^{n-1}i$	$= P(1 + i)^n$
				$= S$

The single-payment compound-amount factor may be used to find the compound-amount, S, of a present principal sum, P. The relationship is expressed as follows:

$$S = P(1 + i)^n.$$

Referring to the example of Table 4.2, if $1,000 is invested at 6 per cent interest compounded annually at the beginning of year one, the compound amount at the end of the fourth year will be

$$S = \$1,000(1 + 0.06)^4 = \$1,000(1.262) = \$1,262.$$

Single-payment present-worth factor. The single-payment compound-amount relationship may be solved for P as follows:

$$P = S\left[\frac{1}{(1 + i)^n}\right].$$

[1]Values for interest factors for annual compounding interest-annual payments are given in Appendix D, Tables D.1 through D.9.

The resulting factor, $1/(1 + i)^n$, is known as the *single-payment present-worth factor*. This factor may be used to find the present worth, P, of a future amount, S. As an example, if a \$1,262 payment is to be received four years hence, its present worth at 6 per cent compounded annually is

$$P = \$1,262\left[\frac{1}{(1 + 0.06)^4}\right] = \$1,262(0.7921) = \$1,000.$$

Note that the single-payment compound-amount factor and the single-payment present-worth factor are reciprocals.

Equal-payment-series compound-amount factor. In many engineering economy problems, a series of equal payments occurring at the end of succeeding annual interest periods is encountered. The sum of the compound amounts of the several payments may be calculated by use of the single-payment compound-amount factor. For example, the calculation of the compound amount of a series of five \$100 payments made at the end of each year at 6 per cent interest compounded annually is illustrated in Table 4.4.

Table 4.4. THE COMPOUND AMOUNT OF A SERIES OF YEAR-END PAYMENTS

End of year	Year-end payment times compound-amount factor	Compound amount at end of 5 year period	Total compound amount
1	\$100 $(1.06)^4$	\$126	
2	\$100 $(1.06)^3$	\$119	
3	\$100 $(1.06)^2$	\$113	
4	\$100 $(1.06)^1$	\$106	
5	\$100 $(1.06)^0$	\$100	\$564

It is apparent that the method illustrated will be cumbersome for calculating the compound amount of an extensive series. Therefore, it is desirable that a compact solution for this type of problem be available. Using the previously defined terms, and referring to Table 4.4, it may be deduced that

$$S = R(1) + R(1 + i) + \ldots + R(1 + i)^{n-2} + R(1 + i)^{n-1}.$$

Multiplying this equation by $(1 + i)$ results in

$$S(1 + i) = R(1 + i) + R(1 + i)^2 + \ldots + R(1 + i)^{n-1} + R(1 + i)^n.$$

Subtracting the first equation from the second gives

$$S(1 + i) - S = -R + R(1 + i)^n$$

$$S = R\left[\frac{(1 + i)^n - 1}{i}\right].$$

The resulting factor, $[(1 + i)^n - 1]/i$, is known as the *equal-payment-series compound-amount factor*. This factor may be used to find the compound amount, S, of an equal-payment-series, R. For example, the compound amount of the five $100 payments mentioned above will be

$$S = \$100\left[\frac{(1 + 0.06)^5 - 1}{0.06}\right] = \$100(5.637) = \$563.70$$

which agrees with the result found in Table 4.4.

Equal-payment-series sinking-fund factor. The equal-payment-series compound-amount relationship may be solved for R as follows:

$$R = S\left[\frac{i}{(1 + i)^n - 1}\right].$$

The resulting factor, $i/[(1 + i)^n - 1]$, is known as the *equal-payment series sinking-fund factor*. This factor may be used to find the required year end payments, R, to accumulate a future sum, S. If, for example, it is desired to accumulate $563.70 by making a series of five annual payments at 6 per cent interest compounded annually, the required amount of each payment will be

$$R = \$563.70\left[\frac{0.06}{(1 + 0.06)^5 - 1}\right]$$
$$= \$536.70(0.18097) = \$100.$$

The derivation and this example illustrate that the equal-payment-series compound-amount factor and the equal-payment-series sinking-fund factor are reciprocals.

Equal-payment-series capital-recovery factor. The substitution of $P(1 + i)^n$ for S in the equal-payment-series sinking-fund relationship results in

$$R = P(1 + i)^n \left[\frac{i}{(1 + i)^n - 1} \right]$$

$$= P \left[\frac{i(1 + i)^n}{(1 + i)^n - 1} \right].$$

The resulting factor, $i(1 + i)^n/[(1 + i)^n - 1]$ is known as the *equal-payment-series capital-recovery factor*. This factor may be used to find the year end payments, R, that will be provided by a present amount, P. For example, \$1,000 invested at 5 per cent interest compounded annually will provide for eight equal year end payments of

$$R = \$1,000 \left[\frac{0.05(1 + 0.05)^8}{(1 + 0.05)^8 - 1} \right]$$

$$= \$1,000(0.15472) = \$154.72.$$

Equal-payment-series present-worth factor. The equal-payment-series capital-recovery factor may be solved for P as follows:

$$P = R \left[\frac{(1 + i)^n - 1}{i(1 + i)^n} \right].$$

The resulting factor, $[(1 + i)^n - 1]/i(1 + i)^n$, is known as the *equal-payment-series present-worth factor*. This factor may be used to find the present worth, P, of a series of equal annual payments, R. For example, the present worth of a series of eight equal annual payments of \$154.72 at an interest rate of 5 per cent compounded annually will be

$$P = \$154.72 \left[\frac{(1 + 0.05)^8 - 1}{0.05(1 + 0.05)^8} \right]$$

$$= \$154.72(6.463) = \$1,000.$$

This example and the derivation illustrate that the equal-payment-series capital-recovery factor and the equal-payment-series present-worth factor are reciprocals.

4.8. NOMINAL AND EFFECTIVE INTEREST RATES

For simplicity, the discussion to this point has embraced interest periods of only one year. The interest rate used was referred to the nominal annual interest rate. However, agreements may specify that interest shall be paid more frequently, such as each half year, each quarter, or each month. Such agreements result in interest periods of one-half year, one-quarter year, or one-twelfth year, and the compounding of interest twice, four times, or twelve times a year, respectively. The effect of this more frequent compounding is an *effective interest rate* higher than the nominal interest rate.

For example, consider a nominal annual interest rate of 6 per cent with an interest period of one-half year. In this case, the true rate is actually 3 per cent for one-half year. The compound amount of $1 for one year at 3 per cent for one-half year is equal to $1(1.03)^2 = $1.0609. Therefore, the effective interest rate is 1.0609 minus 1.0000 = 0.0609, or 6.09 per cent.

An expression for the effective annual interest rate may be derived from the above reasoning. If φ is the nominal interest rate and if c is the number of interest periods per year, then the

$$\text{effective interest rate} = \left(1 + \frac{\varphi}{c}\right)^c - 1.$$

As a limit, interest may be considered to be compounded an infinite number of times per year; that is, continuously. Under these conditions, the effective interest rate may be derived as follows:

$$\left(1 + \frac{\varphi}{c}\right)^c - 1 = \left[\left(1 + \frac{\varphi}{c}\right)^{c/\varphi}\right]^\varphi - 1,$$

but

$$\lim_{c \to \infty} \left(1 + \frac{\varphi}{c}\right)^{c/\varphi} = e,$$

hence

$$\left[\left(1 + \frac{\varphi}{c}\right)^{c/\varphi}\right]^\varphi - 1 = e^\varphi - 1.$$

Therefore, where interest is compounded continuously, the

$$\text{effective interest rate} = e^\varphi - 1.$$

The effective interest rates corresponding to a nominal annual interest rate of 6 per cent compounded annually, semiannually, quarterly, monthly, weekly, daily, and continuously are respectively 6.000 per cent, 6.090 per cent, 6.136 per cent, 6.168 per cent, 6.180 per cent, 6.183 per cent, and 6.184 per cent.

The interest formulas for annual compounding interest-annual payments were derived on the basis of an interest rate for an interest period; specifically, for a nominal annual interest rate compounded annually. However, they may be used when the nominal annual interest rate is compounded more frequently. This may be done in one of two ways: (1) find the effective interest rate from the relationships derived above or from the effective rates tabulated[2] and use this rate in place of the nominal annual rate, or (2) match the interest rate to the interest period and use the formula directly or its corresponding tabulated value. Consider the following example in which it is desired to find the compound amount of $1,000 four years from now at a nominal annual interest rate of 6 per cent compounded semiannually. The effective interest rate is 6.09 per cent and may be used with the single-payment compound-amount factor as follows:

$$S = \$1,000(1 + 0.0609)^4 = \$1,267.$$

Or, since the nominal annual interest rate is 6 per cent compounded semiannually, the interest rate is 3 per cent for an interest period of one-half year. The required calculation is as follows:

$$S = \$1,000(1 + 0.03)^8 = \$1,267.$$

This analysis may be used for nominal annual interest rates compounded with any frequency up to and including continuous compounding. Note, however, that compounding frequencies in excess of 24 times per year differ only slightly from the assumption of continuous compounding.

4.9. INTEREST FORMULAS, CONTINUOUS COMPOUNDING INTERST-ANNUAL PAYMENTS

In certain economic evaluations, it is reasonable to assume that continuous compounding interest more nearly represents the true situation than does annual compounding. Also, the assumption of continuous compounding may be more convenient from a computational standpoint in some applications. Therefore, this section will present interest formulas that may be used in those cases where

---

[2]Effective interest rates corresponding to nominal annual rates for various compounding frequencies are given in Appendix D, Table D.10.

annual payments and continuous compounding interest seems appropriate. The following symbols will be used. Let

φ = the nominal annual interest rate;

n = the number of annual periods;

P = a present principal sum;

R = a single payment, in a series of n equal payments, made at the end of each annual period;

S = a future sum, n annual periods hence, equal to the compound amount of a present principal sum, P, or equal to the sum of the compound amounts of payments, R in a series.

Single-payment compound-amount factor. When interest is permitted to compound continuously, the interest earned is instantaneously added to the principal at the end of each instantaneous interest period. Let the compound amount after time x be S and after time $x + dx$ be $S + dS$. Then, if dS is the interest accumulated during the small time interval dx,

$$dS = S\varphi \, dx$$

and
$$\frac{dS}{S} = \varphi \, dx;$$

by integration
$$[\ln S]_{x=0}^{x=n} = [\varphi x]_{x=0}^{x=n},$$

$$\ln S - \ln P = n\varphi,$$

$$\frac{S}{P} = e^{n\varphi},$$

and
$$S = Pe^{n\varphi}.$$

The resulting factor, $e^{n\varphi}$, is the *single-payment compound-amount factor*[3] for continuous compounding interest.

Single-payment present-worth factor. The single-payment compound-amount relationship may be solved for P as follows:

$$P = S\frac{1}{e^{n\varphi}}.$$

---

[3]Values for interest factors for continuous compounding interest-annual payments are given in Appendix D, Tables D.11 through D.19.

The resulting factor, $e^{-n\varphi}$, is the *single-payment present-worth factor* for continuous compounding interest.

Equal-payment-series present-worth factor. By considering each payment in the series individually, the total present worth of the series is a sum of the individual present-worth amounts as follows:

$$P = R(e^{-\varphi}) + R(e^{-2\varphi}) + \ldots + R(e^{-n\varphi})$$
$$= Re^{-\varphi}(1 + e^{-\varphi} + e^{-2\varphi} + \ldots + e^{-(n-1)\varphi})$$
$$= Re^{-\varphi}\left[\frac{1 - e^{-n\varphi}}{1 - e^{-\varphi}}\right]$$
$$= R\left[\frac{1 - e^{-n\varphi}}{e^{\varphi} - 1}\right].$$

The resulting factor, $(1 - e^{-n\varphi})/(e^{\varphi} - 1)$, is the *equal-payment series present-worth factor* for continuous compounding interest.

Equal-payment-series capital-recovery factor. The equal-payment-series present-worth relationship may be solved for R as follows:

$$R = P\left[\frac{e^{\varphi} - 1}{1 - e^{-n\varphi}}\right].$$

The resulting factor, $(e^{\varphi} - 1)/(1 - e^{-n\varphi})$, is the *equal-payment-series capital-recovery factor* for continuous compounding interest.

Equal-payment-series sinking-fund factor. The substitution of $Se^{-n\varphi}$ for P in the equal-payment-series capital-recovery relationship results in

$$R = Se^{-n\varphi}\left[\frac{e^{\varphi} - 1}{1 - e^{-n\varphi}}\right]$$
$$= S\left[\frac{e^{\varphi} - 1}{e^{n\varphi} - 1}\right].$$

The resulting factor, $(e^{\varphi} - 1)/(e^{n\varphi} - 1)$, is the *equal-payment-series sinking-fund factor* for continuous compounding interest.

Equal-payment-series compound-amount factor. The equal-payment-series sinking-fund relationship may be solved for S as follows:

$$S = R\left[\frac{e^{n\varphi} - 1}{e^{\varphi} - 1}\right].$$

The resulting factor, $(e^{n\varphi} - 1)/(e^{\varphi} - 1)$, is the *equal-payment-series compound-amount factor* for continuous compounding interest.

4.10. SUMMARY OF INTEREST FACTORS FOR ANNUAL PAYMENTS

The factors for annual compounding interest-annual payments may be summarized as follows:

Single-payment compound-amount factor: $(1 + i)^n$

Single-payment present-worth factor: $\dfrac{1}{(1 + i)^n}$

Equal-payment-series compound-amount factor: $\dfrac{(1 + i)^n - 1}{i}$

Equal-payment-series sinking-fund factor: $\dfrac{i}{(1 + i)^n - 1}$

Equal-payment-series present-worth factor: $\dfrac{(1 + i)^n - 1}{i(1 + i)^n}$

Equal-payment-series capital-recovery factor: $\dfrac{i(1 + i)^n}{(1 + i)^n - 1}$

The factors for continuous compounding interest-annual payments may be summarized as follows:

Single-payment compound-amount factor: $e^{n\varphi}$

Single-payment present-worth factor: $\dfrac{1}{e^{n\varphi}}$

Equal-payment-series compound-amount factor: $\dfrac{e^{n\varphi} - 1}{e^{\varphi} - 1}$

Equal-payment-series sinking-fund factor: $\dfrac{e^{\varphi} - 1}{e^{n\varphi} - 1}$

Equal-payment-series present-worth factor: $\dfrac{1 - e^{-n\varphi}}{e^{\varphi} - 1}$

Equal-payment-series capital-recovery factor: $\dfrac{e^{\varphi} - 1}{1 - e^{-n\varphi}}$

4.11. DESIGNATION OF INTEREST FACTORS FOR ANNUAL PAYMENTS

Most problems in engineering economy that involve interest will be solved by the use of interest tables. Therefore, it will be convenient to have a logical scheme for identifying the source of the tabulated values. The designation to be used in this text for annual compounding interest-annual payments is as follows:

Single-payment compound-amount factor: $\begin{pmatrix} SP\ i\text{-}n \\ \quad \end{pmatrix}$

Single-payment present-worth factor: $\begin{pmatrix} PS\ i\text{-}n \\ \quad \end{pmatrix}$

Equal-payment-series compound-amount factor: $\begin{pmatrix} SR\ i\text{-}n \\ \quad \end{pmatrix}$

Equal-payment-series sinking fund factor: $\begin{pmatrix} RS\ i\text{-}n \\ \quad \end{pmatrix}$

Equal-payment-series present-worth factor: $\begin{pmatrix} PR\ i\text{-}n \\ \quad \end{pmatrix}$

Equal-payment-series capital-recovery factor: $\begin{pmatrix} RP\ i\text{-}n \\ \quad \end{pmatrix}$

Numerical values corresponding to each of the above factor designations for the most frequently used values of i and n appear in Appendix D, Tables D.1 through D.9.

The designation for continuous compounding interest-annual payments to be used in this text is as follows:

Single-payment compound-amount factor: $\begin{pmatrix} SP\ \varphi\text{-}n \\ \quad \end{pmatrix}$

Single-payment present-worth factor: $\begin{pmatrix} PS\ \varphi\text{-}n \\ \quad \end{pmatrix}$

Equal-payment-series compound-amount factor: $\begin{pmatrix} SR\ \varphi\text{-}n \\ \quad \end{pmatrix}$

Equal-payment-series sinking-fund factor: $\begin{pmatrix} RS\ \varphi\text{-}n \\ \quad \end{pmatrix}$

Equal-payment-series present-worth factor: $\begin{pmatrix} PR\ \varphi\text{-}n \\ \quad \end{pmatrix}$

Equal-payment-series capital-recovery factor: $\begin{pmatrix} RP\ \varphi\text{-}n \\ \quad \end{pmatrix}$

Numerical values corresponding to each of the above factor designations for the most frequently used values of φ and n appear in Appendix D, Tables D.11 through D.19.

Two important advantages of this scheme for designating factors are: (1) the equations for solving problems may be set up prior to looking up any values of factors from the tables and inserting them in the parentheses, and (2) the source and the identity of values taken from the tables are maintained throughout the solution. For example, in solving a problem where it is required to find the present worth of $800 six years hence at 4 per cent interest compounded annually, the following designation may be used:

$$P = S(\overset{\text{PS } i\text{-}n}{\quad})$$

$$P = \$800(\overset{\text{PS 4-6}}{0.79031})$$

$$P = \$632.24.$$

4.12. USE OF INTEREST FACTORS FOR ANNUAL PAYMENTS

In engineering economy analysis, disbursements made to initiate an alternative are considered to take place at the beginning of the period embraced by the alternative. Payments occurring during the period of the alternative are usually assumed to occur at the end of the year or interest period in which they occur. To use the several interest factors that have been developed, it is necessary that the monetary transactions conform to the pattern for which the factors are applicable. The schematic arrangement of the factors in Table 4.5 should be helpful in this connection.

Five important points should be noted in the use of interest factors for annual payments:

1. The end of one year is the beginning of the next year.
2. P is at the beginning of a year at a time regarded as being the present.
3. S is at the end of the nth year from a time regarded as being the present.
4. An R occurs at the *end* of each year of the period under consideration. When P and R are involved, the first R of the series occurs one year after P. When S and R are involved, the last R of the series occurs at the same time as S.
5. In the solution of problems, the quantities P, S, and R must be set up to conform with the pattern applicable to the factors used.

Table 4.5. SCHEMATIC ILLUSTRATION OF THE USE OF FACTORS

End of year	Single Payment		Equal Payment Series			
	Use of compound-amount factor	Use of present-worth factor	Use of compound-amount factor	Use of sinking-fund factor	Use of present-worth factor	Use of capital-recovery factor
0	P	P	—	—	P	P
1			R	R	R	R
2			R	R	R	R
3			R	R	R	R
r			R	R	R	R
n	S	S	R $\quad S$	S $\quad R$	R	R
	$S = P(\underset{\text{SP } i\text{-}n}{\quad})$	$P = S(\underset{\text{PS } i\text{-}n}{\quad})$	$S = R(\underset{\text{SR } i\text{-}n}{\quad})$	$R = S(\underset{\text{RS } i\text{-}n}{\quad})$	$P = R(\underset{\text{PR } i\text{-}n}{\quad})$	$R = P(\underset{\text{RP } i\text{-}n}{\quad})$

4.13. INTEREST FORMULAS, CONTINUOUS COMPOUNDING INTEREST-CONTINUOUS PAYMENTS

In the previous derivations, payments were considered to be concentrated at discrete points in time. However, in many instances, it is reasonable to assume that monetary transactions occur on a relatively uniform basis throughout the year. In this case, a uniform flow of money best describes the nature of the transaction. Situations such as this involve a *funds-flow process* which may be described in terms of a nominal annual flow rate. The following symbols will be used. Let

φ = the nominal annual interest rate;

n = the time expressed in years;

P = a present principal sum;

F = the nominal annual flow rate;

S = a future sum equal to the compound amount of the nominal annual flow rate after time n;

dS = the interest accumulated during the small time interval dx minus the payments received from F in the small time interval dx.

Then
$$dS = S\varphi\, dx - F dx,$$

$$\frac{\varphi dS}{S\varphi - F} = \varphi\, dx,$$

by integration
$$[\ln S\varphi - F]_{x=0}^{x=n} = [\varphi x]_{x=0}^{x=n},$$

$$\ln(S\varphi - F) - \ln(P\varphi - F) = \varphi n,$$

and
$$\frac{S\varphi - F}{P\varphi - F} = e^{n\varphi}.$$

Where there is no flow of payments, as in the case with annual payments, the compound amount and the present-worth factors are identical to those for continuous compounding interest-annual payments. This may be shown by setting $F = 0$ as follows:

$$\frac{S\varphi - 0}{P\varphi - 0} = e^{n\varphi}$$

or $S = Pe^{n\varphi}$, which was shown previously. Its reciprocal, $P = Se^{-n\varphi}$, is also the same as was previously shown.

Funds-flow capital-recovery factor. The assumption of no compound amount in the general funds-flow relationship derived above yields

$$\frac{0 - F}{P\varphi - F} = e^{n\varphi}$$

$$-F(1 - e^{n\varphi}) = P\varphi e^{n\varphi},$$

and
$$F = P\left[\frac{\varphi e^{n\varphi}}{e^{n\varphi} - 1}\right].$$

The resulting factor, $\varphi e^{n\varphi}/(e^{n\varphi} - 1)$, is the *funds-flow capital-recovery factor*.

Funds-flow present-worth factor. The funds-flow capital-recovery relationship may be solved for P as follows:

$$P = F\left[\frac{e^{n\varphi} - 1}{\varphi e^{n\varphi}}\right].$$

The resulting factor, $(e^{n\varphi} - 1)/\varphi e^{n\varphi}$, is the *funds-flow present worth factor*.

Funds-flow sinking-fund factor. The assumption of no present worth in the general funds-flow relationship derived previously yields

$$\frac{S\varphi - F}{0 - F} = e^{n\varphi}$$

$$-F(e^{n\varphi} - 1) = S\varphi$$

$$-F = S\left[\frac{\varphi}{e^{n\varphi} - 1}\right].$$

The resulting factor, $\varphi/(e^{n\varphi} - 1)$, is the *funds-flow sinking-fund factor*. The negative sign on F indicates that the amount in question is being deposited rather than received.

Funds-flow compound-amount factor. The funds-flow sinking-fund relationship may be solved for S as follows:

$$S = -F\left[\frac{e^{n\varphi} - 1}{\varphi}\right].$$

The resulting factor, $(e^{n\varphi} - 1)/\varphi$, is the *funds-flow compound-amount factor*. As before, the negative sign on F indicates a deposit.

4.14 SUMMARY AND DESIGNATION OF FUNDS-FLOW FACTORS

For ease of reference the previously derived funds-flow factors may be summarized as follows:

Funds-flow capital-recovery factor: $\dfrac{\varphi e^{n\varphi}}{e^{n\varphi} - 1}$

Funds-flow present-worth factor: $\dfrac{e^{n\varphi} - 1}{\varphi e^{n\varphi}}$

Funds-flow sinking-fund factor: $\dfrac{\varphi}{e^{n\varphi} - 1}$

Funds-flow compound-amount factor: $\dfrac{e^{n\varphi} - 1}{\varphi}$

The designation for funds-flow factors will follow the scheme established previously and will be as follows:

Funds-flow capital-recovery factor: $\left(\overset{\text{FP } \varphi\text{-}n}{} \right)$

Funds-flow present-worth factor: $\left(\overset{\text{PF } \varphi\text{-}n}{} \right)$

Funds-flow sinking-fund factor: $\left(\overset{\text{FS } \varphi\text{-}n}{} \right)$

Funds-flow compound-amount factor: $\left(\overset{\text{SF } \varphi\text{-}n}{} \right)$

Examples regarding the use of the funds-flow factors will be presented in Chapter 5.

PROBLEMS

1. If an investment of \$1,400 earns \$42 in 9 months, what is the annual rate of interest?

2. How long will \$4,000 have to be invested to amount to \$4,200 if it earns 4 per cent simple interest per annum?

3. What is the principal amount if the amount of interest at the end of $2\frac{1}{2}$ years is \$450 for a simple interest rate of 6 per cent per annum?

4. Compare the interest earned by \$100 for 10 years at 5 per cent simple interest with that earned by the same amount for 10 years at 5 per cent compounded annually.

5. The principal plus interest earned from a $600 investment at 6 per cent simple interest made 4 years ago is invested at 5 per cent compounded annually for 12 years. What will be the total proceeds at the end of the 16-year period?

6. What amount will be accumulated by each of these present investments?

    (a) $4,100 in 10 years at 6 per cent compounded annually.

    (b) $800 in 3 years at 4 per cent compounded semiannually.

    (c) $15,000 in 38 years at 8 per cent compounded annually.

    (d) $1,720 in 6 years at 2 per cent compounded quarterly.

7. What is the present worth of these future payments?

    (a) $9,000 12 years from now at 8 per cent compounded annually.

    (b) $9,000 12 years from now at 8 per cent compounded quarterly.

    (c) $1,200 8 years from now at 4 per cent compounded annually.

    (d) $2,900 14 years from now at 5 per cent compounded annually.

8. What is the accumulated value of each of the following series of payments?

    (a) $1,250 at end of each year for 9 years at 5 per cent compounded annually.

    (b) $800 at the end of every 6 months for 5 years at 6 per cent compounded semiannually.

    (c) $6,000 every six months for 16 years at 7 per cent compounded semiannually.

    (d) $450 every year for 42 years at 4 per cent compounded annually.

9. What is the present value of the following prospective future payments?

    (a) $700 a year for 14 years at 5 per cent compounded annually.

    (b) $1,000 semiannually for 11 years at 6 per cent compounded semiannually.

    (c) $1,400 a year for 7 years and $4,000 at the end of 7 years at 7 per cent compounded annually.

    (d) $2,200 every six months for 10 years at 7 per cent compounded semiannually.

10. What equal annual payments are necessary to repay the following present amounts?

    (a) $7,000 in 12 years at 4 per cent compounded annually.

(b) $12,000 in 27 years at 3 per cent compounded quarterly.

(c) $25,000 in 37 years at 5 per cent compounded annually.

(d) $4,000 in 6 years at 8 per cent compounded annually.

11. What equal annual payments must be paid into a sinking fund to accumulate the following amounts?

(a) $12,000 in 15 years at 5 per cent compounded annually.

(b) $8,000 in 9 years at 8 per cent compounded annually.

(c) $14,000 in 41 years at 4 per cent compounded semiannually.

(d) $17,000 in 27 years at 3 per cent compounded annually.

12. How many years will it take for an investment to double itself if interest is compounded annually for an interest rate of 4 per cent; 6 per cent?

13. What rate of interest compounded annually is involved if:

(a) An investment of $5,400 made now will result in a receipt of $7,200 5 years from now?

(b) An investment of $8,000 made 6 years ago has increased in value to $10,360?

14. How many years will be required for:

(a) An investment of $700 to increase to $1,200 if interest is 4 per cent compounded annually?

(b) An investment of $1,500 to increase to $1,800 if interest is 6 per cent compounded annually?

15. What interest rate compounded annually is paid if:

(a) Payments of $515 per year for 8 years will repay an original loan of $3,000?

(b) Ten semiannual deposits of $85 will result in $1,000 at the end of 5 years.

16. With interest at 6 per cent compounded annually find:

(a) How much will be required 7 years hence to repay an $800 loan made now?

(b) How much can be loaned now if $600 will be repaid at the end of 8 years?

17. With interest at 4 per cent compounded semiannually, find:

(a) What payment can be made now to prevent an expense of $250 every 6 months for the next 12 years?

(b) What semiannual deposit into a fund is required to total $5,000 in 10 years?

18. An interest rate of 10 per cent compounded annually is desired on an investment of $8,600. How many years will be required to recover the capital with the desired return if $1,750 is received each year?

19. How many years will it take to accumulate $12,000 if $650 is deposited in a sinking fund every 6 months? Interest at 4 per cent compounded semiannually is received on the sinking fund.

20. How would you determine a desired equal-payment-series compound-amount factor if you only had a table of:
    (a) Single-payment compound-amount factors?
    (b) Single-payment present-worth factors?
    (c) Equal-payment-series sinking-fund factors?
    (d) Equal-payment-series capital-recovery factors?

21. How would you determine a desired equal-payment-series present-worth factor if you only had a table of:
    (a) Single-payment present-worth factors?
    (b) Equal-payment-series capital-recovery factors?
    (c) Equal-payment-series sinking-fund factors?
    (d) Equal-payment-series compound-amount factors?
    (e) Single-payment compound-amount factors?

22. Rewrite the formula given for the single-payment compound-amount factor to apply to the compounding of interest at the end of each period, where p represents the number of compounding periods per year, y represents the number of years, and j represents the nominal annual rate of interest. Use P as the present sum and S as the compound amount and express S in terms of P, j, p, and y.

23. Develop a formula for finding the accumulated amount S at the end of n interest periods which will result from a series of beginning-of-period payments each equal to B, if the latter are placed in a sinking fund for which the interest rate per period is i, compounded each period.

24. What effective annual interest rate corresponds to the following:
    (a) Nominal interest rate of 10 per cent compounded semiannually.
    (b) Nominal interest rate of 8 per cent compounded monthly.
    (c) Nominal interest rate of 6 per cent compounded quarterly.
    (d) Nominal interest rate of 8 per cent compounded weekly.

25. An effective interest rate of 6 per cent is desired:

(a) What nominal rate should be asked if compounding is to be semi-annually?

(b) What nominal rate should be asked if compounding is to be quarterly?

26. What is the effective interest rate if a nominal rate of 8 per cent is compounded continuously? If an effective interest rate of 8 per cent is desired, what must the nominal rate be if compounding is continuous?

27. The Honest Deal Loan Company offers money at $\frac{1}{2}$ per cent interest per week compounded weekly. What is the effective annual interest rate?

28. What is the present worth of the following prospective payments?

(a) $2,700 in 17 years at an interest rate of 6 per cent compounded continuously.

(b) $1,200 in 5 years at an interest rate of 5 per cent compounded weekly.

29. What is the present worth of a uniform series of year-end payments of $175 each for 12 years if the interest rate is 7 per cent compounded continuously?

30. How many years will it take an investment to triple itself if the interest rate is 5 per cent compounded annually; compounded continuously?

31. What will be the required annual payment to repay a loan of $3,000 in 6 years if the interest rate is 6 per cent compounded continuously?

32. What is the accumulated value of each of the following series of payments?

(a) $1,200 at the end of each year for 9 years at 5 per cent interest compounded continuously.

(b) $400 at the end of each year for 42 years at 6 per cent interest compounded continuously.

33. What equal annual payment must be deposited into a sinking fund to accumulate $12,000 in 16 years at 5 per cent interest compounded continuously?

34. An interest rate of 10 per cent compounded continuously is desired on an investment of $8,600. How many years will be required to recover the capital with the desired return if $1,750 is received each year? Compare the result with Problem 18.

CHAPTER 5

CALCULATIONS OF EQUIVALENCE
INVOLVING INTEREST

If two or more situations are to be compared, their characteristics must be placed on an equivalent basis. Which is worth more, 4 ounces of Product A or 1,800 grains of Product A? In order to answer this question, it is necessary to place the two amounts on an equivalent basis by use of the proper conversion factor. After conversion of ounces to grains, the question becomes: Which is worth more, 1,750 grains of Product A or 1,800 grains of Product A? The answer is now obvious.

Many calculations in engineering economy require that prospective receipts and disbursements of two or more alternative proposals be placed on an equivalent basis for comparison. Thus, it is important that the application of the interest formulas developed in the previous chapter be thoroughly understood. This chapter will present computational methods required when interest formulas are used and will illustrate the economic meaning of equivalence.

5.1. THE MEANING OF EQUIVALENCE

Two things are said to be equivalent when they have the same effect. For instance, the torques produced by applying forces of 100 pounds and 200 pounds 2 feet and 1 foot, respectively, from the fulcrum of a lever are equivalent. This equivalence can be expressed as follows:

$$100 \text{ lb.} \times 2 \text{ ft.} = 200 \text{ lb.} \times 1 \text{ ft.}$$
$$200 \text{ lb.-ft.} = 200 \text{ lb.-ft.}$$

Another concept is that two things are equivalent when they have the same value in exchange. For instance, 4 tons of Material A at $18 per ton are equivalent to 12 tons of Material B at $6 per ton, since

$$4 \text{ tons} \times \frac{\$18}{\text{ton}} = 12 \text{ tons} \times \frac{\$6}{\text{ton}}$$

$$\$72 = \$72.$$

Similarly, $384.64 on June 6, 1962 is equivalent to $526.40 on June 6, 1970, for an interest rate of 4 per cent per annum. This is so because persons who consider 4 per cent a satisfactory rate of interest would be willing to pay $384.64 on June 6, 1962 to receive $526.40 on June 6, 1970 or vice versa. The equivalence above may be expressed thus:

$$\$384.64 = \frac{1}{(1 + 0.04)^8} \times \$526.40$$

$$\begin{array}{c} \text{PS 4-8} \\ = (0.73069) \times \$526.40 = \$384.64. \end{array}$$

The equivalence above might also have been expressed thus:

$$\$526.40 = (1 + 0.04)^8 \times \$384.64$$

$$\begin{array}{c} \text{SP 4-8} \\ = (1.369) \times \$384.64 = \$526.40. \end{array}$$

Three factors are involved in the equivalence of sums of money. These are (1) the amount of the sums, (2) the time of occurrence of the sums, and (3) the interest rate. The interest factors that have been developed embody consideration of time and the interest rate. They constitute a convenient way for taking the time value of money into consideration in placing sums of money occurring at different times upon an equivalent basis.

5.2. EQUIVALENCE IS NOT DIRECTLY APPARENT

The relative economy of several alternatives is usually not apparent from a statement of their future receipts and disbursements until the latter have been placed on an equivalent basis. Consider the following example. Electric current is desired at an isolated location by the Sun Company. It is estimated that 80,000 kilowatt-hours (kw.-hr.) of current will be needed each year during the next ten years. A power company makes two proposals for supplying the needed current.

In one proposal the power company agrees to build the necessary connecting transmission equipment and supply the 80,000 kw.-hr. of power at a rate of $0.05 per kw.-hr. This alternative will result in an annual power bill of $4,000.

In the second proposal the power company agrees to supply the 80,000 kw.-hr. of power at a rate of $0.02 per kw.-hr. This will result in an annual bill of only $1,600, but the Sun Company is to provide the connecting transmission equipment. Sun Company engineers estimate that the transmission equipment will cost $18,000 to install, that its maintenance during the ten years will be negligible, and that at the end of the ten years it will be possible to sell the used equipment for $6,000. The Sun Company considers an interest rate of 8 per cent adequate in making a comparison of these alternatives.

Identical service will be provided by either Proposal A or Proposal B. The question to be answered is: Which proposal will supply 80,000 kw.-hr. of energy per year for a period of ten years at lower cost? The patterns of disbursements in prospect for these proposals are given in Table 5.1.

Table 5.1. PATTERN OF DISBURSEMENTS FOR PROPOSAL A AND PROPOSAL B

End of year number	Disbursements proposal A	Disbursements proposal B
0	$ 000	$18,000
1	4,000	1,600
2	4,000	1,600
3	4,000	1,600
4	4,000	1,600
5	4,000	1,600
6	4,000	1,600
7	4,000	1,600
8	4,000	1,600
9	4,000	1,600
10	4,000	1,600 — 6,000*

*A receipt, i.e., a negative disbursement.

It is not apparent from a cursory examination of the disbursements of the two proposals which if financially the most desirable. The disbursements of the two proposals can be placed on a comparable basis by calculating their present worths or by calculating the equivalent annual cost of each.

The present worths of the disbursements for Proposals A and B are respectively \$26,840 and \$25,957. This means in effect that ten years of service will cost the equivalent of a present expenditure of \$26,840 if A is selected and \$25,957 if B is selected. These figures are directly comparable. Thus, the desired service may be provided at least cost by Proposal B.

5.3. EQUIVALENCE CALCULATIONS REQUIRING THE USE OF A SINGLE FACTOR

The interest formulas derived in Chapter 4 express relationships that exist between the several elements making up the formulas. Those for annual compounding interest-annual payments exhibit relationships between P, R, S, i, and n. The formulas for continuous compounding interest-annual payments exhibit relationships between P, R, S, φ, and n. The paragraphs which follow will illustrate methods for calculating equivalence where these interest formulas are involved. In the examples, the quantities P, R, and S will be set up to conform to the pattern applicable to the particular factor used, as was illustrated in Table 4.5, Chapter 4.

Single-payment compound-amount factor calculations. The single-payment compound-amount factors yield a sum S, at a given time in the future, that is equivalent to a principal amount P for a specified interest rate i compounded annually, or φ compounded continuously. For example, the solution for finding the compound amount on January 1, 1973 that is equivalent to a principal sum of \$200 on January 1, 1965 for an interest rate of 5 per cent compounded annually is

$$S = P(\overset{\text{SP } i\text{-}n}{\qquad})$$

$$\overset{\text{SP } 5\text{-}8}{= \$200(1.477) = \$295.40.}$$

If interest is compounded continuously, the solution is

$$S = P(\overset{\text{SP } \varphi\text{-}n}{\qquad})$$

$$= \overset{\text{SP 5-8}}{\$200(1.492)} = \$298.40.$$

If the principal P, the compound amount S, and the number of years n are known, the interest rate i, or φ, may be determined by interpolation of the interest tables. For example, if $P = \$300$, $S = \$525$, and $n = 9$, the solution for i is

$$S = P(\overset{\text{SP } i\text{-}n}{\qquad})$$

$$\$525 = \$300(\overset{\text{SP } i\text{-}9}{\qquad})$$

$$\overset{\text{SP } i\text{-}9}{(1.750)} = \frac{\$525}{\$300}.$$

A search of the interest tables for annual compounding interest reveals that 1.750 falls between the single payment compound-amount factors in the 6 and 7 per cent tables for $n = 9$. The value from the 6 per cent table is 1.689 and the value from the 7 per cent table is 1.838. By linear proportion

$$i = 6 + (1)\frac{1.689 - 1.750}{1.689 - 1.838}$$

$$= 6 + \frac{0.061}{0.149} = 6.41 \text{ per cent.}$$

The linear interpolation used for i is illustrated by Figure 5.1.

Solution for i might have been done without the use of tables as follows:

$$S = P(1 + i)^n$$

$$\$525 = \$300(1 + i)^9$$

$$(1 + i)^9 = \frac{525}{300}$$

$$i = \sqrt[9]{1.750} - 1$$

$$i = 1.0641 - 1 = 0.0641, \text{ or } 6.41 \text{ per cent.}$$

If the interest rate quoted was compounded continuously, the table for continuous compounding interest would have been used in the tabular solution. For the direct solution, the formula for continuous compounding interest would have been used.

If the principal sum, P, its compound amount, S, and the interest rate, i, are known, the number of years n may be determined by interpolation of the interest tables. For example, if $P = \$400$, $S = \$704.40$, and $i = 0.07$, the solution for n is

$$S = P(\overset{\text{SP } i\text{-}n}{\qquad})$$

$$\$704.40 = \$400(\overset{\text{SP } 7\text{-}n}{\qquad})$$

$$\overset{\text{SP } 7\text{-}n}{(1.761)} = \frac{\$704.40}{\$400}.$$

A search of the 7 per cent interest table reveals that 1.761 falls between the single-payment compound-amount factors for $n = 8$ and $n = 9$. For $n = 8$, the factor is 1.718 and for $n = 9$, the factor is 1.838. By linear proportion

$$n = 8 + (1)\frac{1.718 - 1.761}{1.761 - 1.838}$$

$$= 8 + \frac{0.043}{0.120} = 8.36 \text{ years.}$$

The linear interpolation used for n is illustrated by Figure 5.2.

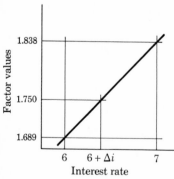

Figure 5.1. Interpolation for i.

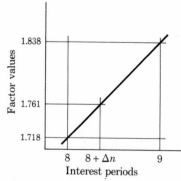

Figure 5.2. Interpolation for n.

Solution for n might have been done without the use of tables as follows:

$$S = P(1 + i)^n$$

$$\$704.40 = \$400(1 + 0.07)^n$$

$$(1.07)^n = \frac{\$704.40}{\$400} = 1.761$$

$$n = 8.37 \text{ years.}$$

If the interest rate quoted was compounded continuously, the table for continuous compounding interest would have been used in the tabular solution. For the direct solution, the formula for continuous compounding interest would have been used. Since the solution required for continuous compounding requires only a different table, the examples which follow will be limited to the case of annual compounding interest.

Single-payment present-worth factor calculations. The single-payment present-worth factors yield a principal sum P, at a time regarded as being the present, which is equivalent to a future sum S. For example, the solution for finding the present worth on September 1, 1964, of a sum equal to $400 on September 1, 1976, for an interest rate of 6 per cent compounded annually, is

$$P = S(\overset{\text{PS } i\text{-}n}{\qquad})$$

$$= \$400(\overset{\text{PS } 6\text{-}12}{0.49697}) = \$198.80.$$

If the future sum S, its present worth P, and the number of years n are known, the interest rate i may be determined by interpolation of the interest tables. For example, if $S = \$400$, $P = \$294.80$, $n = 6$, and if $i =$ the nominal interest rate compounded semiannually, then

$$P = S(\overset{\text{PS } j\text{-}12}{\qquad}), \qquad \text{where } j = \frac{i}{2}$$

$$\$294.80 = \$400(\overset{\text{PS } j\text{-}12}{\qquad})$$

$$(\overset{\text{PS } j\text{-}12}{0.7370}) = \frac{\$294.80}{\$400}.$$

A search of the interest tables reveals that 0.7370 falls between the single-payment present-worth factors in the 2 and the 3 per cent tables for $n = 12$. The value from the 2 per cent table is 0.78849 and the value from the 3 per cent table is 0.70138. By linear proportion

$$j = 2 + (1)\frac{0.7885 - 0.7370}{0.7885 - 0.7014}$$

$$= 2 + \frac{0.0515}{0.0871} = 2.59 \text{ per cent}$$

$$i = 2 \times 2.59 \text{ per cent}$$

$$= 5.18 \text{ per cent.}$$

If a future sum S, its present worth P, and the interest rate i are known, the number of interest periods n may be determined by interpolation of the interest tables. For example, if $S = \$800$, $P = \$491.36$, and $i = 0.04$, the solution for n is

$$P = S(\overset{\text{PS } i\text{-}n}{\quad})$$

$$\$491.36 = \$800(\overset{\text{PS } 4\text{-}n}{\quad})$$

$$\overset{\text{PS } 4\text{-}n}{(0.6142)} = \frac{\$491.36}{800}.$$

A search of the 4 per cent interest table reveals that 0.6142 falls between the single-payment present-worth factors for $n = 12$ and $n = 13$. The value for $n = 12$ is 0.62460 and the value for $n = 13$ is 0.60057. By linear proportion

$$n = 12 + (1)\frac{0.6246 - 0.6142}{0.6246 - 0.6006}$$

$$= 12 + \frac{0.0104}{0.0240} = 12.43 \text{ years.}$$

Equal-payment-series compound-amount factor calculations. The equal-payment-series compound-amount factors yield a sum S at a given time in the future, which is equivalent to a series of payments R, occurring at the end of successive years such that the last R concurs with S. The solution for finding the compound amount, on January 1, 1971, of a series of seven $40 year-end payments whose final payment occurs simultaneously with the compound amount being determined, for an interest rate of 6 per cent is

$$S = R(\overset{\text{SR } i\text{-}n}{\qquad})$$

$$= \$40(\overset{\text{SR } 6\text{-}7}{8.394}) = \$335.76.$$

If the compound amount S, the annual payments R, and the number of years n are known, the interest rate i may be determined by interpolation of the interest tables. For example, if $S = \$441.10$, $R = \$100$, and $n = 4$ the solution for i is

$$S = R(\overset{\text{SR } i\text{-}n}{\qquad})$$

$$\$441.10 = \$100(\overset{\text{SR } i\text{-}4}{\qquad})$$

$$\overset{\text{SR } i\text{-}4}{(4.411)} = \frac{\$441.10}{\$100}.$$

This value falls between the equal-payment-series compound-amount factors in the 6 and the 7 per cent tables for $n = 4$. The value from the 6 per cent table is 4.375 and the value from the 7 per cent table is 4.440. By linear proportion

$$i = 6 + (1)\frac{4.375 - 4.411}{4.375 - 4.440}$$

$$= 6 + \frac{0.036}{0.065} = 6.55 \text{ per cent.}$$

If the compound amount S, the annual payments R, and the interest rate i are known, the number of years n may be solved by interpolation in the interest tables. For example, if $S = \$3874.26$, $R = \$200$, and $i = 0.04$, the solution for n is

$$S = R(\overset{\text{SR } i\text{-}n}{\qquad})$$

$$\$3847.26 = \$200(\overset{\text{SR } 4\text{-}n}{\qquad})$$

$$\overset{\text{SR } 4\text{-}n}{(19.2363)} = \frac{\$3847.26}{\$200}.$$

This value falls between the equal-payment series compound-amount factor for $n = 14$ and $n = 15$ in the 4 per cent table. For $n = 14$, the factor is 18.292 and for $n = 15$, the factor is 20.024. By linear proportion

$$n = 14 + (1)\frac{18.202 - 19.236}{18.292 - 20.024}$$

$$= 14 + \frac{0.944}{1.732} = 14.55 \text{ years.}$$

Equal-payment-series sinking-fund factor calculations. The equal-payment-series sinking-fund factors are used to determine the amount R of each payment of a series of payments, occurring at the end of successive years, which are equivalent to a future sum S. The solution for finding the amount of annual sinking-fund deposits R for the period June 1, 1964 to June 1, 1971, that are equivalent to a sinking fund S equal to \$400 on June 1, 1971 at 5 per cent interest is

$$R = S(\overset{\text{RS } i\text{-}n}{\quad\quad})$$

$$\overset{\text{RS } 5\text{-}6}{= \$400(0.14702) = \$58.81.}$$

Solution for i and n when S, R, and n or i are known may be done by interpolation in the interest tables as was illustrated for the equal-payment-series compound-amount factor.

Equal-payment-series present-worth factor calculations. The equal-payment-series present-worth factors are used to find the present worth P, of an equal-payment series R, occurring at the end of successive years following the time taken to be the present. For example, the solution for finding the present worth P on June 30, 1968 which is equivalent to a series of seven \$60 year-end payments beginning at the end of the first interest period after June 30, 1968, for an interest rate of 5 per cent, is

$$P = R(\overset{\text{PR } i\text{-}n}{\quad\quad})$$

$$\overset{\text{PR } 5\text{-}7}{= \$60(5.78637) = \$347.16.}$$

Solution for i and n when P, R, and n or i are known may be done by interpolation in the interest tables as was illustrated for the equal-payment-series compound-amount factor.

Equal-payment-series capital-recovery factor calculations. The equal-payment-series capital-recovery factors are used to deter--mine the amount R of each payment of a series of payments occurring at the end of successive years which are equivalent to a present sum P. For example, the solution for finding the amount R of annual year-end payments for the period July 1, 1964 to July 1, 1969 which are equivalent to a sum P of \$300 on July 1, 1964 at 6 per cent interest is

$$R = P(\overset{\text{RP } i\text{-}n}{)}$$

$$= \$300(\overset{\text{RP } 6\text{-}5}{0.23740}) = \$71.22.$$

Solution for i and n when P, R, and n or i are known may be done by interpolation in the interest tables as was illustrated for the equal-payment-series compound-amount factor.

5.4. EQUIVALENCE CALCULATIONS REQUIRING THE USE OF SEVERAL FACTORS

Where a number of calculations of equivalence involving several interest factors are to be made, some difficulty may be experienced in laying out a plan of attack. Also, until considerable experience has been gained with this type of calculation it may be difficult to keep track of the lapse of time.

For complex problems, the speed and accuracy can usually be improved by a schematic representation. For example, suppose that it is desired to determine what present-worth amount on May 1, 1965 is equivalent to the following described payments for an interest rate of 5 per cent: \$300 on May 1, 1970; \$60 on May 1, 1973, 1974, 1975, and 1976; \$210 on May 1, 1977; and \$80 on May 1, 1979, 1980, and 1981. These payments may be represented schematically as illustrated in Figure 5.3.

The plan of attack is to determine the sum of the present-worth amounts of the given payments as of May 1, 1965. In the formulas to be used, P payments occur at the beginning of interest periods and R payments occur at the end of interest periods. To satisfy this condition, the present worth of the several payments was calculated as of May 1, 1965 which is one interest period prior to the first R payment, set for May 1, 1966. Note also that one interest period intervenes between \$212.76 and the first \$60 payment. This is in accordance with the characteristics of the conversion formula used,

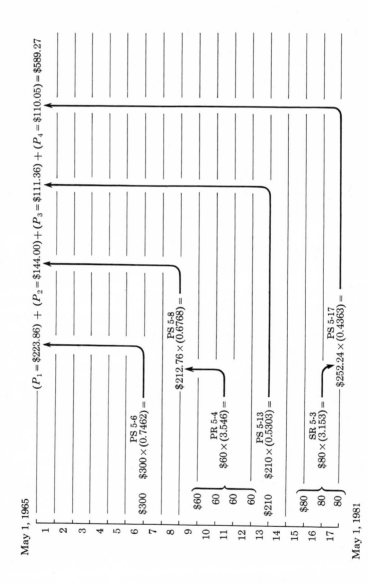

Figure 5.3. Schematic illustration of equivalence.

which requires that the sum P occur one interest period prior to the first R payment. In the diagram, the $252.24 as of May 1, 1981 represents the future worth of the three $80 payments. Note that the $252.24 amount concurs with the last $80. This is in accordance with the characteristics of the formula used, which require that the sum S concur with the final R payment.

The sequence of calculations in the solution of this problem is clearly indicated in the diagram. The position of the arrowhead following each multiplication represents the position of the result with respect to time. The intermediate quantities $212.76 and $252.24 need not have been found. Much time may be saved if all calculations to be made in solving a problem are indicated prior to looking up factor values from the tables and making calculations. In the above example this might have been done as follows:

$$P_1 = \$300(\overset{\text{PS 5-6}}{\quad}) \qquad\qquad =$$

$$P_2 = \$\ 60(\overset{\text{PR 5-4}}{\quad})(\overset{\text{PS 5-8}}{\quad}) \qquad =$$

$$P_3 = \$210(\overset{\text{PS 5-13}}{\quad}) \qquad\qquad =$$

$$P_4 = \$\ 80(\overset{\text{SR 5-3}}{\quad})(\overset{\text{PS 5-17}}{\quad}) \qquad =$$

Next, all factor values are found from the tables and inserted in the parentheses. Calculations are then made as follows to obtain the results printed in **bold face type**:

$$P_1 = \$300\overset{\text{PS 5-6}}{(0.74622)} \qquad\qquad = \textbf{\$223.86}$$

$$P_2 = \$\ 60\overset{\text{PR 5-4}}{(3.54595)}\overset{\text{PS 5-8}}{(0.67684)} = \textbf{144.00}$$

$$P_3 = \$210\overset{\text{PS 5-13}}{(0.53032)} \qquad\qquad = \textbf{111.36}$$

$$P_4 = \$\ 80\overset{\text{SR 5-3}}{(3.153)}\overset{\text{PS 5-17}}{(0.43630)} \quad = \textbf{110.05}$$

If interest had been 5 per cent compounded continuosly instead of 5 per cent compounded annually, values would have been taken from the table for continuous compounding interest. All other calculations would have remained the same.

5.5. EQUIVALENCE CALCULATIONS FOR THE FUNDS-FLOW PROCESS

The tabulated values for interest factors for continuous compounding interest-annual payments may be modified and used for the funds-flow factors. The required conversion factor may be derived by finding the year end equivalent of a summation of an infinite number of payments occurring during the year. The equal payment-series compound-amount factor

$$S = R\left[\frac{e^{n\varphi} - 1}{e^{\varphi} - 1}\right]$$

may be modified to reflect c interest periods per year as follows:

$$S = \frac{R}{c}\left[\frac{e^{c(\varphi/c)} - 1}{e^{\varphi/c} - 1}\right] = \frac{R}{c}\left[\frac{e^{\varphi} - 1}{e^{\varphi/c} - 1}\right]$$

but

$$\lim_{c \to \infty} \frac{R}{c}\left[\frac{e^{\varphi} - 1}{e^{\varphi/c} - 1}\right] = F\left[\frac{e^{\varphi} - 1}{\varphi}\right]$$

$$S = F\left[\frac{e^{\varphi} - 1}{\varphi}\right].$$

The resulting conversion factor, $(e^{\varphi} - 1)/\varphi$, is called the *funds-flow conversion factor*[1] and is designated ($\begin{smallmatrix}FFC_\varphi\\ \quad\end{smallmatrix}$). This factor may be used with the interest factors for continuous compounding interest-annual payments to yield values for the funds-flow factors in the following manner:

$$\begin{pmatrix}FP\ \varphi\text{-}n\\ \ \end{pmatrix} = \begin{pmatrix}RP\ \varphi\text{-}n\\ \ \end{pmatrix}\begin{pmatrix}FFC\ \varphi\\ \ \end{pmatrix}$$

$$\begin{pmatrix}PF\ \varphi\text{-}n\\ \ \end{pmatrix} = \begin{pmatrix}PR\ \varphi\text{-}n\\ \ \end{pmatrix}\begin{pmatrix}FFC\ \varphi\\ \ \end{pmatrix}$$

$$\begin{pmatrix}FS\ \varphi\text{-}n\\ \ \end{pmatrix} = \begin{pmatrix}RS\ \varphi\text{-}n\\ \ \end{pmatrix}\begin{pmatrix}FFC\ \varphi\\ \ \end{pmatrix}$$

$$\begin{pmatrix}SF\ \varphi\text{-}n\\ \ \end{pmatrix} = \begin{pmatrix}SR\ \varphi\text{-}n\\ \ \end{pmatrix}\begin{pmatrix}FFC\ \varphi\\ \ \end{pmatrix}.$$

As an example of the use of the funds-flow conversion factor consider the following example. Find the present worth on December

---

[1]Values for the funds-flow conversion factor for various interest rates are given in Appendix D, Table D.20.

31, 1965 of $800 flowing uniformly throughout the year for a period of 6 years in the future at an interest rate of 6 per cent compounded continuously. The required calculations are

$$P = F(\overset{PF\ \varphi\text{-}n}{\ \ \ \ \ \ })$$

$$= F(\overset{PR\ \varphi\text{-}n}{\ \ \ \ })(\overset{FFC\ \varphi}{\ \ \ \ })$$

$$= \$800(\underset{PR\ 6\text{-}6}{4.88908})(\underset{FFC\ 6}{1.030608}) = \$4,024.$$

The interpretation of the situation represented in the example is that $4,024 on December 31, 1965 is equivalent to $800 per year flowing uniformly throughout the year at an interest rate of 6 per cent compounded continuously.

5.6. EQUIVALENCE CALCULATIONS FOR UNEQUAL-PAYMENT SERIES

In many cases, annual payments do not occur in an equal-payment series. For example, a series of payments that would be uniformly increasing is $100, $125, $150 and $175 occurring at the end of the first, second, third, and fourth year. Similarly, a uniformly decreasing series would be $100, $90, $80, and $70 occurring at the end of the first, second, third, and fourth year. In general, a uniformly increasing series of payments may be expressed as R_1, $R_1 + g$, $R_1 + 2g, \ldots, R_1 + ng$ where R_1 denotes the first year-end payment and g the annual change in the magnitude of the payments.

One way of evaluating such a series is to apply the interest formulas developed previously to each member of the series. This method will yield good results but will be very time consuming. Another way is to reduce the unequal series of payments to an equivalent equal-payment series so that the equal-payment series factor can be used. Let

R_1 = payment at the end of the first year;
g = annual change or gradient;
n = the number of years;
R = the equivalent equal payment.

Unequal payment series, annual compounding. The equivalent equal payment, R, corresponding to an initial payment, R_1, uniform gradient, g, number of years, n, and interest rate, i, may be found by starting with the present-worth factor for an equal-payment series

$$P = R\left[\frac{(1 + i)^n - 1}{i(1 + i)^n}\right].$$

An unequal-payment series may be considered to be made up of two separate series, an equal-payment series with annual payments R_1, and an unequal-payment series 0, g, $2g$, ..., $(n\text{-}1)g$ at the end of successive years. Then, the total present worth is

$$R_1(\overset{\text{PR } i\text{-}n}{\quad}) + g(\overset{\text{PS } i\text{-}2}{\quad}) + 2g(\overset{\text{PS } i\text{-}3}{\quad}) + \ldots + (n - 1)g(\overset{\text{PS } i\text{-}n}{\quad})$$

$$= R_1\left[\frac{(1 + i)^n - 1}{i(1 + i)^n}\right] + g(1 + i)^{-2} + 2g(1 + i)^{-3} + \ldots$$
$$+ (n - 1)g(1 + i)^{-n}.$$

Let

$$S = g(1 + i)^{-2} + 2g(1 + i)^{-3} + \ldots + (n - 1)g(1 + i)^{-n}$$

$$(1 + i)S = g(1 + i)^{-1} + 2g(1 + i)^{-2} + \ldots$$
$$+ (n - 1)g(1 + i)^{-(n-1)}$$

$$(1 + i)S - S = g(1 + i)^{-1} + g(1 + i)^{-2} + \ldots + g(1 + i)^{-(n-1)}$$
$$- (n - 1)g(1 + i)^{-n}$$

$$iS = g(1 + i)^{-1}[1 + (1 + i)^{-1} + \ldots + (1 + i)^{-(n-2)}]$$
$$- (n - 1)g(1 + i)^{-n}$$

$$= g(1 + i)^{-1}\left[\frac{1 - (1 + i)^{-(n-1)}}{1 - (1 + i)^{-1}}\right] - (n - 1)g(1 + i)^{-n}$$

$$= \frac{g}{i}[1 - (1 + i)^{-(n-1)}] - (n - 1)g(1 + i)^{-n}.$$

$$S = \frac{g}{i^2}\left[\frac{(1 + i)^{n-1} - 1}{(1 + i)^{n-1}}\right] - \frac{(n - 1)g}{i(1 + i)^n}$$

$$= \frac{1}{i(1 + i)^n}\left\{\frac{g}{i}[(1 + i)^n - 1 - i - (n - 1)i]\right\}$$

$$= \frac{1}{i(1 + i)^n}\left\{g\left[\frac{(1 + i)^n - 1}{i} - n\right]\right\}.$$

Total present worth of the unequal series then becomes

$$R_1 \frac{(1+i)^n - 1}{i(1+i)^n} + \frac{1}{i(1+i)^n} \left\{ g \left[\frac{(1+i)^n - 1}{i} - n \right] \right\}.$$

As the two payment series are equivalent, their present worths must be equal.

$$R \frac{(1+i)^n - 1}{i(1+i)^n} = R_1 \frac{(1+i)^n - 1}{i(1+i)^n} + \frac{1}{i(1+i)^n} \left\{ \frac{g}{i}[(1+i)^n - 1] - ng \right\}$$

Multiplying both sides by $\dfrac{i(1+i)^n}{(1+i)^n - 1}$, we get

$$R = R_1 + \frac{g}{i} - \frac{ng}{i} \left[\frac{i}{(1+i)^n - 1} \right]$$

or

$$R = R_1 + \frac{g}{i} - \frac{ng}{i} (\overset{\text{RS } i\text{-}n}{\quad})$$

$$= R_1 + g \left[\frac{1}{i} - \frac{n}{i} (\overset{\text{RS } i\text{-}n}{\quad}) \right].$$

The resulting factor, $\left[\dfrac{1}{i} - \dfrac{n}{i} (\overset{\text{RS } i\text{-}n}{\quad}) \right]$, is called the *gradient conversion factor*[2] for annual compounding interest and will be designated GCF i-n (   ).

As an example, assume that a man receives an annual salary of \$5,000 increasing at the rate of \$400 a year. What is his equivalent uniform salary for a period of 10 years if the interest rate is 8 per cent compounded annually?

$$R = R_1 + g(\overset{\text{GCF } i\text{-}n}{\quad})$$

$$= 5,000 + 400(\overset{\text{GCF 8-10}}{3.871314})$$

$$= \$6,548.53 \text{ per year.}$$

Unequal payment series, continuous compounding. The equivalent equal payment, R, corresponding to an initial payment, R_1, uniform gradient, g, number of years, n, and interest rate, φ, may be

---

[2]Values for the gradient conversion factor for annual compounding interest are given in Appendix D, Tables D.21 and D.22.

found in a similar manner as for annual compounding. It can be shown that

$$R = R_1 + g\left[\frac{1}{e^\varphi - 1} - \frac{n}{e^{n\varphi} - 1}\right].$$

The resulting factor, $\left[\dfrac{1}{e^\varphi - 1} - \dfrac{n}{e^{n\varphi} - 1}\right]$, is called the *gradient conversion factor*[3] for continuous-compounding interest and will be designated ($\overset{\text{GCF } \varphi\text{-}n}{\quad}$).

For example, at an interest rate of 6 per cent compounded continuously, the equivalent uniform annual payment R of a series of payments beginning at the end of the first year with \$1,000 and decreasing by \$100 per year to zero is

$$R = R_1 - g(\overset{\text{GCF } \varphi\text{-}n}{\quad})$$

$$= \$1,000 - \$100(\overset{\text{GCF 6-10}}{4.007986}) = \$599.20.$$

5.7. DETERMINING THE INTEREST RATE WHEN TWO OR MORE FACTORS ARE INVOLVED

It is sometimes desired to determine the interest rate for which two series of payments will be equivalent. For example, at what rate of interest will the following two series of payments be equivalent?

	Series A	*Series B*
January 1, 1956	\$1,300	
January 1, 1960		\$800
January 1, 1962		600
January 1, 1963		600
January 1, 1964		600
January 1, 1965		600
January 1, 1970	2,000	

This problem may be solved by trial and interpolation. The first step is to guess at an interest rate. Guess is used advisedly; for, until sufficient experience has been gained to permit approximate

---

[3]Values for the gradient conversion factor for continuous compounding interest are given in Appendix D, Tables D.23 and D.24.

calculations to be made to estimate an interest rate, it will usually be less time-consuming to guess at an interest rate to try at the outset.

Suppose that it has been decided to try 6 per cent and to make calculations on the basis of present worth as of January 1, 1956.

Try 6 per cent:

$1,300 \times 1$........ $\overline{\text{PS 6-14}}$	$1,300.00
$2,000 \times (0.4423)$........	884.60
Present-worth Series A for 6 per cent........	$2,184.60
$\overline{\text{PS 6-4}}$ $800 \times (0.7921)$........	$ 633.68
$\overline{\text{PR 6-4}}$ $\overline{\text{PS 6-5}}$ $600 \times (3.465) \times (0.7473)$........	1,553.64
Present-worth Series B for 6 per cent........	$2,187.32

Try 7 per cent:

$1,300$........ $\overline{\text{PS 7-14}}$	$1,300.00
$2,000 \times (0.3878)$........	775.60
Present-worth Series A for 7 per cent........	$2,075.60
$\overline{\text{PS 7-4}}$ $800 \times (0.7629)$........	610.32
$\overline{\text{PR 7-4}}$ $\overline{\text{PS 7-5}}$ $600 \times (3.387) \times (0.7130)$........	1,448.96
Present-worth Series B for 7 per cent........	$2,059.28

Since the present worth of Series A is less than the present worth of Series B at 6 per cent and the present worth of Series A is greater than the present worth of Series B at 7 per cent, the two series will be equal for an interest rate between 6 and 7 per cent. The existing conditions may be summarized for interpolation as follows:

(P.W. Series A for 6%) — (P.W. Series B for 6%) =   −$2.72
(P.W. Series A for i) — (P.W. Series B for i)   =   0.00
(P.W. Series A for 7%) — (P.W. Series B for 7%) = $16.32

By interpolation

$$i = 6 + (1)\frac{-2.72 - 0}{-2.72 - 16.32}$$

$$= 6 + \frac{-2.72}{-19.04} = 6.14 \text{ per cent.}$$

5.8 INTERPOLATION BETWEEN TABULAR VALUES

Since interpolation will be frequently used in the solution of engineering economy problems, a general relationship for linear interpolation will be presented. Let

X correspond to A,
Y correspond to B,
Z correspond to C;
Y is the unknown.

Figures 5.1 and 5.2 indicated that the following proportion will hold true for the case of linear interpolation:

$$\frac{X - Y}{X - Z} = \frac{A - B}{A - C}.$$

Hence

$$X - Y = (X - Z)\left[\frac{A - B}{A - C}\right]$$

and

$$Y = X - (X - Z)\left[\frac{A - B}{A - C}\right].$$

This general form was followed in all interpolation examples presented in this chapter.

Table 5.2. PER CENT ERROR IN 5.5 PER CENT ANNUAL COMPOUNDING INTEREST FACTORS BECAUSE OF LINEAR INTERPOLATION BETWEEN 5 AND 6 PER CENT

Factor	Years					
	5	10	20	30	40	60
Single-payment compound-amount factor........	+ 0.022	+ 0.101	+ 0.428	+ 0.980	+ 1.760	+ 3.990
Equal-payment-series sinking-fund factor........	+ 0.005	+ 0.010	+ 0.089	+ 0.324	+ 0.687	+ 1.950
Equal-payment-series capital-recovery factor..	+ 0.004	+ 0.014	+ 0.041	+ 0.065	+ 0.080	+ 0.079

Within the range of the interest tables, values of factors for all interest rates and years between those tabulated may be obtained by linear interpolation. The error introduced in so doing is slight and is of minor significance in engineering economy analysis. For example, the error due to linear interpolation in the interest table for annual compounding interest — annual payments is shown in Table 5.2.

PROBLEMS

1. The present-worth amount of a series of payments extending over a period of 16 years at 6 per cent interest compounded annually is $5,680. What is the equivalent annual amount of the series of payments?

2. The equivalent annual amount of a series of payments extending over a period of 12 years is $460. What is the present worth of the series at 5 per cent interest compounded annually; compounded continuously?

3. What is the present worth of a salary of $4,200 per year for 30 years if the interest rate is 3 per cent compounded annually?

4. A $1,000, 4 per cent bond is offered for sale for $950. If interest is payable annually and the bond will mature in 7 years, what interest rate will be received?

5. A $1,000 bond will mature in 10 years. The annual rate of interest is 3 per cent payable semiannually. If the bond can be purchased for $960, what annual interest compounded semiannually will be received?

6. A bond is offered for sale for $1,040. Its face value is $1,000 and the interest is 4 per cent payable annually. What rate of interest will be received if the bond matures 9 years hence?

7. A man desires to make an investment in bonds, provided he can realize 5 per cent on his investment. How much can he afford to pay for a $1,000 bond that pays 4 per cent interest annually and will mature 12 years hence?

8. How much can be paid for a $1,000, 5 per cent bond with interest paid semiannually, if the bond matures 8 years hence? Assume the purchaser will be satisfied with 4 per cent interest compounded semiannually, since the bonds were issued by a very stable and solvent company.

9. From the interest tables given in the text, determine the value of the following factors by interpolation:

(a) The single-payment compound-amount factor for 12 periods at $5\frac{1}{2}$ per cent interest compounded annually.

(b) The equal-payment-series sinking-fund factor for 44 periods at 6 per cent interest compounded annually.

(c) The equal-payment-series present-worth factor for 12 periods at $3\frac{1}{4}$ per cent interest compounded annually.

(d) The equal-payment-series compound-amount factor for 39 periods at 8 per cent interest compounded annually.

10. From the interest tables in the text, determine the following value of the factors by interpolation:

(a) Single-payment present-worth factor for 37 periods at $5\frac{1}{2}$ per cent interest compounded continuously.

(b) The equal-payment-series capital-recovery factor for 48 periods at $6\frac{1}{4}$ per cent interest compounded continuously.

11. Mr. A possesses a mine property estimated to contain 90,000 tons of coal. The mine is now leased to a coal company, which pays Mr. A $0.60 royalty per ton of coal removed. Coal is removed at the rate of 15,000 tons per year. The rate is expected to continue until the mine is exhausted, at which time the mine property is estimated to be worth $4,000. Mr. A now employs a checker whose duty is to measure the coal removed and to bill the coal company for the royalty on the coal removed. The checker receives $2,100 per year.

(a) If interest is at 8 per cent compounded annually and taxes are neglected, for how much can Mr. A afford to sell the property?

(b) If interest is at 6 per cent compounded annually, how much can the coal company afford to pay for the property?

(c) What is the most important factor causing the difference in the results obtained in (a) and (b)?

12. A manufacturer pays a patent royalty of $0.70 per unit of a product he manufactures, payable at the end of each year. The patent will be in force for an additional 4 years. At present, he manufactures 8,000 units of the product per year, but it is estimated that output will be 10,000, 12,000, 14,000, and 16,000 in the four succeeding years. He is considering asking the patent holder to terminate the present royalty contract in exchange for a single payment at present or asking the patent holder to terminate the present contract in exchange for equal annual payments to be made at the beginning of each of the next four years. If 5 per cent interest is used, what is (a) the present single payment and (b) the beginning-of-the-year payments that are equivalent to the royalty payments in prospect under the present agreement?

13. As usually quoted, the prepaid premium of insurance policies covering loss by fire and storm for a 3-year period is 2.5 times the premium for one year of coverage. What rate of interest does a purchaser receive on

the additional present investment if he purchases a 3-year policy now rather than three 1-year policies at the beginning of succeeding years?

14. An investor has $40,000 to invest. He can invest the entire amount in Venture A, which is estimated to yield a return of 7 per cent, or he can invest $10,000 in Venture B, on which the estimated rate of return is 12 per cent. If he undertakes Venture B, what return must be received on the balance of $30,000 in order that he may receive a total return equal to that estimated for Venture A?

15. In order to perpetuate production, part of the income of a machine is put into a sinking fund to replace the machine when it wears out. If $500 is deposited annually at 6 per cent interest, how long must the machine last before a new machine costing $10,000 can be purchased?

16. If $1,500 is deposited annually into a sinking fund with an interest rate of 5 per cent compounded annually, how many years will it take to accumulate $60,000 with which to purchase a new gas turbine?

17. A city power plant wishes to install a feed-water heater in their steam generation system. It is estimated that the increase in efficiency will pay for the heater one year after it is installed, and a contractor has promised he can install the heater in 5 months. If the venture is undertaken and it is found that the heater does pay for itself in a year by saving $300 per month, what amount was paid to the contractor at the last of each month of construction? Assume that the savings of $300 occurs at the last of each month, and that the money paid to the contractor could have been invested elsewhere at 4 per cent compounded monthly.

18. A manufacturing company purchased electrical services to be paid for $50,000 now and $10,000 per year beginning with the sixth year. After two years service the company, having surplus profits, requested to pay for another five years service in advance. If the electrical company elected to accept payment in advance, what would each company set as a fair settlement to be paid if (a) the electrical company considered 6 per cent compounded annually as a fair return, and (b) the manufacturing company considered 4 per cent a fair return.

19. A company is considering two air compressors which will provide equal service. Compressor A costs $1,500 and has a maintenance cost of $150 at the end of each year. Compressor B costs $925 and has the following end-of-year maintenance costs: Year 1-$250; Year 2-$300; Year 3-$350; Year 4-$400. Each compressor has a life of four years and a salvage value of $200. At what interest rate are the two plans equivalent?

20. A machine shop is in need of a vertical mill. The shop can lease one for 6 years with maintenance furnished at no extra cost. The charge for the lease is $1,350 payable now. A vertical mill can be purchased for $1,000 that will have a salvage value of $200 at the end of six years. Annual maintenance cost will be $100 per year, if the mill is purchased. At what interest rate are the two plans equivalent?

21. An engineering firm is seeking a loan of $210,000 to finance production of a newly patented product line. Due to a good reception of the product at its introductory showing, the bank has agreed to loan the firm an amount equal to the present worth of firm orders received for delivery during the next 5 years. The orders are as follows:

Year 1..	20,000
Year 2..	16,000
Year 3..	12,000
Year 4..	8,000
Year 5..	4,000

If the product will sell for $4 each, show that the present worth of the orders received will justify the loan required. Interest is 4 per cent compounded annually.

22. A petroleum engineer estimates that the present production of 300,000 barrels of oil per year from a group of 10 wells will decrease at the rate of 15,000 barrels per year for the next 19 years. Oil is estimated to be worth $3 per barrel for the next 13 years and $2.50 per barrel thereafter. If the interest rate is 6 per cent compounded annually, what is the equivalent present amount of the prospective future receipts from the wells?

23. Find the annual uniform payment series which would be equivalent to a uniform flow of payments at the rate of $360 per year for 7 years. Interest is 4 per cent compounded continuously.

24. What uniform flow of payments will repay a loan of $10,000 in 1 year at an interest rate of 8 per cent compounded continuously; $40,000 in 4 years at an interest rate of 8 per cent compounded continuously?

25. The first cost of an oil well is $100,000. If a profit of $2.50 per barrel is in prospect for a production rate of 2 barrels per hour, 300 days a year, for 3 years, what will be the nominal rate of return; the effective rate of return?

26. Find the annual uniform payment series which would be equivalent to the following increasing series of payments if the interest rate is 7 per cent compounded annually; compounded continuously.

$300 at the end of the first year
$320 at the end of the second year
$340 at the end of the third year
$360 at the end of the fourth year
$380 at the end of the fifth year
$400 at the end of the sixth year
$420 at the end of the seventh year

CHAPTER 6

DEPRECIATION
AND DEPRECIATION CALCULATION

People satisfy their wants by the consumption of goods and services, the production of which is directly dependent upon the employment of large quantities of producer goods. But producer goods are not acquired without considerable investment. One characteristic of modern civilization is the large investment per worker in production facilities. Although this investment results in high worker productivity it should be recognized that this economy must be sufficient to absorb the reduction in value of these facilities as they are consumed in the production process.

Alternative engineering proposals will affect the type and quantity of producer goods required. As an essential ingredient in the process of want satisfaction, producer goods give rise to capital consumption and investment costs which must be considered in evaluating alternative engineering proposals. An understanding of the depreciation concept is essential if it is to be included as an integral part of engineering economy analysis.

6.1. CLASSIFICATIONS OF DEPRECIATION

Depreciation may be defined as the lessening in value of a physical asset with the passage of time. With the possible exception of land, this phenomenon is a characteristic of all physical assets. A common classification of the types of depreciation include (1) physical depreciation, (2) functional depreciation, and (3) accidents. Each of these types will be defined and explained in the paragraphs which follow.

Physical depreciation. Depreciation resulting in physical impairment of an asset is known as *physical depreciation.* Physical depreciation manifests itself in such tangible ways as the wearing of particles of metal from a bearing and the corrosion of the tubes in a heat exchanger. This type of depreciation results in the lowering of the ability of a physical asset to render its intended service. The primary causes of physical depreciation are:

1. Deterioration due to action of the elements including the corrosion of pipe, the rotting of timbers, chemical decomposition, bacterial action, etc. Deterioration is substantially independent of use.

2. Wear and tear from use which subjects the asset to abrasion, shock, vibration, impact, etc. These forces are occasioned primarily by use and result in a loss of value over time.

Functional depreciation. *Functional depreciation* results not from a deterioration in the asset's ability to serve its intended purpose, but from a change in the demand for the services it can render. The demand for the services of an asset may change because it is more profitable to use a more efficient unit, there is no longer work for the asset to do, or the work to be done exceeds the capacity of the asset. Depreciation resulting from a change in the need for the service of an asset may be the result of:

1. Obsolescence resulting from the discovery of another asset that is sufficiently superior to make it uneconomical to continue using the original asset. Assets also become obsolete when they are no longer needed.

2. Inadequacy or the inability to meet the demand placed upon it. This situation arises from changes in demand not contemplated when the asset was acquired.

Suppose that a manufacturer has a hand riveter in good physical condition, but he has found it more profitable to dispose of it and purchase an automatic riveter because of the reduction in riveting costs that the latter makes possible. The difference between the use value of the hand-operated riveter and the amount received for it on disposal represents a decrease in value due to the availability of the automatic riveter. This cause of loss in value is termed obsolescence. Literally, the hand riveter had become *obsolete* as a result of an improvement in the art of riveting.

As a second example, consider the case of a manufacturer who has ceased producing a certain item and finds that he has machines in good operating condition which he no longer needs. If he disposes of them at a value less than their former use value to him, the difference will be termed depreciation, or loss resulting from obsolescence. The inference is that the machine has become obsolete or out of date as far as the user is concerned.

Inadequacy, a cause of functional depreciation, occurs when changes in demand for the services of an asset result in a demand beyond the scope of the asset. For example, a small electric generating plant has a single 500-kilovolt-amperes (kva) generating unit whose capacity will soon be exceeded by the demand for current. Analyses show that it will cost less in the long run to replace the present unit with a 750-kva unit, which is estimated to meet the need for some time, than to supplement the present unit with a 250-kva unit.

In such a case the original 500-kva unit is said to be *inadequate* and to have been *superseded* by the larger unit. Any loss in the value of the unit below its use value is the result of inadequacy or supersession. The former term is preferred for designating this type of depreciation.

Rapid advances in technology and rapid growth and change in industrial output make obsolescence and inadequacy important causes of depreciation and, therefore, important factors in economy.

A disposition to replace machines when it becomes profitable to do so instead of when they are worn out has probably been an important factor in the rapid development of this nation. The sailing ship has given way to the steamship; in street transportation, the sequence of obsolescence has been horse cars, cable cars, electric cars, and automotive buses; steam locomotives are rapidly being replaced by internal-combustion-engine locomotives. In power generation, steam turbines have replaced steam engines. In manufacturing, improvements in the arts of processing have resulted in widespread obsolescence and inadequacy of equipment. Each technological advance produces improvements that result in the obsolescence of existing assets.

Accidents. Accidents may result in a very rapid loss of value. In general, accidents are not predictable and since the resulting loss may be high it has become a common practice to insure against losses resulting from such accidents as fire, flood, windstorms, collisions, and explosion. Insurable losses are usually not treated as depreciation due to their magnitude. However, minor damage caused by accident is regarded as being part of the risk of ownership. Minor accidents are unavoidable and may be classified as part of the wear and tear from use and treated as depreciation.

6.2. ACCOUNTING FOR THE CONSUMPTION OF CAPTIAL ASSETS

An understanding of the concept of depreciation is complicated by the fact that there are two aspects to be considered. One is the actual lessening in value of an asset with use and the passage of time, and the other is the accounting for this lessening in value.

An asset such as a machine is a unit of capital. Such a unit of capital loses value over a period of time in which it is used in carrying on the productive activities of a business. This loss of value of an asset represents actual piecemeal consumption or expenditure of capital. For instance, a truck tire is a unit of capital. The particles of rubber that wear away with use are actually small physical units of capital consumed in the intended service of the tire. In a like manner, the wear of machine parts and the deterioration of structural elements are physical consumptions of capital. Expenditures of capital in this way are often difficult to observe and are usually difficult to evaluate in monetary terms, but they are nevertheless real.

One aim in accounting for depreciation is to have, continuously, a monetary measure of the value of an enterprise's unexpended physical capital, both collectively and by individual units such as specific machines. This aim can only be approximated with the accuracy with which the future life of the asset and the effect of deterioration can be estimated.

A second aim is to arrive at the physical expenditure of physical capital, in monetary terms, that has been occasioned by each unit of goods as it is produced. This aim is difficult to realize because the depreciation per unit of product depends upon the total depreciation and the total number of units that are processed, neither of which can be known until after the asset in question has ceased to be used.

In an enterprise, physical capital in the form of machines, buildings, and the like is used in carrying on production activities. As machines wear out in productive activities, physical capital is converted to value in the product. Thus the capital that is lost in wear by machines is recovered in the product processed on them. This needs to be accounted for in order to determine production costs and to account for the recovered capital.

6.3. THE VALUE-TIME FUNCTION

In considering depreciation as a cost of production, the pattern of the future value of an asset must be predicted. It is customary to assume that the value of an asset decreases yearly in accordance with one of several mathematical functions. However, choice of the particular model that is to represent the lessening in value of an asset over time is a difficult task. It involves decisions as to the life of the asset, its salvage value, and the form of the mathematical function. Once a value-time function has been chosen, it is used to represent the value of the asset at any point during its life. A general value-time function is shown in Figure 6.1.

The calculated amount of decrease in value depends jointly upon

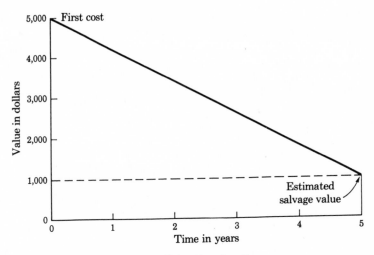

Figure 6.1. Value-time function.

the method of depreciation chosen and the estimated salvage value at the end of an estimated life. Once estimates have been made in regard to depreciation, they are acted upon as though they represent actual facts until another decision is made. When a new decision is made, it is based upon the facts as they exist at the time of decision.

Capital recovered plus return. Capital assets are purchased in the belief that they will earn more than they cost. One part of the prospective earnings will be considered to be *capital recovered*. Capital invested in an asset is recovered in the form of income derived from the services rendered by the asset and from its sale at the end of its useful life. If a machine provided services valued at $800 during its life, and if $200 was received from its sale, a total of $1,000 would be recovered capital. If the machine had cost $1,000, the capital invested in it would have been fully recovered.

A second part of the prospective earnings will be considered to be *return*. Since capital invested in an asset is ordinarily recovered piecemeal, it is necessary to consider the interest on the undepreciated balance as a cost of ownership. Thus, an investment in an asset is expected to result in income sufficient not only to recover the amount of the original investment, but also to provide for a return on the diminishing investment remaining in the asset at any time during its life. This gives rise to the phrase *capital recovered plus return*.

6.4. STRAIGHT-LINE METHOD OF DEPRECIATION

The straight-line depreciation model assumes that the value of an asset decreases at a constant rate. Thus, if an asset has a first cost of $5,000, an estimated life of 5 years, and an estimated salvage value of $1,000, the total depreciation will be $4,000 and the depreciation each year will be $800. In this example, the *capital recovered* will be equal to $800 each year during the life of the asset.

For the conditions assumed, the investment in the asset during the first year is $5,000; during the second $4,200; during the third $3,400; and so forth. If the desired rate of return on the invested capital is 6 per cent, the *return* for the first year should be $5,000 × 0.06 = $300; for the second year $4,200 × 0.06 = $252; for the third year $3,400 × 0.06 = $204; etc. The capital recovered, capital unrecovered, return, and capital recovered plus return for each year of the asset's life is given in Table 6.1.

Table 6.1. AN EXAMPLE OF THE STRAIGHT-LINE METHOD OF DEPRECIATION

Year No.	Capital recovered	Capital unrecovered beginning of year	Return on the capital unrecovered	Capital recovered plus return
1	$800	$5,000	$300	$1,100
2	$800	$4,200	$252	$1,052
3	$800	$3,400	$204	$1,004
4	$800	$2,600	$156	$ 956
5	$800	$1,800	$108	$ 908

General expressions for capital recovered, capital unrecovered, return, and capital recovered plus return may be developed for each year of the asset's life. Let

P = first cost of the asset;
L = estimated salvage value;
n = estimated life;
i = interest rate.

The resulting general expressions are exhibited in Table 6.2.

These general expressions may be used to describe any given facet of the straight-line depreciation model. By substitution of the assigned values for P, L, n, and i, stated in the numerical example above, the values given in Table 6.1 may be verified.

The equivalent end of service life value of capital recovered plus return may be found by multiplying the capital recovered plus return for the rth year by the compound-amount factor for the rth year and summing over all r years. Let S = the equivalent end of service life value of capital recovered plus return, then

$$S = \sum_{r=1}^{n} \left\{ \frac{P-L}{n} + \left[P - (r-1)\left(\frac{P-L}{n}\right)\right]i\right\}(1+i)^{n-r}$$

$$= \sum_{r=1}^{n} \left[\frac{P-L}{n} + Pi + \frac{P-L}{n}i\right](1+i)^{n-r}$$
$$- \sum_{r=1}^{n} i\left(\frac{P-L}{n}\right)r(1+i)^{n-r}$$

$$= \left[\frac{P-L}{n}(1+i) + Pi\right]\sum_{r=1}^{n}(1+i)^{n-r}$$
$$- i\left[\frac{P-L}{n}\right]\sum_{r=1}^{n} r(1+i)^{n-r}.$$

Table 6.2. GENERAL EXPRESSIONS FOR THE STRAIGHT-LINE METHOD OF DEPRECIATION

Year No.	Capital recovered	Capital unrecovered beginning of year	Return on the capital unrecovered	Capital recovered plus return
1	$\dfrac{P-L}{n}$	P	Pi	$\dfrac{P-L}{n} + Pi$
2	$\dfrac{P-L}{n}$	$P - \left(\dfrac{P-L}{n}\right)$	$\left[P - \left(\dfrac{P-L}{n}\right)\right]i$	$\dfrac{P-L}{n} + \left[P - \left(\dfrac{P-L}{n}\right)\right]i$
3	$\dfrac{P-L}{n}$	$P - 2\left(\dfrac{P-L}{n}\right)$	$\left[P - 2\left(\dfrac{P-L}{n}\right)\right]i$	$\dfrac{P-L}{n} + \left[P - 2\left(\dfrac{P-L}{n}\right)\right]i$
r	$\dfrac{P-L}{n}$	$P - (r-1)\left(\dfrac{P-L}{n}\right)$	$\left[P - (r-1)\left(\dfrac{P-L}{n}\right)\right]i$	$\dfrac{P-L}{n} + \left[P - (r-1)\left(\dfrac{P-L}{n}\right)\right]i$
n	$\dfrac{P-L}{n}$	$P - (n-1)\left(\dfrac{P-L}{n}\right)$	$\left[P - (n-1)\left(\dfrac{P-L}{n}\right)\right]i$	$\dfrac{P-L}{n} + \left[P - (n-1)\left(\dfrac{P-L}{n}\right)\right]i$

But $\displaystyle\sum_{r=1}^{n} (1 + i)^{n-r} = (1 + i)^{n-1} + (1 + i)^{n-2} + \ldots + (1 + i) + 1$

$$= \frac{(1 + i)^n - 1}{i}$$

Let $\quad \sigma = \displaystyle\sum_{r=1}^{n} r(1 + i)^{n-r}$

$$= (1 + i)^{n-1} + 2(1 + i)^{n-2} + \ldots + (n - 1)(1 + i) + n$$

$$(1 + i)\sigma = (1 + i)^n + 2(1 + i)^{n-1} + \ldots + n(1 + i) + 1 - 1.$$

Subtracting σ from $(1 + i)$ σ term-by-term

$$i\sigma = (1 + i)^n + \sum_{r=1}^{n} (1 + i)^{n-r} - (n + 1)$$

$$= (1 + i)^n + \frac{(1 + i)^n - 1}{i} - (n + 1).$$

Substituting these evaluations into the expression for S, we get

$$S = \left[\frac{P - L}{n}(1 + i) + Pi\right]\frac{(1 + i)^n - 1}{i}$$

$$- i\left(\frac{P - L}{n}\right)\left[\frac{(1 + i)^n}{i} + \frac{(1 + i)^n - 1}{i^2} - \frac{n + 1}{i}\right]$$

$$= Pi\frac{(1 + i)^n - 1}{i} + \frac{P - L}{n}\left[\frac{(1 + i)^n - 1}{i} + (1 + i)^n - 1\right.$$

$$\left. - (1 + i)^n - \frac{(1 + i)^n - 1}{i} + n + 1\right]$$

$$= P(1 + i)^n - P + \frac{P - L}{n}(n) = P(1 + i)^n - L.$$

An expression for the equivalent annual capital recovered plus return may be derived by multiplying the equivalent end of service life value of capital recovered plus return by the sinking fund factor as follows

$$= [P(1 + i)^n - L]\left[\frac{i}{(1 + i)^n - 1}\right]$$

$$= P\left[\frac{i(1 + i)^n}{(1 + i)^n - 1}\right] - L\left[\frac{i}{(1 + i)^n - 1}\right]$$

$$= P\left[\frac{i(1 + i)^n}{(1 + i)^n - 1}\right] - L\left[\frac{i(1 + i)^n}{(1 + i)^n - 1} - i\right]$$

$$= (P - L)\left[\frac{i(1 + i)^n}{(1 + i)^n - 1}\right] + Li$$

$$= (P - L)(\overset{\text{RP } i\text{-}n}{}) + Li.$$

6.5. SINKING-FUND METHOD OF DEPRECIATION

The sinking-fund depreciation model assumes that the value of an asset decreases at an increasing rate. One of a series of equal amounts is assumed to be deposited into a sinking fund at the end of each year of the asset's life. The sinking fund is ordinarily compounded annually and, at the end of the estimated life of the asset, the amount accumulated equals the total depreciation of the asset. Thus, if an asset has a first cost of $5,000, an estimated life of 5 years, an estimated salvage value of $1,000, and if the interest rate is 6 per cent, the amount deposited into the sinking fund at the end of each year is

$$\text{RS 6-5}$$
$$(\$5,000 - \$1,000)(0.17740) = \$709.60.$$

The *capital recovered* during any year is the sum of the amount deposited into the sinking fund at the end of the year and the amount of interest earned on the sinking fund during the year. For the conditions assumed, the capital recovered during the first year is $709.60; during the second year $709.60 + 0.06 × $709.60 = $752.18; during the third year $709.60 + 0.06 × $1,461.78 = $797.31; etc. These values are given in the first section of Table 6.3.

Table 6.3. AN EXAMPLE OF THE SINKING FUND METHOD OF DEPRECIATION

Year No.	Capital recovered	Capital unrecovered beginning of year	Return on the capital unrecovered	Capital recovered plus return
1	$709.60	$5,000.00	$300.00	$1,009.60
2	$752.18	$4,290.40	$257.42	$1,009.60
3	$797.31	$3,538.22	$212.29	$1,009.60
4	$845.15	$2,740.91	$164.45	$1,009.60
5	$895.85	$1,895.76	$113.75	$1,009.60

The investment in the asset during the first year is $5,000; during the second $4,290.40; during the third $3,538.22; etc. The *return* for the first year should be $5,000 × 0.06 = $300; for the second year $4,290.40 × 0.06 = $257.42; for the third year $3538.22 × 0.06 = $212.29; etc. The capital unrecovered, return, and capital recovered plus return for each year of the asset's life are also given in Table 6.3.

Table 6.4. GENERAL EXPRESSIONS FOR THE SINKING FUND METHOD OF DEPRECIATION

Year No.	Capital recovered	Capital unrecovered beginning of year	Return on the capital unrecovered	Capital recovered plus return
1	$\dfrac{(P-L)\,i}{(1+i)^n - 1}$	P	Pi	$Pi + \dfrac{(P-L)\,i}{(1+i)^n - 1}$
2	$\dfrac{(P-L)\,i\,(1+i)}{(1+i)^n - 1}$	$P - \dfrac{(P-L)\,i}{(1+i)^n - 1}$	$Pi - \dfrac{(P-L)\,i^2}{(1+i)^n - 1}$	$Pi + \dfrac{(P-L)\,i}{(1+i)^n - 1}$
3	$\dfrac{(P-L)\,i\,(1+i)^2}{(1+i)^n - 1}$	$P - \dfrac{(P-L)\,[(1+i)^2 - 1]}{(1+i)^n - 1}$	$Pi - \dfrac{(P-L)\,i\,[(1+i)^2 - 1]}{(1+i)^n - 1}$	$Pi + \dfrac{(P-L)\,i}{(1+i)^n - 1}$
r	$\dfrac{(P-L)\,i\,(1+i)^{r-1}}{(1+i)^n - 1}$	$P - \dfrac{(P-L)\,[(1+i)^{r-1} - 1]}{(1+i)^n - 1}$	$Pi - \dfrac{(P-L)\,i\,[(1+i)^{r-1} - 1]}{(1+i)^n - 1}$	$Pi + \dfrac{(P-L)\,i}{(1+i)^n - 1}$
n	$\dfrac{(P-L)\,i\,(1+i)^{n-1}}{(1+i)^n - 1}$	$P - \dfrac{(P-L)\,[(1+i)^{n-1} - 1]}{(1+i)^n - 1}$	$Pi - \dfrac{(P-L)\,i\,[(1+i)^{n-1} - 1]}{(1+i)^n - 1}$	$Pi + \dfrac{(P-L)\,i}{(1+i)^n - 1}$

General expressions for capital recovered, capital unrecovered, return, and capital recovered plus return may be developed for each year of the asset's life. These derivations are exhibited in Table 6.4.

Substitution of the values for P, L, n, and i, stated in the example above, will yield the values given in Table 6.3. Thus, any given question concerning the sinking-fund method of depreciation may be answered by these general expressions.

By multiplying the capital recovered plus return term for the rth year by the compound-amount factor for the rth year and summing over all r years, $r = 1$ to n, an expression for the equivalent end of service life value of capital recovered plus return may be derived.

$$S = \sum_{r=1}^{n} \left[Pi + \frac{(P - L)i}{(1 + i)^n - 1} \right] (1 + i)^{n-r}.$$

The analysis required is similar to that used for the straight-line method. Therefore, the result, given without proof, is

$$P(1 + i)^n - L.$$

As was expected, the equivalent end of service life amount of captial recovered plus return is the same as for the straight-line method. Therefore, the equivalent annual capital recovered plus return is also

$$(P - L)(\overset{\text{RP } i\text{-}n}{}) + Li.$$

It is interesting to note that the capital recovered plus return expression in Table 6.4 is independent of r, that is, it is the same for all years. This expression is, therefore, the equivalent annual capital recovered plus return and can be reduced to the expression given above.

6.6. FIXED PERCENTAGE METHOD OF DEPRECIATION

The fixed percentage depreciation model assumes that the value of an asset decreases at a decreasing rate. By this method, the *capital recovered* during any year is equal to the unrecovered capital at the beginning of the year times D, where $D \times 100$ is the fixed percentage rate used. It follows that the undepreciated balance remaining at the end of any year equals the unrecovered capital at the beginning of the year times $(1 - D)$. The unrecovered capital at the end of the first year, second year, ..., and nth year is $P(1 - D)$, $P(1 - D)^2$, ..., and $P(1 - D)^n$ with $P(1 - D)^n = L$. The general expression for determining D, given P, L, and n is

$$D = 1 - \sqrt[n]{\frac{L}{P}}.$$

If an asset has a first cost of \$5,000, an estimated life of 5 years, and an estimated salvage value of \$1,000, the value for D is

$$1 - \sqrt[5]{\frac{1,000}{5,000}} = 1 - 0.72478 = 0.27522.$$

The capital recovered in the first year is \$5,000 $\times$ 0.27522 = \$1,376.10; during the second year (\$5,000 $-$ \$1376.10) 0.27522 = \$997.37; etc. These values are given in the first section of Table 6.5.

The investment in the asset during the first year is \$5,000; during the second year \$3,623.90; etc. For an interest rate of 6 per cent, the return for the first year should be \$5,000 $\times$ 0.06 = \$300; for the second year \$3623.90 $\times$ 0.06 = \$217.42; etc. The capital unrecovered, return, and capital recovered plus return for each year of the asset's life are also given in Table 6.5.

Table 6.5. AN EXAMPLE OF THE FIXED PERCENTAGE METHOD OF DEPRECIATION

Year No.	Capital recovered	Capital unrecovered beginning of year	Return on the capital unrecovered	Capital recovered plus return
1	\$1,376.10	\$5,000.00	\$300.00	\$1,676.10
2	\$ 997.37	\$3,623.90	\$217.42	\$1,214.79
3	\$ 722.87	\$2,626.53	\$157.59	\$ 880.46
4	\$ 523.93	\$1,903.66	\$114.22	\$ 638.15
5	\$ 379.73	\$1,379.73	\$ 82.78	\$ 462.51

As for the straight-line and sinking-fund methods of depreciation, general expressions for capital recovered, capital unrecovered, return, and capital recovered plus return may be developed for each year of the asset's life. These derivations are given in Table 6.6.

Substitution of the values for P, L, n, and i, stated in the example above, will give the values shown in Table 6.5. Thus, these general

Table 6.6. GENERAL EXPRESSIONS FOR THE FIXED PERCENTAGE METHOD OF DEPRECIATION

Year No.	Capital recovered	Capital unrecovered beginning of year	Return on the capital unrecovered	Capital recovered plus return
1	$P\left[1 - \sqrt[n]{\dfrac{L}{P}}\right]$	P	Pi	$P\left(1 - \sqrt[n]{\dfrac{L}{P}}\right) + Pi$
2	$P\left[1 - \sqrt[n]{\dfrac{L}{P}}\right]\left(\dfrac{L}{P}\right)^{1/n}$	$P\left(\dfrac{L}{P}\right)^{1/n}$	$Pi\left(\dfrac{L}{P}\right)^{1/n}$	$\left[P\left(1 - \sqrt[n]{\dfrac{L}{P}}\right) + Pi\right]\left(\dfrac{L}{P}\right)^{1/n}$
3	$P\left[1 - \sqrt[n]{\dfrac{L}{P}}\right]\left(\dfrac{L}{P}\right)^{2/n}$	$P\left(\dfrac{L}{P}\right)^{2/n}$	$Pi\left(\dfrac{L}{P}\right)^{2/n}$	$\left[P\left(1 - \sqrt[n]{\dfrac{L}{P}}\right) + Pi\right]\left(\dfrac{L}{P}\right)^{2/n}$
r	$P\left[1 - \sqrt[n]{\dfrac{L}{P}}\right]\left(\dfrac{L}{P}\right)^{(r-1)/n}$	$P\left(\dfrac{L}{P}\right)^{(r-1)/n}$	$Pi\left(\dfrac{L}{P}\right)^{(r-1)/n}$	$\left[P\left(1 - \sqrt[n]{\dfrac{L}{P}}\right) + Pi\right]\left(\dfrac{L}{P}\right)^{(r-1)/n}$
n	$P\left[1 - \sqrt[n]{\dfrac{L}{P}}\right]\left(\dfrac{L}{P}\right)^{(n-1)/n}$	$P\left(\dfrac{L}{P}\right)^{(n-1)/n}$	$Pi\left(\dfrac{L}{P}\right)^{(n-1)/n}$	$\left[P\left(1 - \sqrt[n]{\dfrac{L}{P}}\right) + Pi\right]\left(\dfrac{L}{P}\right)^{(n-1)/n}$

expressions may be used to answer any question concerning the fixed percentage method of depreciation.

As before, the equivalent end of service life value of capital recovered plus return may be found by multiplying the capital recovered plus return for the rth year by the compound-amount factor for the rth year, and summing over all r years; $r = 1$ to n. The result is stated without proof, but

$$S = \sum_{r=1}^{n} \left\{ \left[P\left(1 - n\sqrt{\frac{L}{P}}\right) + Pi \right] \left(\frac{L}{P}\right)^{(r-1)/n} \right\} (1 + i)^{n-r}$$
$$= P(1 + i)^n - L$$

the analysis required is similar to that used for the straight-line method. The result agrees with the result for straight-line and sinking-fund depreciation so the previous expression for equivalent annual capital recovered plus return will apply here also.

Equivalent annual capital recovered plus return is

$$(P - L)(\overset{\text{RP } i\text{-}n}{}) + Li.$$

6.7. SUM OF THE YEARS METHOD OF DEPRECIATION

The sum of the years depreciation model assumes that the value of an asset decreases at a decreasing rate. If an asset has an estimated life of 5 years, the sum of the years will be $1 + 2 + 3 + 4 + 5 = 15$. Thus, if the first cost of the asset is \$5,000, and the estimated salvage value is \$1,000, the capital recovered during the first year will be $(\$5,000 - \$1,000)\frac{5}{15} = \$1,333.33$. During the second year, the depreciation will be $(\$5,000 - \$1,000)\frac{4}{15} = \$1,066.67$, etc. These values are given in the first section of Table 6.7.

Table 6.7. AN EXAMPLE OF THE SUM OF THE YEARS' METHOD OF DEPRECIATION

Year No.	Capital recovered	Capital unrecovered beginning of year	Return on the capital unrecovered	Capital recovered plus return
1	\$1,333.33	\$5,000.00	\$300.00	\$1,633.33
2	\$1,066.67	\$3,666.67	\$220.00	\$1,286.67
3	\$ 800.00	\$2,600.00	\$156.00	\$ 956.00
4	\$ 533.33	\$1,800.00	\$108.00	\$ 641.33
5	\$ 266.67	\$1,266.67	\$ 76.00	\$ 342.67

Table 6.8. GENERAL EXPRESSIONS FOR THE SUM OF THE YEARS' METHOD OF DEPRECIATION

Year No.	Capital recovered	Capital unrecovered beginning of year	Return on the capital unrecovered	Capital recovered plus return
1	$\dfrac{n}{\Sigma n}(P-L)$	P	Pi	$\dfrac{n}{\Sigma n}(P-L)+Pi$
2	$\dfrac{n-1}{\Sigma n}(P-L)$	$\dfrac{\Sigma(n-1)}{\Sigma n}(P-L)+L$	$\left[\dfrac{\Sigma(n-1)}{\Sigma n}(P-L)+L\right]i$	$\dfrac{n-1}{\Sigma n}(P-L)+\left[\dfrac{\Sigma(n-1)}{\Sigma n}(P-L)+L\right]i$
3	$\dfrac{n-2}{\Sigma n}(P-L)$	$\dfrac{\Sigma(n-2)}{\Sigma n}(P-L)+L$	$\left[\dfrac{\Sigma(n-2)}{\Sigma n}(P-L)+L\right]i$	$\dfrac{n-2}{\Sigma n}(P-L)+\left[\dfrac{\Sigma(n-2)}{\Sigma n}(P-L)+L\right]i$
r	$\dfrac{n-r+1}{\Sigma n}(P-L)$	$\dfrac{\Sigma(n-r+1)}{\Sigma n}(P-L)+L$	$\left[\dfrac{\Sigma(n-r+1)}{\Sigma n}(P-L)+L\right]i$	$\dfrac{n-r+1}{\Sigma n}(P-L)+\left[\dfrac{\Sigma(n-r+1)}{\Sigma n}(P-L)+L\right]i$
n	$\dfrac{1}{\Sigma n}(P-L)$	$\dfrac{1}{\Sigma n}(P-L)+L$	$\left[\dfrac{1}{\Sigma n}(P-L)+L\right]i$	$\dfrac{1}{\Sigma n}(P-L)+\left[\dfrac{1}{\Sigma n}(P-L)+L\right]i$

The unrecovered capital during the first year is \$5,000; during the second year \$5,000 − \$1,333.33 = \$3,666.67; etc. If the interest rate is 6 per cent, the return for the first year should be \$5,000 × 0.06 = \$300; for the second year \$3,666.67 × 0.06 = \$220; etc. The capital unrecovered, return, and capital recovered plus return for each year of the asset's life are also given in Table 6.7.

As was done previously, general expressions for capital recovered, capital unrecovered, return, and capital recovered plus return may be derived for each year of the asset's life. The resulting expressions are exhibited in Table 6.8.

Substitution of the values for P, L, n, and i, stated for the example above, will yield the values given in Table 6.7. As before, the general expressions may be used to describe any particular facet of the sum of the years method of depreciation.

As was indicated for the previous methods of depreciation, the equivalent end of service life value of capital recovered plus return may be found by multiplying the capital recovered plus return for the rth year by the compound-amount factor for the rth year, and summing over all r years; $r = 1$ to n. Then

$$S = \sum_{r=1}^{n} \left\{ \frac{n - r + 1}{\Sigma n}(P - L)\left[\frac{\Sigma(n - r + 1)}{\Sigma n}(P - L) + L \right]i \right\} (1 + i)^{n-r}$$

$$= P(1 + i)^{n} - L.$$

This result is stated without proof, but again the analysis required is similar to that used in the straight-line method. The result agrees with the previous results so the equivalent annual capital recovered plus return expression will be applicable for sum of the years depreciation also.

Equivalent annual capital recovered plus return is

$$(P - L)(\overset{\text{RP } i\text{-}n}{\quad}) + Li.$$

6.8. SERVICE OUTPUT METHOD OF DEPRECIATION

In some cases, it may not be advisable to assume that capital is recovered in accordance with a theoretical value-time model such as those considered previously. An alternative is to assume that capital recovered occurs on the basis of service performed without regard to the duration of the asset's life. Thus, a trencher might be depreciated on the basis of pipeline trench completed. If the trencher has a first cost of $11,000 and a salvage value of $600, and if it is estimated that the trencher would dig 1,500,000 linear feet of pipeline trench in its life, the *capital recovered* per foot of trench dug may be calculated as

$$\frac{\$11,000 - \$600}{1,500,000} = \$0.006933 \text{ per foot.}$$

The capital unrecovered at the end of each year is a function of the number of feet of trench dug during the year. If, for instance, 300,000 feet of pipeline trench were dug during the first year, the undepreciated balance at the end of the year would be $11,000 − 300,000(\$0.006933) = \$8,920.10$. The *return* expected, if the interest rate is 6 per cent, would be $\$8,920.10 \times 0.06 = \$535.21$. This analysis would be repeated at the end of each year.

6.9. CAPITAL RECOVERED PLUS RETURN IS EQUIVALENT FOR ALL METHODS OF DEPRECIATION

The equivalent annual capital recovered plus return for each of the methods of depreciation considered was shown to be

$$(P - L)(\overset{\text{RP } i\text{-}n}{\quad}) + Li.$$

This result proves that capital recovered plus return is equivalent for the straight-line, sinking-fund, fixed percentage, and sum of years methods of depreciation. It will now be shown that if retirement of any asset takes place at the age and salvage value for which capital recovered and interest on the unrecovered capital were calculated, the sum of capital recovered and return for any method of depreciation will be equivalent.

If $(P - L) = A + B + C + \ldots + N$, where $A, B, C, \ldots, N$ are capital recovered amounts for the successive years, we get the following table:

End of Year No.	Depreciation at End of Year	Interest on Undepreciated Balance at End of Year
0	0	0
1	A	$Ai + Bi + \ldots + Ni + Li$
2	B	$Bi + \ldots + Ni + Li$
n	N	$Ni + Li$

Interest, Li, on the salvage value, L, will be equal for all methods of depreciation and need not be given further consideration. The quantity $B + Bi$ as of the end of Year No. 2 is equivalent to

$$(B + Bi) \times \frac{1}{(1 + i)} = B$$

as of the end of Year No. 1. Addition of this amount, B, to Bi results in a total $(B + Bi)$ as of the end of Year No. 1. This sum is in turn equivalent to B as of the end of Year No. 0. By similar calculations, quantities involving symbols A to N inclusive will be found to have a worth of $A, B, \ldots, N$ as of the end of Year No. 0 respectively. Since $(A + B + \ldots + N)$ equals $(P - L)$, and since $A, B, \ldots, N$ may be chosen to represent depreciation by any method, it may be concluded that the present worth of the depreciation calculated by any method plus the interest on the undepreciated balance is equal to the total depreciation at the beginning of the depreciation period.

In the illustrative example on straight-line depreciation, an asset having a first cost of $5,000 was depreciated to a salvage value of $1,000 in a period of 5 years. The sum of *capital recovered* and *interest on unrecovered balance* is shown in the second column of the following table.

Year No.	Sum of Capital Recovered and Interest on Unrecovered Balance		Single Payment Present Worth Factor		
1	$1,100	×	PS 6-1 (0.9434)	=	$1,037.74
2	1,052	×	PS 6-2 (0.8900)	=	936.28
3	1,004	×	PS 6-3 (0.8396)	=	842.96
4	956	×	PS 6-4 (0.7921)	=	757.25
5	908	×	PS 6-5 (0.7473)	=	678.55
			Total Present Worth		$4,252.78

The comparable figures calculated for sinking-fund depreciation are given in the second column of the following table.

Year No.	Sum of Capital Recovered and Interest on Unrecovered Balance		Single Payment Present Worth Factor		
1	$1,009.60	×	PS 6-1 (0.9434)	=	$ 952.46
2	1,009.60	×	PS 6-2 (0.8900)	=	898.54
3	1,009.60	×	PS 6-3 (0.8396)	=	847.66
4	1,009.60	×	PS 6-4 (0.7921)	=	799.70
5	1,009.60	×	PS 6-5 (0.7473)	=	754.47
			Total Present Worth		$4,252.83

The slight difference between the two resulting values, $4,252.78 and $4,252.83, results from using tables of too few places.

There are ordinarily only two real transactions in an asset's depreciation. These are its purchase and its sale as salvage. In the above example the asset was purchased for $5,000 and its salvage five years later was presumed to have a value of $1,000. The present worth of these two amounts as of the time of purchase follows.

Present worth of $5,000 disbursement at time of purchase of asset, $5000 × 1....................................... $5,000.00

Present worth of $1,000 received from sale of salvage value (a receipt is a negative disbursement), $1,000 × PS 6-5 (0.7473)..... −747.30

Total present worth................................ $4,252.70

Compare this with the two previous results.

6.10. DEPLETION

Depletion differs in theory from depreciation in that the latter is the result of use and the passage of time while the former is the result of the intentional, *piecemeal removal* of certain types of assets. Depletion refers to an activity that tends to exhaust a supply and the word literally means emptying. When natural resources are exploited in production, depletion indicates a lessening in value with the passage of time. Examples of depletion are the removal of coal from a mine, timber from a forest, stone from a quarry, and oil from a reservoir.

In the case of depletion, it is clear that a portion of the asset is

disposed of with each sale. But when a machine tool is used to produce goods for sale, a portion of its productive capacity is a part of
each unit produced and, thus, is disposed of with each sale. A mineral
resource has value only because the mineral may be sold and, similarly, the machine tool has value because what it can produce may
be sold. Both depletion and depreciation represent decreases in value
through the using up of the value of the asset under consideration.

There is a difference in the manner in which the capital recovered
through depletion and depreciation must be handled. In the case of
depreciation, the asset involved usually may be replaced with a like
asset, but in the case of depletion such replacement is usually not
possible. In manufacturing, the amounts charged for depreciation
are reinvested in new equipment to continue operation. However,
in mining, the amounts charged to depletion cannot be used to replace
the ore deposit and the venture may sell itself out of business. The
return in such a case must consist of two portions — the profit earned
on the venture and the owners' capital which was invested. In the
actual operation of ventures dealing with the piecemeal removal of
resources, it is common to acquire new properties, thus enabling the
venture to continue.

6.11. DEPRECIATION AND ENGINEERING ECONOMY ANALYSIS

As was indicated earlier, depreciation is a cost of production.
An asset is actually consumed in producing goods and thus its depreciation is a production cost. If the cost of capital consumption is
neglected, profits will appear to be higher than they are by an amount
equal to the depreciation that has taken place during the production
period.

In economy analysis dealing with physical assets, it is necessary
to compute the equivalent annual cost of capital recovered plus
return, so that alternatives involving competing assets may be compared on an equivalent basis. Regardless of the depreciation model
chosen to represent the value of the asset over time, the equivalent
annual cost of capital recovered and return will be

$$(P - L)(\overset{\text{RP } i\text{-}n}{}) + Li.$$

Therefore, in making annual cost comparisons of alternative engineering proposals involving physical assets, this expression may be used.

Depreciation is based upon estimates. It would be desirable to know the amount and pattern of an asset's depreciation at any point during its life in order that exact charges could be made against products as they are produced. Unfortunately, the depreciation of an asset cannot be known with certainty until after the asset has been retired from service.

Usually, it is impractical to defer calculation of depreciation costs until after an asset has been disposed of at the end of its life. In fact, depreciation costs of an asset should be taken into account prior to the purchase of the asset, as one of the factors to be considered in arriving at the desirability of purchasing it.

Since information on depreciation is needed on a current basis for making decisions, it has become a practice to estimate the amount of depreciation an asset will suffer and the pattern in which this depreciation will occur. This involves estimates of the service life, salvage value, and depreciation method, since the first cost of an asset is known with considerable accuracy. However, since the service life, salvage value, and pattern of depreciation refer to events in the future, they cannot be known with certainty. These estimates are usually based upon experience with similar assets and the judgment of the estimator. Certain aspects of the problem of estimating service life are presented in Appendix A.

QUESTIONS AND PROBLEMS

1. Discuss the difference between physical and functional depreciation.

2. Why is it important to include capital consumption as a cost of production?

3. Why is the cost of capital consumption an important consideration in evaluating alternative engineering proposals?

4. Describe the value-time function and name its essential components.

5. Discuss the meaning of capital recovery and return.

6. A certain asset was purchased in 19x2 for $2,800. It is estimated that the asset could be sold for $2,200 in 19x3, $1,650 in 19x4, $1,200 in 19x5, $950 in 19x6, $700 in 19x7, and $400 in 19x8. On the basis of these estimates, plot the depreciation and the undepreciated balance of the asset for each year of its life.

7. A pin grinder has a first cost of $1,600 with an estimated salvage value of $400 at the end of 6 years. The interest rate is 6 per cent.

(a) Graph the annual depreciation by the straight-line, sinking-fund, and fixed percentage methods for each year.

(b) Graph the depreciated values obtained by the three methods for the end of each year.

(c) Graph the total depreciation of the asset obtained by the three methods for the end of each year.

8. Calculate the depreciated value at the end of each year by the straight line, sinking-fund, and fixed percentage methods of depreciation for an asset with an initial cost of $6,100 and an estimated salvage value of $2,000 after 5 years. Use an interest rate of 10 per cent and present results in tabular form.

9. An asset has a first cost of $5,000 and an estimated salvage value of $1,000 at the end of 4 years. The interest rate is 10 per cent.

(a) Tabulate capital recovery and return for each year by the straight-line and sum of the years methods of depreciation.

(b) Show that the depreciation methods are equivalent by converting each to an equivalent annual cost for the 4 years.

10. A drilling rig was purchased for $3,800. One year later an offer of $4,000 was received for it. Two years later, the offer was $2,800 and three years later, a $1,800 offer was received.

(a) Determine the depreciation of the rig for each year based on the offers received.

(b) Determine the interest on the undepreciated balance for each of the 3 years using an interest rate of 7 per cent.

(c) Determine the uniform year-end amount for the 3-year period which is equivalent to the sum of the depreciation and interest on the undepreciated balance found above.

(d) Determine the annual cost of capital recovery with a return for the 3-year period using the initial cost and the last offer. Compare with (c).

11. A refrigeration unit was purchased for $3,800. From analysis of similar units, it was estimated that the unit would last 12 years and would be worth $200 as scrap. After 7 years of operation, the unit was sold for $800. The interest rate is 6 per cent.

(a) What was the anticipated equivalent annual cost of capital recovery and return?

(b) How much was the equivalent annual cost of capital recovery and return underestimated?

12. For convenience, a contractor uses the sum of straight-line depreciation plus interest on the original investment to calculate the cost of capital recovery with a return on his equipment.

(a) On this basis, what will be the annual cost of capital recovery with a return of an asset that is purchased for $5,500 and has a salvage value of $750 at the end of 10 years, if the interest rate is 8 per cent?

(b) What per cent error is involved in this approximation?

13. A drill press is purchased for $1,100 and has an expected life of 12 years, at which time the salvage value is estimated to be $130. What will be the book value at the end of 8 years by (a) straight-line depreciation, (b) 4 per cent sinking-fund depreciation, (c) fixed percentage depreciation, and (d) sum of the years depreciation?

14. An asset was purchased 10 years ago for $2,400. It is being depreciated in accordance with the straight-line method for an estimated total life of 20 years and salvage value of $400. What is the difference in its book value and the book value that would have resulted if 6 per cent sinking-fund depreciation had been used?

15. Contractor A and Contractor B both purchased concrete mixers for $5,000 each on January 1, 19x2. Contractor A kept his mixer in top condition and at the end of 19x3 he sold it for $4,000. Contractor B, however, did not think ahead to its resale value and, therefore, spent only enough on maintenance to keep it in good running order for the two years that he owned it. At the end of two years, B also sold his mixer but got only $3,000 for it. Contractor A spent $300 the first year and $300 the second year for maintenance in excess of what B spent.

Considering the rate of interest at 10 per cent and also the fact that both mixers gave equal performance during the two years, what was the net equivalent annual value of Contractor A's extra maintenance?

16. A cement mixer is purchased for $2,000 and has an estimated salvage value of $500 and an expected life of 4 years. Approximately 25 cubic yards of concrete per month will be produced by the mixer.

(a) Calculate the annual cost of capital recovery plus return with the interest rate at 5 per cent.

(b) Calculate the cost of capital recovery plus return per yard of concrete produced if the interest rate is 7 per cent.

17. A city engineer wishes to know the annual cost and the cost per foot for a paving machine that will cost the city $26,000 and will have a salvage value of $6,000 at the end of 10 years. The city plans to pave 30,000 running feet of street per year and uses an interest rate of 5 per cent. Develop the required cost figures using sinking-fund depreciation.

18. An engineer with a construction firm is considering the purchase of a machine with an initial cost of $6,200. He estimates that the salvage value of the machine will be $1,200 at the end of 5 years. He wishes to use straight-line depreciation, but wants to express capital recovery and return separately and in the form of equivalent annual amounts. For an interest rate of 6 per cent what is the equivalent annual capital recovery and the equivalent annual return?

19. A certain machine is estimated to provide 4,000 hours of service during its life. The machine costs $4,800 and will have a salvage value of zero after 4,000 hours of use. The space occupied by the machine is worth $300 per year. What will be the cost of capital recovered plus return if the interest rate is 6 per cent compounded annually and if the number of hours the machine is used per year is (a) 2,000, (b) 1,000?

20. Rework Problem 19 under the assumption that interest is compounded continuously.

PART III

PLANNING ENGINEERING
ECONOMY ANALYSIS

CHAPTER 7

CLASSIFICATIONS OF COST
FOR ECONOMY ANALYSIS

The ultimate objective of engineering application is the satisfaction of human wants. But human wants are not satisfied without cost. Alternative engineering proposals will differ in regard to the costs they involve relative to the objective of want satisfaction. The engineering proposal resulting in least cost will be considered best under the assumption that its success is measured by its ultimate ability to create utility in the economic environment.

It was noted in Chapter 1 that the essential steps in want satisfaction are carried out as a part of organized activity, and that the costs associated with this activity will have a direct bearing on the cost of want satisfaction. A number of classifications of cost have come into use to describe the expense involved in organized activity. As concepts, these classifications are useful in calling to mind the source and affect of costs that will have a bearing on the end result of an activity. This chapter will define and illustrate these cost classifications.

7.1. FIRST COST

By definition, *first cost* is considered to involve the cost of getting an activity started. The chief advantage in recognizing this classification is that it calls attention to a group of costs associated with the initiation of a new activity that might not otherwise be given proper consideration. Ordinarily, this classification is limited to those costs which occur only once for any given activity.

The threshold idea, presented as a concept in Chapter 2, illustrated that there is a degree of input below which the effect of action is insignificant. As an analogy, it must be recognized that many activities that otherwise may be profitable cannot be undertaken for the reason that their associated first cost represents a level of input above that which can be met. Many engineering proposals that are otherwise sound are not initiated because the first cost involved is beyond the reach of the controlling organization. Other engineering proposals meet with failure after initiation because it was found that the threshold input required was not successfully met due to financial limitations.

An example involving consideration of first cost. Often it is wise to accept an engineering proposal with an expected return less than that of a competing proposal if the ability to meet the first cost of the latter is in doubt. As an example, consider a proposed mining operation involving the extraction of an estimated 120,000 tons of ore from a mountain. Engineering Proposal A involves the construction of a tunnel beginning at an existing railroad spur and terminating within the mountain at the ore deposit. The ore will be removed by a gravity conveyor within the tunnel. The first cost of the tunnel and installed conveyor is estimated to be $138,000. The conveyor will cost $0.10 per ton to operate and will have a salvage value of $18,000.

Engineering Proposal B involves the removal of a quantity of overburden so the ore deposit will be exposed for loading into trucks. The first cost of removing the overburden and improving an existing road is estimated to be $22,000. Trucks with drivers will be leased to haul the ore to the spur at a cost of $1.30 per ton of ore removed. All other costs for the two proposals are equal. Neglecting interest, the cost difference is calculated as follows:

Proposal A:

$$\$138,000 - \$18,000 + \$0.10(120,000) = \$132,000.$$

Proposal B:

$$\$22,000 + \$1.30(120,000) = \$178,000.$$

Cost difference:

$$\$178,000 - \$132,000 = \$46,000.$$

Suppose that further analysis indicates that the mining operation will result in sufficient income to yield a profit regardless of the proposal chosen, but that financial limitations will not allow the successful completion of Proposal A because of its high first cost. In such a case, the mining operation might be initiated by accepting Proposal B even though it will result in a cost of $46,000 more than A. Although A appears to be best, it would result in failure because of exhaustion of funds before realization of adequate income. Thus, the value of recognizing and considering first cost is illustrated.

7.2. FIXED AND VARIABLE COST

Fixed cost is ordinarily defined as that group of costs involved in a going activity whose total will remain relatively constant throughout the range of operational activity. The concept of fixed cost has a wide application. For example, certain losses in the operation of an engine are in some measure independent of its output of power. Among its fixed costs, in terms of energy for a given speed and load, are those for the power to drive the fan, the valve mechanism, and the oil and fuel pumps. Almost any task involves preparation independent of its extent. Thus, to paint a small area may require as much effort for the cleaning of a brush as to paint a large area. Similarly, manufacturing involves fixed costs that are independent of the volume of output.

Variable cost is ordinarily defined as that group of costs which vary in some relationship to the level of operational activity. For example, the consumption of fuel by an engine may be expected to be proportional to its output of power and the amount of paint used may be expected to be proportional to the area painted. In manufacturing, the amount of material needed per unit of product may be expected to remain constant and, therefore, the material cost will vary directly with the number of units produced.

Fixed costs arise from making preparation for the future. A machine is purchased now in order that labor costs may be reduced in the future. Materials which may never be needed are purchased in large quantities and stored at much expense and with some risk in order that idleness of production facilities and men may be avoided. Research is carried on with no immediate benefit in view on the hope that it will pay in the long run. The investments that give rise to fixed cost are made in the present in the hope that they will be recovered with a profit as a result of reductions in variable costs or of increases in income.

Fixed costs arise from past decisions.

Fixed costs are made up of such cost items as depreciation, maintenance, taxes, insurance, lease rentals, and interest on invested capital, sales programs, certain administrative expenses, and research. It will be observed that these arise from the decisions of the past and in general are not subject to rapid change. Volume of operational activity, on the other hand, may fluctuate widely and rapidly. As a result, fixed costs per unit may easily get out of hand. It is probable that this is the cause of more unsuccessful activity than any other, for few have the foresight or luck to make commitments in the present which will fit requirements of the future even reasonably well. Since fixed costs cannot be changed readily, consideration must be focused upon maintaining a satisfactory volume and character of activity.

In general, all costs such as direct labor, direct material, direct power, and the like, which can readily be allocated to each unit of product, are considered to constitute the variable costs and the balance of the costs of the enterprise are regarded as fixed costs.

In a practical situation, fixed costs are only relatively fixed and their total may be expected to increase somewhat with increased activity. The increase will probably not follow a smooth curve but will vary in accordance with the characteristics of the enterprise.

Consider a plant of several units that has been shut down or is operating at zero volume. No heat, light, janitor, and many other services will have been required. Many of these services must be reinstated if the plant is to operate at all, and if reinstated only on a minimum basis it is probable that these services will be adequate for quite a range of activity. Further increases in activity will require expenditures for other services that cannot be provided to just the extent needed. Thus, what are termed "fixed costs" in business may be expected to increase in some stepped pattern with an increase in activity.

Variable expense may also be expected to increase in a stepped pattern. To increase production beyond a certain extent another machine may be added. Even though its full capacity may not be utilized, it may be necessary to employ a full crew of men to operate it. Also, an increase in productivity may be expected to result in the use of materials in greater quantities, and thus in their purchase at a lower cost per unit due to quantity discounts and volume handling.

The practices followed in designating fixed and variable costs are usually at variance with the strict interpretation of these terms. Analyses in which they are a factor must recognize this fact or the results may be grossly misleading.

Lapse of time and rate of use affect fixed cost. The lapse of time and rate of use of assets materially affect the fixed costs per annum and per unit of output. This may be illustrated by an example. Suppose that a machine can be purchased for $1,000 and that it will reach zero value either from the wear of processing 10,000 units of product or from ten years of deterioration due to action of the elements. This machine has capacity sufficient to process 10,000 units per year. It is estimated that the annual cost of space used by the machine is $60. Interest is taken at 8 per cent.

A tabulation of the fixed costs per annum and per unit of output is given in Table 7.1. At an output of 500 units per annum the machine will have weathered to uselessness when only 5,000 units have been made.

Table 7.1. FIXED COST OF A MACHINE FOR SEVERAL RATES OF USE

Annual output..........	10,000	5,000	2,000	1,000	500
Years of service, n........	1	2	5	10	10
Capital recovery factor for n years...............	1.0800	0.56077	0.25046	0.14903	0.14903
Capital recovery factor $\times$ $1,000................	$1,080	$561	$250	$149	$149
Charge for space.........	60	60	60	60	60
Total annual fixed cost..	$1,140	$621	$310	$209	$209
Fixed cost per unit of output..............	$0.114	$0.124	$0.155	$0.209	$0.418

These analyses serve to show that fixed costs are a function of the amount of investment and the lapse of time. The fixed cost per unit output is markedly affected by the time element and warrants serious consideration as a means of cost reduction. It is also apparent that an unwise investment in an asset may be the source of high costs throughout its life. The problem of controlling fixed cost per unit of product is further complicated by depreciation due to obsolescence or inadequacy, which can result in the retirement of a machine before it either wears or weathers to scrap.

An example embracing fixed and variable costs. The ideas involved in the fixed costs and variable costs are theoretical in nature. From a practical standpoint, it is difficult to accurately identify all costs of an activity as being either fixed or variable. Nevertheless, these concepts are useful as a cost classification scheme in evaluating alternatives.

As an aid to understanding fixed and variable costs, consider an activity consisting of the manufacturing and marketing of a certain plastic drafting template. The machine required in the operation will cost $1,400 and will have an estimated life of 8 years. It is estimated that the cost of production including power, labor, space, and selling expense will be $0.11 per unit sold. Material will cost $0.095 per unit. An interest rate of 8 per cent is considered necessary to justify the required investment. The costs associated with this activity are:

	Fixed Costs (Annual)	Variable Costs (Per Unit)
RP 8-8		
Capital recovery and return $1,400 × (0.17401)	$244	
Insurance and taxes..........................	34	
Repairs and maintenance....................	22	$0.005
Material...		0.095
Labor, electricity, and space................		0.11
Total...	$300	$0.210

The difficulty of making a clear-cut separation between fixed and variable costs becomes apparent when attention is focused on the item for repair and maintenance in the above classification. In practice it is very difficult to distinguish between repairs that are a result of deterioration that takes place with the passage of time and those that result from the wear and tear of use. However, in theory, the separation can be made as shown in this example and is in accord with fact, with the exception, perhaps, of the assumption that repairs from wear and tear will be in direct proportion to the number of units manufactured. To be in accord with actualities, depreciation also undoubtedly should have been separated so that a part would appear as variable cost. Let

C_f = annual fixed cost = \$300;

C_v = annual variable cost = $c \times n$;

c = variable cost per unit = \$0.21;

n = annual output;

C_t = total annual cost;

C_u = cost of production per unit;

s = sale price per unit = \$0.30;

I = income per year = $n \times s$.

The following expressions apply;

$$C_t = C_f + C_v = C_f + (c \times n)$$

If C_t is plotted as n varies from 0 to 6,000, the result will be as shown in Figure 7.1.

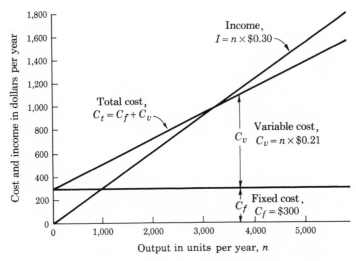

Figure 7.1. Fixed cost, variable cost, and income per year.

The cost of producing templates will vary with the number made per year. The production cost per unit is given by

$$C_u = \frac{C_f}{n} + c.$$

Values of C_u, the production cost per unit, as n varies from 0 to 6,000, are given in Figure 7.2.

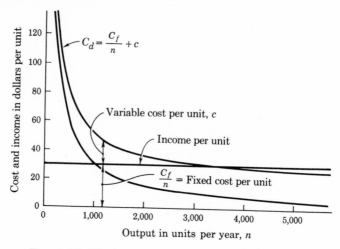

Figure 7.2. Fixed cost, variable cost, and income per unit.

It will be noted that the fixed cost per unit may range to an infinite amount. Thus, in determining unit costs, fixed cost has little meaning unless the number of units to which it applies is known.

Income for most enterprises is directly proportional to the number of units sold. In the example above the income is expressed as $I = ns$.

The income per unit may easily be exceeded by the sum of the fixed and the variable cost per unit for low production volumes. This is shown by comparing the total cost per unit curve and the income per unit curve shown in Figure 7.1. Additional concepts and analyses relative to fixed and variable costs applied to the analysis of industrial operations will be presented in Chapter 18.

7.3. INCREMENT, DIFFERENTIAL, AND MARGINAL COST

The terms *increment cost, differential cost, and marginal cost* refer to essentially the same concept. The word increment means increase and an *increment cost* means an increase in cost. Usually, reference is made to an increase of cost in relation to some other factor, thus resulting in such expressions as increment cost per ton, increment cost per gallon, or increment cost per unit of production.

With reference to the basic increment cost, *differential cost* is used to mean the ratio of a small increment of cost and a small increase of output. The term *marginal cost* refers specifically to an increment of output whose cost is barely covered by the return derived from it; in other words, a marginal cost is an incremental cost that is on the borderline of attaining a contemplated result. With reference to the concept of diminishing returns, marginal cost would fall where net return is zero.

The increment cost of producing 10 items between outputs of 60 and 70 units per year is shown in Figure 7.3. The increment output, Δ output, = 70 − 60 = 10 units.

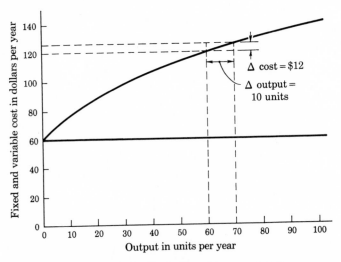

Figure 7.3. An illustration of increment cost.

The increment cost, Δ cost, as read from the curve, is $12. The average increment cost of the 10 units in question is $12/10 or $1.20 per unit.

The average cost of producing 60 units per year is $120/60 or $2 per unit. The average cost of producing 70 units per year is $132/70, or approximately $1.89 per unit.

The concept of increment costs is very useful in considering economy. Suppose, for instance, that in the above example 60 units per year are being sold at $2.20 per year when an offer of $1.50 per unit is made for 10 additional units. In view of the average cost of $2 and $1.89 for 60 and 70 units per year respectively, it might be concluded that acceptance of the offer would result in a loss, when in fact an average gain of $0.30 per unit is in prospect.

Increment costs are difficult to determine. In the example above, a curve was given which enabled the increment cost to be precisely determined as $12 for 10 units. As a practical matter in actual situations it is ordinarily difficult to determine increment cost. There is no general approach to the problem, but each case must be analyzed on the basis of the facts that apply to it at the time and the future period involved. Increment costs can be overestimated or underestimated, and either error may be costly. The overestimation of increment costs may obscure a profit possibility; on the other hand, if they are underestimated, an activity may be undertaken which will result in a loss. Thus, accurate information is necessary if sound decisions are to be made.

Pattern for consideration of increment costs. Where increment costs are to be considered, the question is: Will it be profitable to add a certain activity or subtract a certain activity from the total activities now in progress? To answer this question, basic data are needed to give a true picture of the present situation in a physical sense. These data should take the form of such concrete terms as pounds of scrap produced, square feet of floor space used, number of hours that Machine N-116 operates, number of hours that Machine 20 can operate before an overhaul will be needed, pounds of steam used, and so forth. Factual information on such items over the period that the contemplated increment of activity will be in force forms the base line for evaluating the increment.

The next step is to determine, in similarly concrete terms, the changes that will take place as a result of undertaking the increment of activity. The accuracy and completeness with which this can be done ranges all the way from the point where predictions are almost a certainty, to the point where success of prediction is a matter of chance. In any event, the changes that the increment of activity will bring about should be set down item by item. The plan above is analogous to the use of a free-body diagram in mechanics to arrive at the effect of a force.

After the changes that will take place as a result of an increment of activity have been isolated as far as possible, the next step is to convert the changes as found into monetary values. The point to recognize is that the monetary values that can be assigned to happenings in the future can at best be no more accurate than the data to which they apply. They may be less accurate. Even where it is known that an event will take place, it may be impossible to determine the expenditure it will entail.

Increment costs based on experimentation. There are a surprising number of situations in which costs that are unknown can be determined by investigation or experimentation. A relatively small sum spent experimentally may determine the result of a future activity under consideration. This is the idea behind the construction and operation of pilot plants. Not only are these plants effective in determining the feasibility of taking on a new product, but they also permit experimentation to arrive at improvements which, with a full-scale installation, it would not be feasible to work out.

In many cases information is available and needs merely to be brought to bear on the problem. Information is often available in handbooks and technical literature. Supervisors and operators of machines often have valuable concrete information. In other cases information is at hand and needs only to be used. In a recent conversion from the manufacture of aluminum to the production of steel pistons, no one took the trouble to determine the bulk of the shavings that would be produced as the result of the change. Thus provisions for removing them were inadequate and expensive changes had to be made after the manufacturing line had been installed. This large cost could have been avoided by calculating from the blueprints the amount of shavings that would be produced.

Increment costs based on cost accounts. The most prevalent data available on costs, and particularly unit costs, are those produced by accounting and cost accounting systems. Unfortunately such data are often not to be relied on in determining the effect of an increment of activity.

It has been brought out, for instance, that accounting records give "book values" of equipment instead of the true depreciated balance. Cost accounting systems are compromises between the cost of getting accurate cost figures and the value of their accuracy in the operation of an enterprise.

Furthermore, cost data are based on estimates of future volume of activity in order that cost data may be predictive and serve as a basis for planning. Many bases for distributing burden rates, such as direct labor dollars, direct labor hours, and machine hours, are satisfactory from a practical standpoint and as an over-all guide but are inadequate for the determination of the specific costs needed for the analysis of incremental activities.

A firm that was punching a circular disk from a square blank conceived the idea of altering the die so that four advertising novelties were punched out of the formerly wasted corners of the blank. After the punching, the burrs were removed and the pieces were flash plated. At first the product was given to salesmen without bothering to determine costs. As the demand grew, costs were determined on the basis of the scrap value of the actual weight of metal in each piece and the cost of burring and flash plating. No labor was charged to the novelty for the punching operation; this was considered to be carried by the disk. On this basis the incremental cost was inordinately low and the company's salesmen not only gave the pieces to their customers freely but also offered a quantity for sale, basing their price upon an incremental cost of $0.0024 per piece. When the orders were totaled, the number required greatly exceeded the number that could be made in conjunction with the disks. When the pieces were made separately, where all costs had to be borne by the novelty, the cost was $0.0208 per piece — over nine times as much as before — and resulted in a high percentage loss.

In this case, the cost of production of $0.0024 was an incremental cost and so recognized by the firm, but it was only true for the number of pieces that could be punched with the disk. Cost accounting, ordinarily, could not be expected to direct attention to the fact that the cost of $0.0024 only held good for a quantity proportional to the number of disks produced.

Increment costs based on judgment. Where no cost accounts are available and where it is not feasible to determine increment cost by investigation or experimentation, it will be necessary to arrive at costs through judgment. This amounts to an informal consideration of the facts involved, or thought to be involved, in the future in light of facts, opinions, impressions, biases, and conjectures of the past. As faulty as judgment may sometimes be, the fact remains that it must necessarily be the basis for deciding on much activity for which there is insufficient objective knowledge. Judgments often must be made to undertake this or to drop that increment of activity even though objective data are lacking, for the decision not to act is itself a decision relative to the question in hand.

7.4. SUNK COST

The intent in making an investment in a capital asset, such as a bulldozer, is to receive a net income from its services sufficient to at least equal the investment. When the net income equals or exceeds the amount invested, the investment is said to have been recovered. When the net income received is less than the amount invested, an unrecovered balance remains. The unrecovered balance is referred to as a *sunk cost*. Thus, the term *sunk cost* may be defined as the difference between the amount invested in an asset and the net worth of services and incomes resulting from its employment. Sunk costs arise from decisions based on plans that are not realized.

Sunk cost arising from overestimation of productive value. As an illustration of the concept of sunk costs, consider the following theoretical example in which interest will be ignored for simplicity. A manufacturer purchased a machine for $2,800 that was expected to have a service value of $1,000 per annum. When purchased, the machine was estimated to have a service life of five years, a salvage value of $200 at the end of its life, and an annual operating cost of $400 per year. On the basis of these estimates, the future years were pictured as shown in Table 7.2.

On the basis of the estimates that had been made, the machine was expected to render services whose net value plus the $200 to be received from salvage was expected to be sufficient to recover the investment in the machine plus $400 in a five-year period.

Actually the above estimates had been in error. Instead of the machine's services having an annual value of $1,000, the services turned out to be worth only $700 per year. Operating costs totaled $600 instead of the estimated $400. Instead of having a service life of five years, the machine became so worn that it was sold for $300 at

Table 7.2. ESTIMATED RECEIPTS AND DISBURSEMENTS

Receipts and disbursements	Year No. 0	Year No. 1	Year No. 2	Year No. 3	Year No. 4	Year No. 5
Value of service rendered by machine during the year................	...	$1,000	$1,000	$1,000	$1,000	$1,000
Amount received from salvage.............	...	...	...	...	...	200
Operating cost during year................	...	400	400	400	400	400
Amount of investment recovered during year...	...	600	600	600	600	800
Unearned balance of investment in machine at the end of year.......	$2,800	2,200	1,600	1,000	400	−400

the end of three years. Thus the service value and the life of the machine had been overestimated and its salvage value had been underestimated. The actual history of the investment is shown in Table 7.3. Therefore, on the basis of the facts pertinent to the venture, $2,200 of the investment was not recovered. The unrecovered capital is a *sunk cost*.

In the example above, the supposition was that an investment in an asset is recovered as a result of the worth of services and incomes received from the item. This is a correct view but a most difficult one to apply. It is usually impossible to determine the worth of the

Table 7.3. ACTUAL RECEIPTS AND DISBURSEMENTS

Receipts and disbursements	Year No. 0	Year No. 1	Year No. 2	Year No. 3
Value of service rendered by machine during the year................	...	$ 700	$ 700	$ 700
Amount received from salvage.....	...	...	...	300
Operating cost during year........	...	600	600	600
Amount of investment recovered during year....................	...	100	100	400
Unrecovered balance of investment in machine at the end of year....	$2,800	2,700	2,600	2,200

services rendered by a production unit. Suppose that a machine, labor to operate the machine, and a quantity of material were purchased and expended in one year, and that as a result of this action a person was able to earn $5,000 more than he might otherwise have done. Obviously the $5,000 income is attributable jointly to machine, material, and labor. The amount that is attributable to the machine alone cannot be determined objectively.

Because of the difficulty of establishing the worth of services performed by physical property, the worth is estimated to be equal in value to the cost of providing it. A method commonly followed for making this estimate will be illustrated by example. Suppose that a machine that has been purchased for $5,000 has an expected salvage value of $1,000 at the end of a service life of five years.

From the above estimates the amount of capital investment to be recovered in five years is $5,000 − $1,000, or $4,000. Assume that straight-line depreciation is to be used. Then the amount of investment to be recovered per year is $4,000 ÷ 5, or $800 per year. This amount can only be recovered by the worth of the services provided by the machine. But, since it is all but impossible to determine the worth of a machine's services, the usual practice is to account for capital recovery by making a charge for a machine's service equal to an amount estimated necessary to recover the capital invested in it. In the above example, the amount estimated necessary to recover the capital invested in the machine is equal to the annual depreciation of $800 per annum for five years. If this amount can be charged to products processed on the machine, the capital invested in it will be considered to be recovered.

Thus capital invested in a machine is considered to be recovered to the extent that charges are made for the machine's services against the products that benefit thereby. The aim of most cost accounting procedures is to make such charges equal per unit of similar product and of such amount that the estimated depreciation of an asset will be recovered during its life.

Thus capital recovery as practiced consists of allocating the cost of depreciation of an asset to its output on some proportional basis. But the number of units that will be processed by a machine during its lifetime cannot be known prior to its retirement. For this reason it is common practice to estimate a *normal* annual output of a machine as a basis for allocating its depreciation costs to the product.

Sunk cost arising from error in estimated life and salvage value. For another viewpoint, consider a situation in which the estimated life and salvage value of an asset are in error. Assume that in the example above the machine was sold for $1,400 at the end of three years for reasons not pertinent to this discussion.

The history of the investment, assuming the production had been at the normal rate of 1,000 units per year, would appear as given in Table 7.4.

Table 7.4. EFFECT OF ERROR IN ESTIMATED LIFE AND SALVAGE VALUE

Receipts and disbursements	Year No. 0	Year No. 1	Year No. 2	Year No. 3
Estimated depreciation during year.	...	$ 800	$ 800	$ 800
Amount considered to be received through charges to products made during year (A)................	...	800	800	800
Amount received from sale of salvage during year (B)................	...	...	...	1,400
Unrecovered balance of investment at end of year, $5,000 − (A + B)	$5,000	4,200	3,400	1,200

On the basis of this record the unrecovered balance, or sunk cost, is shown to be equal to $1,200. It should be remembered that this value is true only to the extent that the data on which it is based actually represent the facts of the case.

It is evident that the machine had not depreciated $800 per year, as shown by the record, but had depreciated $5,000 − $1,400 or $3,600 in three years; $1,200 per year on the average. The sunk cost is equal to the difference between the actual depreciation and the depreciation charged, in this case $3,600 − (3 × $800) = $1,200. Stated another way, sunk cost, as usually determined by depreciation accounting, is equal to the estimated depreciated value or *book value* minus the realized salvage value of the asset, in this case $2,600 − $1,400 = $1,200. The financial facts relating to the machine are shown in Figure 7.4.

In the above case an investment of $5,000 was made in a machine with the expectation that the total investment with a return would be recovered. The expectation was in error, $1,200 has been lost as a sunk cost, and nothing further can be done about it.

Errors in depreciation rates are sometimes incorrectly adjusted by

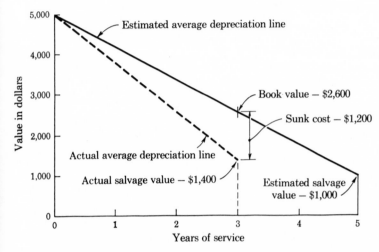

Figure 7.4. Estimated and actual depreciation showing sunk cost.

charging for depreciation during the balance of the asset's life at a rate sufficient to compensate for the error in the original rate. Another erroneous practice is to add the difference of the book value and the actual value of an asset to the cost of a replacement. The effect of these practices is to embrace the errors of past depreciation in rates charged to the products made in the future.

As painful as it may be to admit error in setting up depreciation rates, the difference between book value and actual value should be admitted and charged to Profit and Loss or Surplus. This practice removes the influence of past errors and permits the accounts to reflect the facts accurately.

QUESTIONS AND PROBLEMS

1. Define first cost and explain how it is related to the threshold concept.
2. Discuss the difference between fixed cost and variable cost.
3. Define increment cost and list methods for its determination.
4. Define sunk cost and list the conditions under which it may arise.

5. The total cost of manufacturing 260 units of a product is $3,200. If 340 units are manufactured, the total cost will be $3,800.

   (a) What is the average manufacturing cost for the first 260 units?

   (b) What is the variable cost per unit?

   (c) What is the total fixed cost?

   (d) What is the average fixed cost per unit for the first 260 units?

6. The total cost of installing 900 similar structural members is $6,300. The variable cost for the first 600 units is 2 times the fixed cost and the variable cost for the remaining 300 units is 3.5 times the fixed cost.

   (a) What is the fixed cost per unit?

   (b) What is the total installation cost per unit for the first 600 units?

   (c) If $7.50 is received for each unit installed between 600 and 750 units, what is the profit or loss?

7. The fixed cost of a machine (depreciation, interest, space charges, maintenance, indirect labor, supervision, insurance, and taxes) is F dollars per year. The variable cost of operating the machine (power, supplies, and similar items, excluding direct labor) is V dollars per hour of operation. N is the number of hours the machine is operated per year, A the annual total cost of operating the machine, C_h the hourly cost of operating the machine, t the time in hours to process one unit of product, M_p the machine cost of processing a unit of product, and n the number of units of product processed per year. In terms of these symbols, write expressions for (a) A, (b) C_h, (c) M_p.

8. In Prob. 7, F = $600 per year, t = 0.2 hour, V = $0.50 per hour, and n varies from 0 to 10,000 in increments of 1,000.

   (a) Plot values of M_p as a function of n.

   (b) Write the expression for C_p, the total cost of direct labor and machine cost per unit using the symbols given in Problem 7 and letting W equal the hourly cost of direct labor.

9. A semiautomatic arc welding machine that is used for a certain joining process costs $10,000. The machine has a life of 5 years, and a salvage value of $1,000. Maintenance, taxes, interest, and other fixed costs amount to $500 per year. The cost of power and supplies is $2 per hour, and the operator receives $2.50 per hour. The cycle time per unit of product is 60 minutes. If interest is 4 per cent, calculate the cost per unit of processing the product if (a) 200, (b) 600, (c) 1,200, (d) 2,500 units of product are made per year. Plot the cost per unit as a function of the number of units produced per year.

10. Mr. A drives a car 72,000 miles per year. Mr. B drives a car 72,000 miles in 6 years. Each car costs $2,600 and has a trade-in value of $1,800 at the end of one year and 72,000 miles, and a trade-in value of $500 at the end of 6 years and 72,000 miles. Fuel, oil, grease, and tires cost $0.03 per mile. Storage batteries cost $17 each and have an average life of 2 years. Storage cost is $6 per month and insurance costs $90 per year. Each car is washed twice a month at a cost of $1.50 per washing and is waxed four times a year at a cost of $8 per waxing. To keep his car neat in appearance, Mr. B deems it necessary to have it painted at the end of 3 years at a cost of $120. Mechanical maintenance is estimated at $6 per 1,000 miles for each car.

(a) With interest at 6 per cent, determine the fixed, variable, and total cost of operation per mile for each car.

(b) Mechanical maintenance was estimated for simplicity at $6 per 1,000 miles for both Mr. A's car and Mr. B's car. Which car would likely have the higher maintenance? Why?

11. It will cost $16,000 to design and build a special machine. The salvage value at the end of an estimated life of 8,000 hours of operation will be $1,000. The cost of space for the machine is estimated at $460 per year. Maintenance of the machine is estimated at $0.32 per hour and its power consumption is estimated at $0.44 per hour of operation. Labor costs per hour of operation are to be taken at $2.14 and interest is 6 per cent. It will require one hour to process a unit of the product to be made on the machine. Calculate the cost per unit of processing the product if (a) 8,000, (b) 4,000, (c) 2,000, and (d) 1,000 units are produced per year.

12. The total annual cost of producing 6,400 units of a product is $12,000. How great an increase in annual fixed cost is justified for facilities that will reduce variable cost per unit of product produced by $0.40?

13. It is estimated that it costs $620 per month plus $0.09 per mile to operate a truck. This estimate includes the driver's salary and a fair share of the control office expense. Calculate the cost of operating the truck for an increment of 2,000 to 2,200 miles per month.

14. An asset was purchased for $6,400 six years ago. Its life and salvage value were estimated at ten years and $400, respectively. If the asset is now sold for $1,200, what will be the sunk cost if depreciation has been by

(a) The straight-line method?

(b) The sum of the years method?

15. A chemical piping system was installed at a cost of $9,400. Cost calculations were based on an estimated life of four years with zero salvage value. At the end of 3 years, it had deteriorated so badly that it was replaced. Depreciation was calculated by the straight-line method.

   (a) What was the estimated annual depreciation?

   (b) What was the actual annual depreciation?

   (c) What was the sunk cost at the time of replacement?

16. A parking lot was paved at a cost of $10,000. It was anticipated that the service life would be 10 years with no salvage value. However, the paving became so worn that after 8 years it had to be replaced. Use straight-line depreciation and calculate:

   (a) The anticipated annual depreciation.

   (b) The actual annual depreciation.

   (c) The sunk cost involved.

17. An oil company purchased a plot of land on a highway for $3,000 and built a filling station at a cost of $22,000. It was estimated that the value of the land would remain constant, but that the value of the station would depreciate to $7,000 in 15 years. On the basis of these estimates, net profits were calculated to be $7,200, $8,200, and $8,800 for the first, second, and third years of operation, respectively. At the end of the third year, a new highway was built which isolated the station from the main flow of traffic. As a result, the land and station was sold for $13,000.

   (a) Using 6 per cent sinking-fund depreciation, calculate the sunk cost.

   (b) Calculate the actual net profit for the three years of operation.

18. Show by graphical means the situation described in Problem 17.

CHAPTER 8

A PATTERN
FOR ENGINEERING ECONOMY ANALYSIS

The objective of an engineering economy study is to improve the want-satisfying potential of engineering application. Profit will result if an activity results in a return that is in excess of cost. In terms of economic efficiency, this means that the activity must involve an input-output ratio that is in excess of unity, or 100 per cent.

Both individuals and enterprises possess limited resources. This gives rise to the necessity to produce the greatest output for a given input; that is, to operate at high efficiency. Thus, the search is not merely for a fair, plausible, or good opportunity for the employment of limited resources, but for the best opportunity. The objective of most engineering endeavors should be to apply available resources to the best advantage. Thus, it is important that elements limiting the efficiency of an enterprise be known and that a logical pattern for engineering economy analysis be available. This chapter will describe the important elements that must be considered in economy studies and will outline a plan useful in engineering economy analysis.

8.1. PROFIT IS A RESULTANT OF INCOME AND OUTLAY

Profit is the resultant of two components, one of which is the economy associated with the performance of an activity and the other the economy associated with income from the activity.

It is obvious that some activities have greater profit potentialities than others. In fact some activities can only result in loss. When profit is a consideration, it is important that activities be selected for their profit potentialities. This is a first step and an important one, since once the decision to perform an activity has been made, the success of subsequent acts has been limited.

The second step, after an activity has been selected, is to perform the activity with economy; to obtain the desired performance with the least possible outlay.

The idea of profit as a resultant of the economies of income and outlay associated with an activity is presented diagrammatically in Figure 8.1.

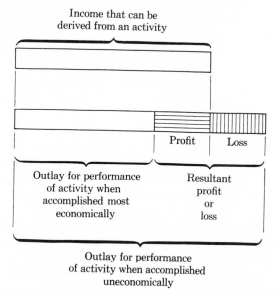

Figure 8.1. Profit or loss as a resultant of income and outlay.

After income estimates have been made, they should be next translated into certain products to be manufactured in certain quantities at certain times at a certain cost. Once production schedules have been determined, production facilities to meet them can be worked out on the basis of economy.

The income from many new activities lags behind the expenses associated with them for a considerable period of time. In some instances this lag, in terms of time and amount of funds needed, is known with considerable accuracy. For example, contracts for buildings, bridges, and large units of equipment usually stipulate a schedule of payments to be made based upon progress of the work.

8.2. MEASURES OF SUCCESS

Any activity that is undertaken requires an input of thought, effort, material, etc. for its performance. In a purposeful activity, an input of some value is surrendered in the hope of securing an output of greater value. The terms input and output as used here have the same meaning as when they are used to designate, for instance, the number of heat units that are supplied to an engine and the number of energy units it contributes for a defined purpose.

Success of a venture in terms of economy is determined by considering the relationship between the input and output of the venture. The profit of a venture is the difference between output and input. If the output consists of goods that are sold for dollars and input consists of materials and services bought for dollars, the resulting profit will be in terms of dollars and will be highly quantitative. The profit of a venture A is the summation of the profits of its subordinate parts a_1, a_2, and a_3. If P_A represents the profit of the major venture and p_{a_1}, p_{a_2}, and p_{a_3}, represent the profits of the subordinate ventures, then

$$P_A = p_{a_1} + p_{a_2} + p_{a_3}.$$

Let inputs and outputs of the above major and subordinate ventures be designated respectively be I_A, i_{a_1}, i_{a_2}, and i_{a_3} and by O_A, o_{a_1}, o_{a_2}, and o_{a_3}. Then

$$P_A = O_A - I_A$$
$$= (o_{a_1} - i_{a_1}) + (o_{a_2} - i_{a_2}) + (o_{a_3} - i_{a_3})$$

and also $$P_A = (o_{a_1} + o_{a_2} + o_{a_3}) - (i_{a_1} + i_{a_2} + i_{a_3}).$$

As a measure, absolute profit, as expressed by $P_A = O_A - I_A$ and $p_{a_1} = o_{a_1} - i_{a_1}$, for example, has the advantage that the profit of major objectives may be obtained as a summation of the profits of subordinate objectives. It is frequently used.

Absolute profit as a measure has the disadvantage that it does not reveal the magnitude of the venture that resulted in the profit. In this connection, consider the following analysis embracing ventures A and B.

Venture	Output	Input	Profit
A	$1,100	$1,000	$100
B	150	50	100

Measured in terms of absolute profit, ventures A and B are equal.

Another widely used measure of success is the ratio of output to input. This ratio will be recognized by engineers as an expression of efficiency. Following the scheme of symbols used above, the ratios of outputs to inputs may be expressed by R_A, r_{a_1}, r_{a_2}, and r_{a_3}. Then

$$R_A = \frac{O_A}{I_A}$$

and

$$r_{a_1} = \frac{O_{a_1}}{i_{a_1}}, \text{ etc.}$$

Also let R_B represent the ratio of output O_B and the input I_B of a venture B. Then the success of ventures A and B in the concrete example above may be stated as follows:

Venture	Output	Input	Ratio R Output over Input
A	$1,100	$1,000	1.1
B	150	50	3.0

Considering R as a measure of success, venture B is nearly three times as successful as venture A. The significance of the ratio of output over input is perhaps more clearly seen if it is considered to be the number of units of output per unit of input. Resources available for use in making a gain are usually limited. Thus, it is desirable that each unit of resource be employed in ventures that will result in the greatest output per unit of input.

8.3. THE ELEMENTS OF ECONOMY ANALYSIS

Since engineering is utilitarian, the primary purpose of its employment is the profitable manipulation of the elements of the physical environment as a means of creating utility in the economic environment. The first step in making a profit is to secure an income. But, to acquire an income necessitates certain activities resulting in certain costs. Profit is, therefore, a resultant of activities which produce income and involve outlay which may be expressed as

$$\text{profit} = \text{income} - \text{outlay}.$$

Outlays may be classified under several subheadings in accordance with the special treatments they require in economy analysis. The common classification includes operating costs, depreciation, interest, and income taxes. These items can only be provided for out of income. Therefore, the success of an activity may be measured by the expression:

$$N = G - (O + D + I + T)$$

where:

N = net income;

G = gross income;

O = operating costs;

D = depreciation;

I = interest;

T = taxes.

Much of the endeavor in engineering economy analysis is directed toward methods for manipulating mathematically the terms of the expression above. Two of these terms, interest and depreciation, were the topics of Part II. Applications of these two elements and methods for considering each of the others are the topics of the chapters which follow. Since the economic success of an activity is a function of these terms, it is important that each be given careful consideration prior to the initiation of a venture.

8.4. INPUT

The elements involved in the production of goods and services may be thought of in terms of inputs and outputs, the ratio of which is a measure particularly useful in evaluating the comparative success of the enterprise. The inputs of private and governmental enterprise involve a wide variety of items. A number of these common to most organizations are presented in the following sections.

Human service. A most important item of input is services of people for which wages are paid. In a commercial organization the total input of human services, as measured by the cost for a given period of time, is ordinarily reflected accurately by the amount of wage payments. Where involuntary service is secured, as in military services of governments, it will be clear that the input of human services is not necessarily reflected by amounts paid out as wages. In a commercial organization the input of human services may be classified under the headings of direct labor, indirect labor, promotional effort, investigation and research. Of these, direct labor is the only item whose amount is known with reasonable accuracy and whose identity is preserved until it becomes a part of output.

Input devoted to investigation and research is particularly hard to relate to particular units of output. Much research is conducted with no particular specified goal in mind and much of it results in no appreciable benefit that can be associated with a particular output. Expenditures for people for investigation and research may be made for some period of time before this type of service has a concrete effect upon output. Successful research of the past may continue to affect output for a long time in the future. The fact that expenditures for this type of service do not parallel in time the benefits provided makes it very difficult to relate them to an organization's output.

Expenditures for promotional effort have many of the characteristics of expenditures for investigation and research in relationship between time of input and effect on output.

Indirect labor, supervision, and management have characteristics falling between those of direct labor and of investigation and research. The input of indirect labor and, to a lesser extent, that of supervision, parallel the output fairly closely in time, but their effects can ordinarily be identified only with broad classes of output items.

Management is associated with the operations of an organization as a whole. Its important function of seeking out desirable opportunities is similar in character to research. Input in the form of management effort is difficult to associate with output either in relation to time or to classes of product.

As difficult as it may be to associate certain inputs with a final measurable output, such as of products sold on the market, input can ordinarily be identified closely with intermediate ends that may or may not be measurable in concrete terms. For example, the cost of the input of human effort assigned to the safety engineering department, the legal department, the labor relations department, and the engineering department are reflected with a high degree of accuracy by the payrolls of each. However, the worth of the output of the personnel assigned to these departments may and usually does defy even reasonably accurate measurement.

Where quantitative data on human service input is needed for economy studies, it is often necessary to use estimates, or, in other words, to evaluate input by judgment.

Material items. Many items of material are acquired to meet the objectives of commercial and governmental enterprise. For convenience, material items may be classified as direct material, indirect material, equipment, and land and buildings.

Inputs of direct material are directly allocated to final and measurable outputs. The measure of material items of input is their purchase price plus costs for purchasing, storage, and the like. This class of input is subject to reasonably accurate measurement and may be quite definitely related to final output, which in the case of commercial organizations is easily measurable.

Indirect material and power inputs are measurable in much the same way and with essentially the same accuracy as are direct material and power inputs. One of the important functions of accounting is to allocate this class of input in concrete terms to items of output or classes of output. This may ordinarily be done with reasonable accuracy.

An input in the form of an item of equipment requires that an immediate expenditure be made, but its contribution to output takes place piecemeal over a period of time in the future which may vary from a short time to many years, depending upon the use life of the equipment. Inputs of equipment are accurately measurable and can often be accurately allocated to definite output items except in amount. The latter limitation is imposed by the fact that the number and kinds of output to which any equipment may contribute are often not known until years after many units of the product have been distributed. The function of depreciation procedures is to allocate equipment inputs to outputs.

Inputs of land and buildings are treated in essentially the same manner as inputs of equipment. They are somewhat more difficult to allocate to output because of their longer life and because a single item, such as a building, may contribute simultaneously to a great many output items. Allocation is made with the aid of depreciation and cost accounting techniques and practices.

Allocation of inputs of indirect materials, equipment, buildings, and land rests finally upon estimates or judgments. Although this fact is often obscured by the complexities of and the necessary reliance upon accounting practices for day-to-day operations, it should not be lost sight of when economy studies are to be made.

Interest. Capital in the form of money is a very necessary input, although it must ordinarily be exchanged for producer goods in order for it to make a contribution to output. Interest on money used is usually considered to be a cost of production and so may be considered to be an input. Its allocation to output will necessarily be related to the allocation of human effort, services, material, and equipment in which money has been invested.

Taxes. Taxes are essentially the purchase of governmental service required by private enterprise. Since business activity cannot be carried on without the payment of taxes, they comprise a necessary input. There are many types of taxes, such as ad valorem, excise, sales, and income. The amounts may be precisely known and, therefore, are accurately called inputs. However, it is often difficult to allocate taxes to outputs especially in the case of income taxes which are levied after the profit is derived.

Analysis of input. Almost all activities require inputs of human service, material items, interest, and taxes. Where these classes of input are present, an analysis of input for an economy study may usually be summarized as follows:

1. Operating costs:

    Direct labor

    Direct material and services

    Indirect labor

    Indirect material and services

2. Depreciation on:

>   Equipment
>   Buildings
>   Land

3. Interest on:

>   Investment in depreciable items
>   Funds borrowed for operation

4. Taxes on:

>   Inventory
>   Sales
>   Net earnings.

The subheadings in the classification above are in accordance with $O, D, I,$ and T of the profit equation $N = G - (O + D + I + T)$.

Direct labor and direct material as given in the classification are accurately known in cost and destination. Depreciation and interest are the familiar items studied earlier and are calculated in accordance with the methods developed. The input costs of indirect labor and indirect material are ordinarily accurately known, but their exact contribution to specific outputs in an economy study are a matter of estimate. The tax item is difficult to estimate because of the dependence on time and the net earnings. The remaining items under input costs are usually relatively small and not of great concern in economy studies.

8.5. OUTPUT

The outputs of commercial organizations and governmental agencies are endless in variety. Commercial outputs are differentiated from governmental outputs by the fact that it is usually possible to evaluate the former accurately but not the latter. A commercial organization offers its products to the public. Each item of output is evaluated by its purchaser at the point of exchange. Thus the monetary values of past and present outputs of commercial concerns are accurately known item by item.

Since engineering economy is concerned with future economy, it is concerned with future output. Generally, information on two subjects is needed to come to a sound conclusion. One of these is the physical output that may be expected from a certain input. This is a matter for engineering analysis. The second is a measure of output that may be expressed in terms of monetary income.

Monetary income is dependent upon two factors: one is the volume of output, in other words the amount that will be sold; the other is the monetary value of the output per unit. The determination of each of these items for the future must of necessity be based upon estimates. Market surveys and similar techniques are widely used for estimating the future output of commercial concerns.

Internal intermediate outputs of commercial organizations are determined with great difficulty and are usually estimated as dictated by judgment. For example, the value of the contribution of an engineer, a production clerk, or a foreman to a final output is rarely known with reasonable accuracy to either himself or to his superior. Similarly, it is difficult to determine the value of the contributions of most intermediate activities to the final result.

The outputs of many governmental activities are distributed without regard to the amount of taxes paid by the recipient. When there is no evaluation at the point of exchange, it appears utterly impossible to evaluate many governmental activities. John Doe may recognize the desirability of the national military establishment, the U. S. Forest Service, or Public Health activities, but he will find it impossible to demonstrate their worth in monetary terms. However, some government outputs, particularly those which are localized, such as highways, drainage, irrigation, and power projects, may be fairly accurately evaluated in monetary terms by calculating the reduction in cost or the increase in income they result in for the user.

8.6. A PLAN FOR ENGINEERING ECONOMY ANALYSIS

In engineering economy analysis, engineering and economic considerations are joined. Such analysis can be made haphazardly or it can be made on the basis of a logical plan. The purpose of a plan of analysis is to outline a procedure that will aid in arriving at sound conclusions. A good plan of attack points out the nature and sequence of analysis that will be required in most situations. If followed, a sound plan is effective in eliminating errors of omission for it focuses attention on the steps that should be taken. Where the analysis has to be examined by many persons, a standardized plan of approach will greatly facilitate interpretation.

In the discussion of the engineering process presented in Chapter 1, it was noted that the employment of engineering economy contributed to the creative nature of engineering application. Such employment leads to a four-step plan useful in engineering economy analysis. These steps are:

The creative step;

The definitive step;

The conversion step;

The decision step.

These steps will be described in the sections which follow. Each will be related to the creative engineering process and the essential steps in want satisfaction.

8.7. THE CREATIVE STEP

Engineers, whether engaged in physical research or in general administrative activities, are concerned with the profitable employment of resources. When known opportunities fail to hold sufficient promise for the profitable employment of resources, more promising opportunities are sought. People with vision are those who accept the premise that better opportunities exist than are known to them. This view accompanied by initiative leads to exploratory activities aimed at finding the better opportunities. Exploration, research, investigation, and similar activities are creative. In such activities steps are taken into the unknown to find new possibilities, which may then be evaluated to determine if they are superior to those that are known. Such activities consist essentially of prospecting for new opportunities.

The person who concludes that there is no better way makes a self-fulfilling prophecy. When the belief is held that there is no better way, a search for one will not be made, and a better way will not be found.

Opportunities are not made; they are discovered. The possibility of flight in heavier-than-air machines, for example, has always existed and merely awaited discovery.

The universe may be considered to consist of a summation of factors, or, in other words, a summation of all that exists. If individual facts are designated by such symbols as a_1, a_2, and a_3, then the following representation applies:

$$\text{the universe} = a_1 + a_2 + a_3 + \ldots + a_n.$$

Some of the facts of the universe are known. Most are unknown. Any situation embraces groups of facts of which some may be known and others unknown. The material out of which new opportunities for profit are to be fashioned are the facts as they exist.

Search for facts and new combinations of facts. Many successful ideas are merely new combinations of commonly known facts. The highly successful confection widely sold under many names and best described as a piece of chocolate-covered ice cream on a stick is the result of combining several simple known facts or ideas. The principal constituents are a stick, ice cream, and chocloate. It was known that people liked ice cream in conjunction with chocloate. Chocolate coverings for candies had been known for years. The stick had been previously used with candy in the "all-day sucker." Nevertheless, the exploiters of the resulting new combination of these ideas are reported to have made a fortune.

Some successful ideas are dependent upon the discovery of new facts. New facts may become known through research effort or by accident. Research is effort consciously directed to the learning of new facts. In pure research, facts are sought without regard for their specific usefulness, on the premise that a stockpile of knowledge will in some way contribute to man's welfare. Much of man's progress rests without doubt upon facts discovered from efforts to satisfy curiosity.

Both new facts and new combinations of facts may be consciously sought after. The creative aspect of engineering economy consists in finding new facts and new combinations of facts out of which may be fashioned opportunities to provide profitable service through the application of engineering.

Aside from the often quoted statement that "inspiration is ninety per cent perspiration," there are few guides to creativeness. It appears that both conscious application and inspiration may contribute to creativeness. Some people seem to be endowed with marked aptitudes for conceiving new and unusual ideas.

It may be presumed that a knowledge of facts in a field is a necessity for creativeness in that field. Thus, for example, it appears that a person who is proficient in the science of combustion and machine design is more likely to contrive a superior internal-combustion engine than a person who has little or no such knowledge. It also appears that knowledge of costs and people's desires as well as of engineering is necessary to conceive of opportunities for profit that involve engineering.

The economic opening. The creative step in economy studies consists essentially of finding an opening through a barrier of economic and physical limitations. When aluminum was discovered, uses had to be found for it that would enable it to be marketed, and means had to be found whereby its physical characteristics could be improved and its cost of manufacture reduced. Exploitation of uranium deposits rests upon the phenomenon of fission. The legality of collecting fees for regulations of parking as contrasted to making a charge for the use of parking space on streets was the factor on which exploitation of the parking meter hinged. Titanium has become economically important for its high temperature characteristics. Exploitation of iron ore deposits in Canada and Venezuela follows exhaustion of ore bodies closer to steel centers.

Economic limitations are continually changing with the needs and wants of people. Physical limitations are continually being pushed back through science. In consequence, new openings revealing new opportunities are continually developing.

For each successful venture someone has found an opening through the barrier of economic and physical limitation.

Circumventing factors limiting success. So far, discussion of the creative step has been confined to consideration of seeking new opportunities for profitable employment of resources. Attention will now be turned to a search for means for circumventing factors that limit success of present activities. The aim of circumventing factors limiting success is related to the search for better means for achieving objectives rather than a search for better objectives which was considered in a previous section. Though this is not particularly different in character from the activity first discussed in the creative step, separate consideration is justified because of the more objective approach that is possible.

Where the aim is to improve the success of a given activity, search may be directed to means for circumventing factors that limit success.

A strategic factor is a limiting factor which, if appropriately altered, will remove limitations restricting the success of the entire undertaking. Known strategic factors and those that seem most likely to be strategic factors should be selected for consideration.

The understanding that results from the delineation of limiting factors and their further consideration to arrive at the strategic factors often stimulates the conception of improvements.

There is obviously no point in operating upon some factors. Consider for example a situation in which an operator is hampered because he had difficulty in loading his machine with a heavy piece. Three factors are involved: the pull of gravity, the mass of the piece, and the strength of the man. Not much success would be expected from an attempt to lessen the pull of gravity. Nor is it likely that it is feasible to reduce the mass of the piece. A stronger man might be secured, but it seems more logical to consider overcoming the need for strength by devices to supplement the strength of the man. A consideration of the strength factors would thus lead to consideration of devices that might circumvent the limiting factor of strength.

It is possible that consideration of the factor of the piece's weight could have resulted in a reduction in weight by substitution of material, lighter sections, or a similar change. In this connection it may be noted that weight of pipe was considered a strategic factor in the cost of petroleum pipelines. This factor was circumvented by the use of high-strength steels made possible by the development of new welding processes.

Solutions result from search for limiting factors. In the drilling of oil wells with a rotary drill, a drill bit is rotated at the bottom of the hole by heavy members known as drill pipe joined end to end with screw joints. When it becomes necessary to replace the drill bit, successive joints of drill pipe are raised and unscrewed until the drill bit is reached. One alert person considered the joining method a strategic factor in drilling cost, for each length of drill pipe had to be turned a number of times in making and unmaking joints.

After some consideration he devised the taper thread joint, which has saved millions of dollars in drilling oil wells. This thread becomes disengaged in a few turns, has all the advantages of straight threads and some in addition, and costs about the same as straight thread.

The creative step has been given much emphasis in the discussion above for it is believed to be of first importance in economy studies. It is directly related to the delineation and selection of objectives that are without doubt the most important functions of engineering economy and certainly the first steps toward success in any field of endeavor. Since the mental processes involved are in large measure illogical, this step must be approached with considerable alertness and curiosity and a willingness to consider new ideas and unconventional patterns of thought.

The creative conference. An interesting development has been the *creative conference* in which a group of persons seek new opportunities or ways to circumvent limitations. In such a conference a problem is posed for solution. Those in attendance are encouraged to let their imagination have free reign and suggest solutions to the problem, no matter how fantastic. No criticisms of ideas suggested are permitted on the thought that criticism will inhibit imagination. Ideas produced by the conference are evaluated elsewhere.

8.8. THE DEFINITIVE STEP

The definitive step consists of defining the alternatives that have originated in the creative step or which have been selected for comparison in some other way. In the first stage of the definitive step, the engineer's aim should be to delineate each alternative on the basis of its major and subordinate physical units and activities. The purpose of this stage is to insure that all factors of each alternative and no others will be considered in evaluating it.

The second stage of the definitive step consists of enumerating the prospective items of output and input of each alternative, in quantitative physical terms as far as possible and then in qualitative terms. Though qualitative items cannot be expressed numerically they may often be of major importance. They should be listed carefully so that they may be considered in the final evaluation.

On completion of the definitive step there should be an enumeration giving all items of input and output and the time of their occurrence for each alternative.

Choice is between alternatives. Conception of alternatives is a creative process. A complete, all-inclusive alternative rarely emerges in its final state. It begins as a hazy, but interesting idea. The attention of the individual or group is then directed to analysis and synthesis and the result is a definite proposal. In its final form, an alternative should consist of a complete description of its objectives and its requirements in terms of inputs and outputs.

Except in extreme situations, there are usually several if not many things that are within the powers of an individual or an organization to do. But each choice imposes limitations of resources, time, and place. Thus, though it might be within the power of an individual to go to Place A and Place B, he cannot be at both places simultaneously. Also, he may have the resources, time, talent, and desire to carry Activity A or Activity B to successful conclusions. But he may find that he cannot do both and that he is forced to make a choice between them.

Courses of action between which choice is contemplated are conveniently called alternatives. Both different ends and different methods are embraced by the term alternative. All proposed alternatives are not necessarily attainable. Alternatives are frequently proposed for analysis even though there seems to be little likelihood that they will prove feasible. This is done on the thought that it is better to consider many unprofitable alternatives than to overlook one that is profitable. Alternatives that are not considered cannot be adopted no matter how desirable they might prove to be. Consider a contractor who is trying to evaluate the comparative merit of Method A and Method B when Method C, of which he is not aware, is superior to either of the other methods. The criterion for judging the desirability of an alternative is its result in comparison with the result of other alternatives that may be undertaken.

Not all alternatives can be considered. An objective of economy analysis is to find the best opportunity for the employment of limited resources. However, this objective can rarely be realized; to realize it completely would require that all possible alternatives of a situation be delineated for comparison with each other. It is essential to remember that alternatives are not outlined .and evaluated without cost and the passage of time.

As an example, consider the following situation. The attention of a superintendent was directed to a loss of heat from a bare pipe in his plant. The superintendent calculated the heat loss and found it to amount to $260 per month. A covering that would reduce the heat loss by $240 per month was offered by a salesman for $680. The superintendent thought he could secure the needed covering for less and actually accepted a bid for $632 three weeks later. Thus the lapse of time in seeking a better alternative had resulted in a saving of $48 on the covering and a heat loss of $180 that could have been prevented by accepting the first offer for the covering.

Similarly, the cost of considering alternatives will ordinarily force a choice before all are considered. Suppose that a concern was seeking a location for a plant in which to employ 20 women workers in manufacturing a line of leather novelties. Such a plant could be located in at least a thousand communities in the United States. Obviously the cost of investigating all the possibilities would be prohibitive. Further, suppose that the annual net income of the plant would be $10,000 at the first site considered. Suppose also that an annual income of $1,000 per year in the future is considered to justify a present investment of $5,000[1], and that the cost of evaluating a plant site is $1,600. Thus each investigation of a site after the first should result in an increase in income of

$$\$1,000 \times \frac{\$1,600}{\$5,000} = \$320$$

on the average for each site investigated. If the potential annual income of the first site considered was $10,000, the annual income of the site selected to justify the cost of investigation of a number of sites would be as follows:

Number of Sites Investigated	1	2	4	10	20
Annual Income to Justify Investigation..........	$10,000	$10,320	$10,960	$12,880	$16,080

Ordinarily too few alternatives are probably considered, but the above analysis shows that there is a limit beyond which considera-

---

[1]This corresponds to a capital-recovery period of 10 years at 15 per cent. ($5,000 \times \overset{\text{RP 15-10}}{(0.19925)} = \$996.25$).

tions cannot be justified. The number of alternatives to consider is in itself a matter of economy worthy of study.

Recognizing that all alternatives cannot be considered, the number of alternatives to be considered is limited on the basis of general assumptions. For instance, a fireman works on the assumption that it is his duty to minimize property loss by fire. When an alarm is sounded, his alternatives are limited to the methods by which he may minimize property loss by extinguishing the fire. The assumption under which he works precludes the necessity for him, for instance, to consider the alternative of letting a particular area be destroyed because mankind might be better served thereby.

Alternatives may be limited in a progressive series of assumptions. If the limiting assumptions are sound, no desirable alternatives will have been excluded. Skill and knowledge that will result in judgment that will enable consideration of none but desirable alternatives without excluding any that are desirable is an important function of intellect. Consider the following illustration suggested by Simon.[2]

Suppose the problem is to select a dam site for a storage reservoir. For simplicity, it will be assumed that the desideratum is to secure a specified volume of water storage at minimum cost, and that water storage above the specified amount will be of no value. Usually the real problem is not so simple. The cost of building a dam with the required storage capacity can be estimated for each point along the river. However, to make an accurate estimate, detailed studies would have to be made of the foundation conditions of each point. Then this huge array of cost estimates could be compiled and the dam site with the least cost selected.

Actually, the engineer proceeds quite differently. By inspection of a topographic map, he immediately picks out a half-dozen "plausible" dam sites and forgets about the rest. He is sufficiently familiar with dam construction cost to know with a fair degree of certainty that any other site he might choose would have a higher construction cost. Next, he makes an approximate estimate of dam costs for each of the plausible sites, assuming "normal" foundation conditions. Finally, he selects the most promising sites and makes careful foundation studies as a basis for final estimates.

At each step in this process there is a chance that the dam site which really is most desirable will be eliminated without complete analysis.

The degree of approximation that is allowable at each point in

---

[2]Herbert A. Simon, *Administrative Behavior* (New York: The Macmillan Company, 1948).

procedures similar to the one illustrated depends upon skill or judgment.

Individuals and organizations frequently limit the number of alternatives to be considered by assuming that the best opportunities for them lie within certain areas of activity. Thus, a manufacturer of farm tractors would ordinarily be expected to reject with only cursory consideration an opportunity to manufacture cosmetics or to engage in the distribution of motion pictures.

8.9. THE CONVERSION STEP

In order that alternatives may be compared effectively, it is necessary that they be converted to a common measure. The common denominator usually chosen for economic comparison is value expressed in terms of money.

The first phase of the conversion step is to convert the prospective output and input items enumerated in the definitive step into receipts and disbursements at specified dates. This phase consists essentially of appraising the unit value of each item of output or input and determining their total amounts by computation. On completion, each alternative should be expressed in terms of definite amounts of receipts and disbursements occurring at specified dates in the future, plus an enumeration of qualitative considerations that it has been impossible to reduce to money terms. For such items the term "irreducibles" is often employed. This term seems to be superior to the term "intangibles" in this connection, for many items described in qualitative terms are clearly known even though not expressible in numbers.

The second phase of the conversion step consists of placing the receipts and disbursements of all alternatives on a comparable basis, considering the time value of money. This involves calculation of equivalence. The interest rate to be used should have been determined as a part of the definitive step, where the use of funds to carry on a venture would be considered to be an input. Where money is an input item, it seems most logical to use cost of money for the interest rate in the calculations of equivalence. However, there are many who use the interest rate as a vehicle for expressing risk. This practice will be discussed at some length later. The interest rate received from output items should be that actually received. Where calculations of equivalence involve depreciation, the method used should be based on the pattern of depreciation set forth in the definitive step.

A final phase in the conversion step is to enumerate all irreducibles that remain so that they may be considered in the final decision step.

Economic significance of engineering proposals. Control over the acceptance or rejection of an engineering proposal is exercised more often than not by persons who have not been concerned with the technical phases of the proposal. Also, the persons who control acceptance are likely to lack understanding of technical matters.

A proposal should be explained in terms that will best interpret its significance to those who will control its acceptance. The aim of a presentation should be to take persons concerned with a proposal on an excursion into the future to experience what will happen if the proposal is accepted or rejected.

Suppose that a proposal for a new factory layout is to be presented. Since those who must decide if it should be adopted rarely have the time and background to go into and appreciate all the technical details involved, the significance of these details in terms of economic results must be made clear. Of interest to those in a position to decide will be such things as the present outlay required, capital-recovery period, flexibility of the layout in event of market changes, effect upon cost and quality of product, how employees will be affected, and difficulties of financing. Cost and other data should be broken down and presented so that attention may be easily focused upon pertinent aspects of the proposal. Diagrams, graphs, pictures, and even solid models should be used where these devices will contribute to understanding. The effort expended in developing a sound proposal is often lost through its rejection because of poor presentation.

The aim of economy studies is sound decision. Thus a first consideration should be to present a proposal in terms that will help those who must decide to understand the implications of the proposal to the fullest extent possible.

8.10. THE DECISION STEP

In addition to the alternatives formally set up for evaluation, another alternative is always present. This is the alternative of making no decision on the formal alternative being considered. The decision not to decide may be a result of either active consideration or passive failure to act; it is usually motivated by the thought that there will be opportunities in the future which will prove more profitable than any known at present.

For example, if a venture to build a plant to process and sell fruit is under consideration, there frequently is only one formal alternative to consider. Those concerned will usually decide the issue on how favorably the prospective venture measures up to those generally open for the employment of resources. Thus the decision not to decide is clearly a decision based on a comparison with future, though perhaps unknown, alternatives.

Differences are bases for decision. On completion of the conversion step, quantitative and qualitative outputs and inputs of each alternative, so far as these are known, will form the basis for comparison and decision. Quantitative input may be deducted from quantitative output to obtain quantitative profit, or the ratio of quantitative profit to quantitative input may be found. Each of these measures is then supplemented by what qualitative consideration may have been enumerated.

Decisions between alternatives should be made on the basis of their differences. Thus, all identical factors can be canceled out for the comparison of any two or more alternatives at any step in an economy study. In this process great care must be exercised that factors canceled as being identical are actually of the same significance. Unless it is very clear that factors considered for cancellation are identical, it is best to carry them through the first stage of the decision step. This may entail a greater amount of computation and other paper work, but the slight added complexity and loss of time is ordinarily insignificant in comparison with the value of greater accuracy in decision.

It frequently occurs that alternatives to provide an identical output or service are under consideration. Then output need not be considered and decision is made on the basis of input.

Where all facts about alternatives are known in accurate quantitative terms, the relative merit of each alternative may be expressed in terms of a single number. Decision in this case is simple. Where all factors are known, evaluation may be made on the basis of reason.

Decision must also be made when the quantitative considerations are based on estimates that are subject to error and where quantitative knowledge must be used to fill gaps in knowledge. It must always be remembered that the final calculated amounts embody the errors of the estimated quantities.

When facts are missing judgment must be used. Where alternatives cannot be completely delineated in accurate quantitative terms, the choice is made on the basis of the judgment of one or more individuals. Judgment seeks to predict the outcome of a course of action. Few believe that any person is endowed with a sixth sense or intuition to enable him to peer into the future. Fortune tellers get rich on the "suckers" they serve rather than upon the soundness of their advice.

If judgment is not clairvoyant, the ability to predict the future rests entirely on a cause-and-effect relationship. The only bases for the prediction of the outcome of a course of action are the facts in existence at the time the prediction is made. A person's judgment rests, therefore, upon his knowledge of the facts involved and his ability to use these facts. When complete knowledge of all facts concerned and their relationships exists, reason can supplant judgment and predictions become a certainty. Judgment tends to be qualitative. Reason is both qualitative and quantitative. Judgment is at best an informal consideration and weighing of facts; at its worst it is merely wishful thinking. Judgment appears to be an informal process for considering information, past experience, and feeling in relation to a problem. In this connection, contrast aviators who fly "by the seat of their pants" with those who fly by instruments. No matter how sketchy factual knowledge of a situation may be, some sort of a conclusion can always be drawn in regard to it by judgment.

Figure as far as you can, then add judgment. An important aim of engineering economy analysis is to marshal the facts so that reason may be used to the fullest extent in arriving at a decision. In this way judgment can be reserved for parts of situations where factual knowledge is absent. This idea is embraced in the statement "Figure as far as you can, then add judgment."

Where a diligent search uncovers insufficient information to reason the outcome of a course of action, the problem is to render as accurate a decision as the lack of facts permits. In such situations there is a decided tendency, on the part of many, to make little logical use of the data that are available in coming to a conclusion, on the thought that since some pretty rough estimating has to be done on some elements of the situation, the estimate might as well embrace the entire situation. But an alternative may usually be subdivided into parts, and the available data are often adequate for a complete or nearly complete evaluation of several of the parts. Thus, the final outcome of a portion of the total situation may be predicted with considerable accuracy, leaving a balance about which little is known.

In this connection, consider the situation illustrated in Figure 8.2 where the distance between A and B is to be determined by a man on side A unable to cross the stream.

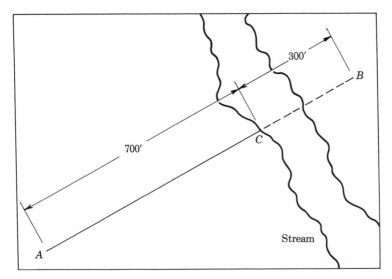

Figure 8.2. Judgment of a situation should be limited to those parts of which more accurate methods of determination cannot be supplied.

The distance from A to B may be estimated in its entirety or AC may be measured and CB estimated. It is interesting to note that a 50 per cent error in an estimate of CB will result in only a 15 per cent error in the conclusion, which is probably less than would have been the case if the distance AB had been estimated. Estimate or judgment should be reserved for those parts of the alternative for which a more accurate method of evaluation cannot be used.

The segregation of the known and unknown parts is in itself additional knowledge. Also, the unknown parts, when subdivided, frequently are recognized as being similar to parts previously encountered and thus become known.

QUESTIONS

1. Describe a situation in which the attainment of a major objective is a summation of the attainments of subordinate objectives.

2. Explain the two common measures of success.

3. List each item in the classification of outlays involved in deriving a net income.

4. List the common items of input encountered in the production of goods and services.

5. What is meant by the output classification as regards the process of production?

6. Apply the plan of engineering economy analysis to an engineering problem of your selection.

7. How is the creative step related to the creative engineering process?

8. List the methods for discovering means to more profitably employ resources.

9. Discuss the nature of the definitive step.

10. Why is it not possible to consider all possible alternatives?

11. What procedure is involved in reducing possible alternatives to a number that is practical to consider?

12. Describe the three phases of the conversion step.

13. What is the nature of the decision step?

14. Discuss the nature of judgment and explain why it is applicable to more situations than reason.

15. Explain why decision must be based on differences occurring in the future.

16. Discuss what is meant by the statement "Figure as far as you can, then add judgment."

CHAPTER 9

TREATMENT OF ESTIMATES
IN ECONOMY ANALYSIS

The scientific approach in estimating the physical environment approximates certainty in many applications. Instances are the pressure that a confined gas will develop under a given temperature, the current flowing in a conductor as a function of the voltage and resistance, and the velocity of a falling body at a given point in time. It was noted in Chapter 2, however, that much less is known with certainty about the economic environment with which the engineering process is concerned. Economic laws depend upon the action of people and are unlike physical laws which depend upon well-ordered cause and effect relationships.

A large portion of creative engineering activity has as its objective the search for activities with profit potential that is high in relation to the risk involved. This search necessitates the estimation of pertinent facets of the anticipated economic outcome of engineering activity. However, since little is known with certainty about the economic environment, careful thought must be given to the estimation procedure. After the best possible estimates have been formulated, it must be recognized that there will still be errors for which allowances must be made. Ordinarily, economic activities are carried on with relatively low margin of profit, this margin usually being lower than that adopted as the usual "factor of safety" in engineering design. For this reason, it seems worthwhile to devote some space to the discussion of estimates and allowances for errors in estimate that pertain to economy analysis.

9.1. ESTIMATING THE FINAL OUTCOME OF A VENTURE

It was shown in the previous chapter that the final economic success of a venture may be measured by the expression

$$N = G - (O + D + I + T).$$

The outcome as a whole may be estimated. Thus, if the purchase of a steam shovel is under consideration, it might be directly estimated that the purchase of the steam shovel will result in an income equivalent to 8 per cent per year on the amount invested. This return will be a resultant of a number of prospective receipts and disbursements, which may be classified as income, operating expenses, depreciation, interest, and taxes. It is a rare intellect that can combine accurately four complex items to obtain their resultant without resort to paper and pencil, even when the items are clearly known. Thus for best results in estimating the final outcome of an undertaking, it will almost always be found advantageous to begin with detailed estimates of income and costs as they may be expected to originate in the future. The detailed estimates are then combined mathematically to obtain their results.

Prospective receipts and disbursements are a secondary result of prospective activities. Estimates of receipts and disbursements should, therefore, be based on these prospective activities. It follows that receipts and disbursements often arise from the same data. For example, if a steam shovel is used to excavate 10,000 cubic yards of earth, this activity may be expected to result in both income and expense. Thus an estimate that an asset, for example, a steam shovel, will be used to do certain work in the future is the basis for estimating prospective income, depreciation, return on investment, operating expense, and income taxes. It is important to recognize that prospective receipts and disbursements have a common origin in the prospective use of the asset under consideration.

Estimating income. If there is a demand for goods or service, an income can be derived from supplying that demand. If the cost of supplying the service is less than the income received, a profit can be made. The firts step toward a profit is an income. Thus, in estimating the desirability of a prospective undertaking, it seems logical to estimate income as a first step. As used here, income also embraces the possibility for making a saving. Estimates of income should be based upon objective information as far as possible.

Estimates of a result will usually be more accurate if they are based upon estimates of the factors having a bearing on the result than if the result is estimated directly. For example, in estimating the volume of a room, it will usually prove more accurate to estimate the several dimensions of the room and calculate the volume than to estimate the volume directly. Similar reasoning applies to estimates of economic factors in prospect.

If, for example, the problem under consideration is the saving that may result from replacing a hand operation by a machine operation, the amount of saving will depend upon the number of units processed in a given time and the saving per unit. The first step is to bring all possible information to bear upon estimating the number of units expected to be processed during each year of the future period to be considered. In this connection, use should be made of such information as the records of past sales, present sales trends, the product's relation to the building trades, general business activity, and anything else that may be useful in arriving at the most accurate estimate of future sales.

In estimating the savings per unit, all items of saving — direct labor, direct material, overhead items, storage, inspection, and any others — should be estimated separately and totaled in preference to estimating the total of the savings of the items directly. The total estimated saving is then determined as a product of the number of units processed and the saving per unit. If more than one product is to be processed on a machine, the savings for each product should be estimated as above and totaled.

Under some circumstances — for example, if the income is represented by the saving resulting from an improvement in a process for manufacturing a staple product made at a constant rate — an estimate of income is easily made. But estimating income for new products with reasonable accuracy may be very difficult. Extensive market surveys and even trial sales campaigns over experimental areas may be necessary to determine volume. When work is done on contract, as is the case with much construction work, for example, the necessity for estimating income is eliminated. Under these circumstances the income to be received is known in advance with certainty from the terms of the contract.

Estimating operating expense. Operating expense as defined in the previous chapter is used here to embrace both direct and indirect costs pertinent to situations under consideration. Operating expense originates as expenditures for such items as fuel, water, electric current, materials, supplies, wages, taxes, insurance, etc.

Some of these items will be based on the same facts that determine income. For instance, the income derived from the manufacture and sale of a given number of units of a product will be based upon the number and the income derived per unit. The number of units sold will also be a factor in estimating the needed materials, labor, power, and other inputs needed in their production. In general, operating expenses should be estimated item by item rather than as a whole.

Estimating depreciation. Depreciation of machines often parallels income. The period and extent of use of single-purpose machines are dependent upon the number of units to be processed, which will have been estimated in arriving at income. Where depreciation is dependent upon wear and tear, the extent of use will be the determining factor; experiences in the past with like or similar machines may be helpful. If weathering or other causative factors of depreciation associated with the passage of time are the determining factors in estimating depreciation, mortality tables may prove to be of aid.

A portion of an investment in a physical asset is lost through physical or functional depreciation. If the loss resulting from depreciation is offset by an equal income from the use of the asset, that portion of the investment has been recovered. The actual undepreciated balance of the asset represented by its salvage value has not been lost and so need not be recovered. The salvage value of the asset is merely reconverted into another medium, usually money, by selling what remains of the asset.

In the recovery of an investment, attention is focused upon realizing an income to offset value lost through depreciation. And since depreciation is taken to be the difference between first cost and the amount realized from salvage, the prime problem in capital recovery is the securing of income equal to depreciation.

A depreciation estimate should be considered to be a summation of four estimates covering (1) installed cost, (2) service life in years, (3) salvage value at the end of service life, and (4) pattern of depreciation during service life.

Little difficulty is ordinarily experienced in making a reasonable estimate of the installed cost of an asset. The pattern of depreciation is not ordinarily of great importance. This leaves estimates of service life and salvage value. Of these, the estimate of service life is most important and perhaps the most difficult to make. The longer the service life of an asset, the less is the significance of error in estimates of salvage value.

It is a common practice in industry to base depreciation on arbitrarily set length-of-service lives that are often much shorter than actual lives. This is usually done to express a policy of conservatism in regard to investment in equipment, particularly in industries where obsolescence is an important factor. As a basis of determining costs this practice seems unrealistic and unsound, for it assumes that an arbitrarily set payout period for a class of equipment is more accurate than an individual estimate of the life of a particular unit of equipment.

Estimating interest. In comparative evaluations of proposed activities it is believed to be sound to take the viewpoint that interest is an item of cost. By considering interest as an expense, the interest rate can be determined more or less objectively. An enterprise that borrows money for its operations may use the rate that it is paying for funds. A concern investing its own funds is justified in using the rate that it can receive for funds for purposes similar to the one under consideration.

Regardless of the method used in arriving at the interest rate, it will be necessary to estimate the total investment to which the rate will be applied. This may be broken down into the return expected on capital unrecovered in physical assets and the return expected on funds used for operating expense. In either case, the return will enter the final analysis as an interest cost and, like operating expense, depreciation, and taxes, will be deducted from gross income yielding a net income. The final magnitude of the estimated net income will depend upon the magnitude of the estimated interest.

As an item of expense, interest for most activities will be relatively small. Thus, the interest rate estimated will have a minimum effect. It is desirable that the rate selected be used in all studies to be compared.

Estimating taxes. Income taxes are difficult to estimate in regard to a specific project that is an element of a larger activity for the reason that the income tax on the project is partly determined by net income of the activity as a whole. Also, tax schedules are subject to the fiscal needs of the nation. Income taxes of a specific project may be based upon the estimated net income of the project and an estimated effective income tax rate.

An estimate of the income taxes of a project may be made on a cost basis as a per cent of the investment in the project. The applicable per cent is the ratio of the income taxes of the total activity and the investment in the total activity. This method is explained in Chapter 16.

9.2. AN EXAMPLE OF A DECISION BASED ON ESTIMATES

An example will be used to illustrate some aspects of estimating, treating estimated data, and arriving at an economic decision. To simplify the discussion of these subjects, the same example will be used throughout the balance of this chapter. Income taxes will not be considered and it will be assumed that all funds invested in the project are equity funds.

The purchase of a machine for a certain operation, now performed in another manner, is considered likely to result in a saving. It is known with absolute certainty that the machine will cost $1,000 installed. All other factors pertinent to the decision are unknown and must be estimated.

Income estimate. From a study of available data and the result of judgment, it has been estimated that a total of 3,000 units of the product involved will be made during the next six years. The number to be made each year is not known; but, since it is believed that production will be fairly well distributed over the six-year period, it is believed that the annual production should be taken as 500 units. A detailed consideration of materials used, time studies of the methods employed, wage rates, and the like, have resulted in an estimated saving of $1.04 per unit, exclusive of the costs incident to the operation of the machine if the machine is used. Combining the estimated production and the estimated unit saving results in an estimated saving (income) of 500 × $1.04, or $520 per year.

Depreciation and interest estimate. The machine is a single-purpose machine and no use is seen for it except in processing the product under consideration. Its service life has been taken to be 6 years to coincide with the estimated production period of 6 years. It is believed that the salvage value of the machine will be offset by the cost of removal at retirement. Thus the estimated net receipts at retirement will be zero.

Interest is considered to be an expense in this evaluation, and the rate of interest has been estimated at 5 per cent. The next step is to combine the estimates of first cost, service life, and salvage value to determine the estimated annual capital recovery with a return. For the first cost of $1,000, a service life of 6 years, a salvage value of zero, and an interest rate of 5 per cent, the resultant estimate of annual depreciation and interest will be:

$$\text{RP 5-6}$$
$$(\$1,000 - 0)(0.19702) + 0 \times 0.05 = \$197.$$

Operation cost estimate. Operating costs will ordinarily be made up of several items such as fuel, maintenance, supplies, and labor. Consider for simplicity that the operating expense of the equipment in this example consists of items a, b, c, and d. Each of these items is estimated on the basis of the number of units of product that it is estimated are to be processed per year. Assume that these items have been estimated as follows:

$$\text{Item } a = \$90 \text{ per year;}$$
$$\text{Item } b = \$60 \text{ per year;}$$
$$\text{Item } c = \$40 \text{ per year;}$$
$$\text{Item } d = \$10 \text{ per year.}$$

The estimated income and cost items of the example may be summarized as follows:

	RP 5-6	
Estimated annual capital recovery and return, $1,000 (0.19702)...		$197
Estimated annual operating cost, $90 + $60 + $40 + $10........		200
Estimated total annual cost.................................		$397
Estimated total annual income..............................		520
Estimated net annual profit for venture......................		$123

This final statement means that the venture will result in a profit of $123 per year for a period of 6 years if the several estimates prove to be accurate.

The resultant annual profit is itself an estimate, and experience teaches that the most certain characteristic of estimates is that they nearly always prove to be in error, sometimes in small degree and often in large degree. Once the best possible estimates have been made, however, whether they eventually prove to be good or bad, they remain the most objective basis on which to base decision. It should be realized that decision can never be an entirely objective process.

9.3. ALLOWANCE FOR ERRORS IN ESTIMATES

The success of the scientific approach depending upon a cause and effect relationship in the physical realm has carried over into other realms. The idea that the future can be predicted if sufficient knowledge is available is now generally accepted. Great emphasis is placed on securing sufficient data and applying it carefully in arriving at estimates that are representative of actualities to the highest possible extent. The better the estimates, the less allowance need be made for error. It should be realized at the outset that allowances for errors (factors of safety) do not make up for deficiency of knowledge in the sense that allowances correct errors. Allowances are merely a means of eliminating some consequences of error at a cost.

In illustration of how allowances for errors in estimates function, consider an example from the engineering field. Let it be assumed that a scientific instrument is to hang from the center of a steel beam that has a horizontal span of 60 inches. It has been decided that the beam is to have a width of one inch; the depth is to be determined. The instrument has a value of $1,000 and an estimated weight of 800 pounds. Tests of several samples of steel from the melt from which the beam is to be made show the steel capable of resisting strains of 50,000 to 52,000 pounds per square inch. This steel costs $0.10 per pound. The depth of the beam is determined by the use of the formula $PL/4 = Sbd^2/6$ as follows:

$$\frac{800 \times 60}{4} = \frac{50,000 \times 1 \times d^2}{6}$$
$$d = 1.2 \text{ in.}$$

The cost of the beam, 1 in. $\times$ 1.2 in. in cross section and 62 inches long (allowing 1 inch for support at each end), made of steel at $0.10 per pound, is $2.11.

In the example above the nature of the length of beam required, its width, the strain-resisting properties of steel, and the formula by which the depth was calculated are such that they may be determined objectively, that is, estimated with a degree of accuracy approaching certainty. Thus a beam with a calculated depth of 1.2 inches and costing $2.11 is almost certain to be adequate to carry the 800 pounds.

But the consequences of a $1,000 loss in case of failure, prompt caution, particularly since a stronger beam can be had for an additional cost equal to only a small fraction of the loss in case of failure. So possible errors for which allowances should be made are sought. The extent of the errors in the estimates of the length, breadth, and depth of the beam and in the strain resistance of steel is so small that no allowance will be made for them. But a question may arise in regard to the estimated load the beam is to carry. May not the estimated weight of the instrument be in error? Is it not possible that a load of greater than 800 pounds may be placed on the beam? A man might decide to cross the span by walking on the beam, for example, or the instrument might suddenly be dropped upon the beam.

Calculation reveals that an additional expenditure of $2.11 will provide a beam that will support four times as much as the original. Since this amount is relatively small in comparison to the loss that would be occasioned by failure of the beam, it is likely that a beam of greater depth than required to hold the instrument will be selected. If this is done, an allowance has been made for an error in the estimated load that the beam will be called upon to carry. By spending $2.11 it is hoped to eliminate the consequences that might have resulted from errors in the original estimate.

In this situation a large factor of safety can be introduced for a small cost. In fact, it might be cheaper to allow for a large error in the estimated load than to exercise much effort in trying to determine its amount.

As calculated above, a beam just adequate to carry a load of 800 pounds will weigh 21.1 pounds. If its depth is doubled to quadruple its load-carrying capacity, its weight will double and will be increased by 21.1 pounds. No cognizance was taken of this fact above. In some applications the increase in weight would be more important than an increase in its cost. It might prove prohibitive to allow for errors in the estimated load by introducing a factor of safety of four that results in increasing the weight of the beam by 21.1 pounds. This is evident when aircraft design is concerned. Great effort is made to determine loads accurately so that the structural elements will not have to withstand unusual loads, thus allowing for minimum allowances for safety factors.

As an example of the effect of an allowance in an economic undertaking, consider the following illustration. A contractor has estimated the cost of a project on which he has been asked to bid at $100,000. If he undertakes the job, he wishes to profit by 10 per cent or $10,000. How shall he make allowance for errors in his cost estimate? If he makes an allowance of 10 per cent for errors in his estimates, comparing to the very low factor of safety of 1.10, his estimated cost becomes $110,000. To allow for his profit margin, he will have to enter a bid of $121,000. But the higher his bid, the less the chance that he will be the successful bidder. If he is not the successful bidder, his allowance for errors in his estimate may have served to insure not only that he did not profit from the venture, but that he was left with a loss equal to the cost of making the bid. This illustration serves to emphasize the necessity for considering the cost of making allowances for errors in estimates.

Allowing for error in estimates by high interest rates. A policy common to many industrial concerns is to require that prospective undertakings be justified on the basis a of high interest rate, say 25 per cent. One basis for this practice is that there are so many opportunities which will result in a return of 25 per cent or more that those yielding less can be ignored. But since this is a much greater return than most concerns make on the average, the high rate of return represents an allowance for error. It is hoped that if undertaking of ventures is limited to those that promise a high rate of return, none or few will be undertaken that will result in a loss.

Returning to the example of the new machine given previously, suppose that the estimated income and the estimated cost of carrying on the venture when the interest rate is taken at 25 per cent are as follows:

Estimated annual income (for six years)......................	$520
Estimated annual capital recovery and return, $1,000 (0.33882) $339 (RP 25-6)	
Estimated annual operating cost.... 200	
Estimated total annual operating cost........................	539
Estimated net annual profit of venture........................	−$ 19

If the calculated loss based on the high interest rate is the deciding factor, the venture will not be undertaken. Though the estimates as given above, except for the interest rate of 25 per cent, might have been correct, the venture would have been rejected because of the arbitrary high interest rate taken, even though the resulting rate of return would be 22.5 per cent.

Suppose that the total operating costs had been estimated as above but that annual income had been estimated at $600. On the basis of a policy to accept ventures promising a return of 25 per cent on investment, the venture would be accepted. But if it turned out that the annual income was, say, only $150, the venture would result in loss regardless of the calculated income with the high interest rate. In other words, an allowance for error embodied in a high rate of return does not prevent a loss that stems from incorrect estimates if a venture is undertaken that will result in loss.

Allowing for error in estimates by rapid payout. The effect of allowing for error in estimates by rapid payout is essentially the same as that of using high interest rates for the same purpose. Let it be assumed that a concern has a policy that equipment purchases must be based upon a three-year payout period when interest is taken at 5 per cent.

Returning to the example of past paragraphs, suppose that the estimated income and the estimated cost of carrying on the venture when a three-year payout period is taken is as follows:

Estimated annual income (Estimated for six years but taken
as being for three years to conform to policy)................. $520

RP 5-3
Estimated annual capital recovery and return, $1,000 (0.36721) $367
Estimated annual operating cost....................... 200

Estimated total annual operating cost........................ 567

Estimated net annual profit for venture....................... −$ 47

Under these conditions the venture would not have been undertaken.

Allowing for error in estimates by choosing conservative values. The effect of choosing conservative values for the components making up an estimate is to improve the certainty of a favorable result, if the outcome results in values that are more favorable than those chosen. This technique is actually a component of the least favorable, fair, and most favorable estimates to be discussed next.

9.4. USE OF LEAST FAVORABLE, FAIR, AND MOST FAVORABLE ESTIMATES

A plan for the treatment of estimates considered to have some merit is to make a least favorable estimate, a fair estimate, and a most favorable estimate of each situation.

The *fair estimate* is the estimate that appears most reasonable to the estimator after a diligent search for and a careful analysis of data. This estimate might also be termed the most likely estimate.

The *least favorable estimate* is the estimate that results when each item of data is given the least favorable interpretation that the estimator feels may reasonably be realized. The least favorable estimate is definitely not the very worst that could happen. This is a difficult estimate to make. Each element of each item should be considered independently in so far as this is possible. The least favorable estimate should definitely not be determined from the fair estimate by multiplying the latter by a factor.

The *most favorable estimate* is the estimate that results when each item of data is given the most favorable interpretation that the estimator feels may reasonably be realized. Comments similar to those made in reference to the least favorable estimate, but of reverse effect, apply to the most favorable estimate.

The use of the three estimates will be illustrated by application to the example of previous paragraphs.

Items Estimated	Least Favorable Estimate	Fair Estimate	Most Favorable Estimate
Annual number of units............	300	500	700
Savings per unit..................	$0.80	$1.04	$1.15
Annual saving.....................	$240	$520	$750
Period of annual savings, n.........	3	6	10
Capital recovery and return,			
$1,000(RP 5-$n$).................	$367	$197	$130
Operating cost			
Item A........................	$ 60	$ 90	$120
Item B........................	60	60	70
Item C........................	50	40	60
Item D........................	20	10	2
Estimated total of capital recovery, return and operating items.......	$557	$397	$382
Estimated net annual saving in prospect for n years................	−$317	$123	$368

An important feature of the least favorable, fair, and most favorable estimate plan of comparison is that it provides for bringing additional information to bear upon the situation under consideration. Additional information results from the estimator's analysis and judgment in answering two questions relative to each item. These questions are: "What is the least favorable value that this item may reasonably be expected to have?" and the reverse, "What is the most favorable value that this item may reasonably be expected to have?"

Judgment should be made item by item, for a summation of judgments can be expected to be more accurate than a single judgment of the whole. A second advantage of the three-estimate plan is that it reveals the consequences of deviations from the fair or most likely estimate. Even though the calculated consequences are themselves estimated, they show what is in prospect for different sets of conditions. It will be found that the small deviations in the direction of unfavorableness may have disastrous consequences in some situations. In others even a considerable deviation may not result in serious consequences.

The results above can be put on other bases for comparison. The present-worth basis has merit in this instance because of the variation in the number of years embraced by the above three estimates. The payout period and saving per unit of product can easily be calculated for other veiwpoints. The estimated present worth of savings is calculated as follows:

Items Estimated	Least Favorable Estimate	Fair Estimate	Most Favorable Estimate
Net annual saving................	−$317	$123	$ 368
Period of annual savings, n.........	3	6	10
Present worth factor, (PR 5-n).......	2.723	5.076	7.722
Present worth of saving............	−$863	$624	$2,842

And, the estimated rate of return is:

Items Estimated	Least Favorable Estimate	Fair Estimte	Most Favorable Estimaate
Annual saving....................	$240	$520	$750
Annual operating cost, items A, B, C, and D.........................	190	200	252
Difference applicable to capital recovery and return at 5 per cent...	50	320	498
Capital recovery period, years.......	3	6	10
Rate of return, per cent...........	minus	22.5	48.9

The net estimated saving per unit of product is:

Items Estimated	Least Favorable Estimate	Fair Estimate	Most Favorable Estimate
Net annual saving................	−$317	$123	$368
Annual number of units............	300	500	700
Net saving per unit of product......	−$1.057	$0.246	$0.526

There are many who feel that it is an aid to judgment to have several bases on which to compare a single situation. Since the cost of making extra calculations is usually insignificant in comparison with the worth of even a small improvement in decision, the practice should be followed by all who feel they benefit from the additional information. But there are limits beyond which further calculations can serve no useful purpose. This occurs when calculations are made that are beyond the scope of the data used. In the example above, it would seem that no useful purpose would be served, for instance, by averaging the results calculated from the three estimates, least favorable, fair, and most favorable.

9.5. USE OF TENTATIVE GUESSES

In evaluating some alternatives in which there are one or two obscure elements, it may be helpful to make a series of tentative guesses about the obscure elements.

The results obtained with different guesses are compared and the effect of the different guesses noted. The results of the guesses may reveal that no guess within the realm of reasonableness will result in the desirability of the alternative; on the other hand, it may be found that the missing element has little bearing on the alternative. Trends with the different guesses may be observed. If one of the guesses makes the alternative seem desirable, the probability that that guess is correct may be considered.

The systematic use of conjecture will nearly always result in a clearer understanding of an obscure situation and is particularly effective in guarding against a wholly disastrous decision.

9.6. RISK IS AN ELEMENT OF COST

Economic activities undertaken for profit are entered into only after it is found that estimated receipts exceed estimated costs. When an activity has failed to yield a profit, it is because disbursements exceeded receipts. This may have resulted because some receipts were less than estimated, because some costs were greater than estimated, or from a combination of both varieties of incorrect estimates.

Estimates of the first cost of an asset, its salvage value, and the interest rate are ordinarily not sources of error of important consequence. The first cost of an asset and the interest rate are usually known within narrow limits and salvage value can generally be estimated with reasonable accuracy when the prospective life of an asset is short. If the life of an asset is long, the error in the estimate of its salvage value will usually be of minor importance. The life of an asset, direct labor, direct material, and overhead are estimated with difficulty and, therefore, have important consequences on the success of a venture. These items are closely related to quantity of output and, therefore, to the total income to be received during the life of the activity in question.

However, once these items have been estimated on the best available information, there seems little point in making allowance for error; if an estimate is believed to be in error, it should be corrected. Furthermore, it seems unrealistic to make adjustments in the estimate of one item for suspected errors in the estimates of others, as is often done when the interest rate and service life are over- or underestimated to compensate for errors in other items.

Risk associated with hazards as contrasted to errors associated with estimates can be entered as a cost of operation if known quantitatively. Risk, as used here, designates a loss that may be experienced by a happening in a situation under consideration. Action based on estimates that are in error may also result in a loss, but in this case the loss results from what is believed to be true.

Risk is known in many situations and is expressed as the probability that certain events will happen in certain ways. For example, experience in the manufacture of a certain article has revealed that one piece in every 132 is lost due to breakage. Analysis also reveals that such loss amounts to $86. Thus, the probable loss per piece due to breakage amounts to $86 divided by 132, or $0.65 per piece. That is, the risk of breakage amounts to $0.65 per piece.

When risk is known, it may be considered to be an item of input cost. This is often done by insuring against risk and entering the amount spent for insurance as an operating cost. Where risk is not known, it may be estimated in quantitative terms and be added as an input cost, or it may be regarded as an irreducible factor to be considered in decision making.

9.7. DEFERRING THE DECISION BECAUSE OF UNCERTAINTY

Where success embodies elements of uncertainty there is often a need to hold capital equipment investment to a minimum until outcomes become clearer, even though such action may result in higher production costs. Such action amounts to a decision to incur higher costs temporarily in order to reserve the privilege of making a second decision when the situation becomes clearer.

The accuracy of estimates with respect to events in the future is at least to some extent inversely proportional to the span of time between the estimate and the event. It is often sound to incur expense for the privilege of deferring decision. This premise may be illustrated by the following example.

A firm has need for warehouse space in a new business territory it is about to enter. It is estimated that the equivalent annual cost of providing a warehouse to meet estimated needs through ownership will amount to $5,000 per year. Warehouse space can be leased for $8,000 for the first year, with an option to renew the lease. In spite of the higher cost, it is desired to lease for the first year until the situation becomes clearer. It is considered possible that during the year (1) the firm will withdraw from the territory, or (2) warehouse needs will be either lesser or greater than estimated. In other words it is considered prudent to spend $3,000 during the first year in order to be free to consider the warehouse problem one year hence.

9.8. MAKING THE DECISION

After a situation has been carefully analyzed and the possible outcomes have been evaluated as accurately as possible, a decision must be made. Even after all the data that can be brought to bear on a situation have been considered, some areas of uncertainty may be expected to remain. If a decision is to be made, these areas of uncertainty must be bridged by consideration of nonquantitative data or, in other words, by the evaluation of intangibles. Some call the type of evaluation involved in the consideration of intangibles *intuition;* others call it *hunch* or *judgment.*

Whatever it be called, it is inescapable that this type of thinking or, perhaps better, this type of feeling, must always be the final part in coming to a decision about the future. There is no other way if action is to be taken. There appears to be a marked difference in people's abilities to come to sound conclusions when some facts relative to a situation are missing. Perhaps much more attention should be devoted to developing sound judgment, for those who possess it are richly rewarded. But as effective as intuition, hunch, or judgment may sometimes be, this type of thinking should be reserved for those areas where facts on which to base a decision are missing.

QUESTIONS

1. Contrast the effectiveness of estimating in the physical environment and the economic environment.

2. Explain why engineering economy analysis must rely heavily upon estimates.

3. Explain why an estimate of a result will probably be more accurate if it is based upon estimates of the factors that have a bearing on the result, than if the result is estimated directly.

4. Why is it best to make an estimate of the components of $N = G - (O + D + I + T)$ as an aid in estimating the success of a venture?

5. Describe the estimating procedure for operating expense, depreciation, interest, and taxes.

6. Why should an estimate of the income of a venture be made before estimating the factors that have a bearing on the result?

7. Relate the usual "factor of safety" concept in engineering design to allowances for error in engineering economy analysis.

8. Discuss the value of allowing for error in estimates by high interest rates, rapid payout, and choosing conservative values.

9. Discuss the value of making least favorable, fair, and most favorable estimates.

10. What is the value of making tentative guesses for unknown facets of an alternative?

11. Discuss risk as an element of cost.

12. What are the advantages and disadvantages of deferring a decision when uncertainty is involved?

13. Why are decisions relative to the future based upon estimates instead of upon the facts that will apply?

14. Why is judgment always necessary to come to a decision relative to an outcome in the future?

PART IV

ENGINEERING ECONOMY ANALYSIS

CHAPTER 10

BASES FOR COMPARISON
OF ALTERNATIVES

Engineering economy analysis is usually concerned with alternatives, each of which will involve prospective outputs and inputs at specific points in time. These outputs and inputs are then converted to monetary receipts and disbursements, insofar as this conversion is possible. The resulting information is quantitative in nature and, therefore, may be manipulated mathematically for comparison. The most common bases for comparison are the present-worth amount, the equivalent annual amount, the capitalized amount, the rate of return, and the service life.

The reduction of alternatives to a common base is necessary so that apparent differences become real differences, with the time value of money considered. When expressed in terms of a common base, the real differences become directly comparable and may be used in decision making. This chapter will be devoted to explanation and illustration of the common bases for comparison of alternatives.

10.1. ACCEPTING OR NOT ACCEPTING A SINGLE ALTERNATIVE

Often decision is limited to the acceptance or rejection of a single alternative. In such a case the decision will be based on the relative merit of the alternative and other opportunities believed to exist, even though none of the latter have been crystallized into definite proposals.

When only one specified alternative exists, it should be evaluated in terms that can be used to compare its desirability with that of opportunities that are believed to exist, but are unspecified. The following example will illustrate several bases of evaluation where the decision to be made is to accept or reject a proposal where there is no specific alternative proposed for comparison.

The purchase of a compressor is under consideration for renting to contractors who need such equipment temporarily. The receipts and disbursements associated with the purchase and subsequent rental of the air compressor are given below.

	Date	Disbursements	Receipts
Cost of compressor............	6-1-19x0	$5,000	
Rental received, 1st year.......	6-1-19x1		$2,400
Operating cost, 1st year........	6-1-19x1	1,000	
Rental received, 2nd year......	6-1-19x2		2,400
Operating cost, 2nd year.......	6-1-19x2	1,000	
Overhaul, 2nd year............	6-1-19x2	700	
Rental received, 3rd year.......	6-1-19x3		2,400
Operating cost, 3rd year.......	6-1-19x3	1,000	
Rental received, 4th year......	6-1-19x4		2,400
Salvage sale of compressor.....	6-1-19x4		1,200
Operating cost, 4th year.......	6-1-19x4	1,000	

These disbursements and receipts tabulated above, with the exception of the purchase cost of the compressor, are estimates because all occur in the future. The life of the compressor has been estimated at four years. For convenience, disbursements and receipts occurring during the year are considered to come at the end of the year in which they occur. In this example the rental of $2,400 received during the first year is considered to occur at the close of May 31, 19x1. The error introduced by this practice is insignificant in comparison with the usual errors in estimates, except for extremely high interest rates. It should be borne in mind that the end of one year may be considered to be the beginning of the next. The cost of money in this example is taken at 5 per cent. Also, June 1, 19x0 will be considered to be the present, in other words the date as of which evaluation is to be made.

Present-worth comparison. The present worth of future monetary values is easily computed and readily understood. It results in an expression that yields a common basis for comparison with other present-worth values and is equivalent to the values it represents.

For the compressor example, the present worth of receipts as of June 1, 19x0 at 5 per cent interest are determined as follows:

$$
\begin{array}{lr}
\overset{\text{PR 5-4}}{\$2,400 \times (3.546)}\dots\dots\dots\dots\dots\dots\dots\dots\dots\dots\dots\dots\dots\dots & \$8,510 \\
\overset{\text{PS 5-4}}{\$1,200 \times (0.8227)}\dots\dots\dots\dots\dots\dots\dots\dots\dots\dots\dots\dots\dots\dots & 987 \\
\hline
 & \$9,497
\end{array}
$$

The present worth of the disbursements as of June 1, 19x0 at 5 per cent interest is:

$$
\begin{array}{lr}
\$5,000 \times 1\dots\dots\dots\dots\dots\dots\dots\dots\dots\dots\dots\dots\dots\dots\dots & \$5,000 \\
\overset{\text{PS 5-1}}{\$1,000 \times (0.9524)}\dots\dots\dots\dots\dots\dots\dots\dots\dots\dots\dots\dots & 952 \\
\overset{\text{PS 5-2}}{(\$1,000 + \$700) \times (0.9070)}\dots\dots\dots\dots\dots\dots\dots\dots\dots & 1,542 \\
\overset{\text{PS 5-3}}{\$1,000 \times (0.8638)}\dots\dots\dots\dots\dots\dots\dots\dots\dots\dots\dots\dots & 864 \\
\overset{\text{PS 5-4}}{\$1,000 \times (0.8227)}\dots\dots\dots\dots\dots\dots\dots\dots\dots\dots\dots\dots & 823 \\
\hline
 & \$9,181
\end{array}
$$

The present worth of receipts less disbursements is $9,497 less $9,181, or $316.

On the assumption that all estimates eventually prove to be correct, the significance of this analysis is that if $5,000 is invested in the compressor on June 1, 19x0 the investor will receive a 5 per cent return on the money he has invested in the enterprise plus the equivalent of a receipt of $316 on June 1, 19x0. Note that the amount invested in the enterprise begins at $5,000 and diminishes until the entire investment has been recovered.

To decide whether or not to purchase the compressor, the prospective purchaser should compare the gain in prospect from it against a feeling or opinion regarding nonspecified opportunities that appear to be in prospect or against the prospects from some specific alternative. In the latter case, as will be demonstrated later, the net present worth of receipts less disbursements for the latter specified alternative can be calculated for comparison.

Equivalent annual comparison. The equivalent annual difference between receipts and disbursements at 5 per cent interest may be calculated. Ordinarily the first step in this calculation is to find the present worths of receipts and disbursements; this was done for the present-worth evaluation above. Next these quantities are converted to an annual basis in the following manner:

Equivalent annual receipts, 6-1-x0 to 6-1-x4:

$$\$9{,}497 \times \overset{\text{RP 5-4}}{(0.28201)} \dots\dots\dots\dots\dots\dots\dots\dots\dots\dots\dots\dots \quad \$2{,}678$$

Equivalent annual disbursements, 6-1-x0 to 6-1-x4:

$$\$9{,}181 \times \overset{\text{RP 5-4}}{(0.28201)} \dots\dots\dots\dots\dots\dots\dots\dots\dots\dots\dots\dots \quad 2{,}589$$

Equivalent annual receipts less disbursements. . . . . $ 89

This result means that if $5,000 is invested in the compressor on June 1, 19x0, a 5 per cent return will be received on the amount invested in the compressor for the time it is invested plus the equivalent of receipts of $89 on June 1, 19x1, 19x2, 19x3, and 19x4.

Capitalized comparison. The capitalized basis of evaluation is in favor in some quarters for consideration of long-term opportunities. This method is not used for short-lived assets except as a means of illustration. Typical of such opportunities are highway and railway cuts, fills, embankments, water power developments, and other assets of long life. On a capitalized basis, the income and disbursements will be calculated as though they will continue in perpetuity or, in other words, forever. This basis of evaluation is not ordinarily used for assets of short life.

The capitalized basis of evaluation consists of finding a single amount in the present whose return at a given rate of interest will be equivalent to the net difference of receipts and disbursements if the given patterns of disbursements and receipts were repeated in perpetuity. This would take place in the example if a new compressor were purchased each fourth year in the future and if given disbursements and receipts were repeated during the life of each compressor.

Calculations for a capitalized evaluation may begin with the equivalent annual receipts and disbursements previously calculated to be $2,678 and $2,589 for each year-end of the first four years. To capitalize these amounts, it is only necessary to determine amounts in the present whose annual return at 5 per cent will be $2,678 and $2,589, respectively.

Capitalized receipts as of 6-1-x0:

$$\$2{,}678 \div .05 \dots\dots\dots\dots\dots\dots\dots\dots\dots\dots\dots\dots\dots\dots \quad \$53{,}560$$

Capitalized disbursements as of 6-1-x0:

$$\$2{,}589 \div .05 \dots\dots\dots\dots\dots\dots\dots\dots\dots\dots\dots\dots\dots\dots \quad 51{,}780$$

Capitalized receipts less capitalized disbursements. . . . . $ 1,780

This result means that an investment of $5,000 followed by re-
newals of compressors out of earnings each four years forever, provided that the patterns of receipts and disbursements of the first
compressor are repeated, will have results equivalent to an investment
of $5,000 at 5 per cent interest forever, plus a receipt of $1,780 on
June 1, 19x0.

Rate-of-return comparison. This method is probably the best
for comparing a concrete proposal with other opportunities believed
to exist but not delineated. Rate of return is a universal measure
of economic success. The meaning of rates of return is widely understood. Also, the rates of return to be expected from different classes
of opportunities are usually well established and generally known.
Thus rates of return are norms representative of opportunities in
general. These characteristics make this basis of comparison particularly well adapted to situations where the choice is between engaging
in an opportunity or not engaging in it.

The compressor proposal can be evaluated on the basis of the rate
of return that may be secured on the funds invested in it. This can
be done by determining the rate of interest for which the present worth
of disbursements and receipts will be equal. This may be done by
trial-and-error calculations for different rates of interest and interpolation. The necessary calculation of present worths will follow the
pattern illustrated previously under present-worth evaluation.
For an interest rate of 7 per cent:

Present worth of receipts at 7%............................	$9,044
Present worth of disbursements at 7%......................	8,999
Present worth of receipts less disbursements at 7%..........	$ 45

For an interest rate of 8 per cent:

Present worth of receipts at 8%............................	$8,831
Present worth of disbursements at 8%......................	8,912
Present worth of receipts less disbursements at 8%..........	−$ 81

To find the desired value of i, remember that the present worth
of receipts less present worth of disbursements equals zero when the
interest rate equals i. By interpolation:

$$i = 7 + (1)\frac{45 - 0}{45 - (-81)} = 7.36 \text{ per cent.}$$

This result means that, if $5,000 is invested in the compressor on June 1, 19x0, a return of 7.36 per cent will be received on the amount invested for the time it is invested. This evaluation is probably the most meaningful in a comparison of this type.

Service life comparison. Expressions like "This machine will pay for itself in less than three years" are common in industry and are indicative of the tendency to evaluate assets in terms of their service life. It is generally conceded that the longer the life, the greater the uncertainty. One merit of the service life comparison is that it specifically directs attention to the length of life embraced by an alternative. The hazard of an opportunity may often be pointedly revealed by calculating results for service lives less than that originally estimated. The service life method of evaluation is useful as a supplement to other methods of comparison.

Service life or payout life is usually determined on the basis of an interest rate of zero. The service life is then the period of time required for the difference between operating receipts and disbursements to equal the capital cost of the asset at zero interest. In other words, service life is equal to the period of time required for an asset to *pay for itself* from net operating returns.

The period of time required for the compressor to pay for itself may be calculated as follows:

Three year service life:

Receipts: 3($2,400) + $1,200................................ $8,400
Disbursements: 3($1,000) + $700.......................... 3,700

Receipts less disbursements............................ $4,700

Four year service life:

Receipts: 4($2,400) + $1,200................................ $10,800
Disbursements: 4($1,000) + $700.......................... $ 4,700

Receipts less disbursements............................ $ 6,100

$$\text{Service life} = 3 + (1)\frac{\$4,700 - \$5,000}{\$4,700 - \$6,100} = 3.21 \text{ years.}$$

This result means that operating receipts less operating disbursements will be equal for a life of 3.21 years. Or, the compressor will pay for itself in 3.21 years.

10.2. ALTERNATIVES THAT PROVIDE SERVICE OF EQUAL VALUE

In many, if not most, problems in engineering economy analysis the comparison is between alternatives with outputs that are identical or equal in value. In such situations the objective is to provide the desired service at least cost.

Suppose that it is proposed to route one highway over another. The desired service, or output, is the smooth flow of traffic resulting from the elimination of an intersection. This may be provided, for example by a reinforced concrete overpass or by a tunnel underpass. If both alternatives will provide service that is identical or equal in value, their outputs will cancel and the choice between them can be made entirely on the basis of cost.

Two alternatives will be considered to provide identical service when they meet needs that are the same in all significant particulars. As an example, where ability to carry a load is the only consideration, concrete mixtures resulting in the same strength per unit area will be considered identical. However, if color, surface roughness or imperviousness to moisture is of economic significance, mixtures will be considered to be identical only if they are identical in the qualities enumerated. When this condition is met the services of one alternative will offset or cancel those of the other. Therefore, the comparison of alternatives that provide identical service can be made on the basis of the cost of providing them.

As an illustration of the application of the several bases for comparison of alternatives to the choice between alternatives that provide service of identical or equal value the following example will be used. Two alternative methods have been proposed for providing needed warehouse space for a period of 12 years. Alternative A will require an immediate investment of $30,000 in a building that will depreciate to zero in the 12-year period. The cost of maintenance, heat, light, insurance, and taxes is estimated to be $2,200 per year. Alternative B will require an immediate investment of $20,000 in a building that will have no salvage value at the end of the 12-year period. The estimated annual cost of maintenance, heat, light, insurance, and taxes is $3,200 per year. The interest rate is 5 per cent.

Present-worth cost comparison. Since the choice of either alternative will result in satisfying the need for warehouse space, each will provide identical service and it is only necessary to compare their respective cost elements in the following manner:

Present-worth cost of Alternative A:

Initial investment..	$30,000
Operating cost, $2,200 $\overset{\text{PR 5-12}}{(8.863)}$...........................	$19,499
	$49,499

Present-worth cost of Alternative B:

Initial investment..	$20,000
Operating cost, $3,200 $\overset{\text{PR 5-12}}{(8.863)}$...........................	$28,361
	$48,361

The sum of $49,499 for Alternative A can be thought of as the lump-sum present cost of 12 years of service for interest at 5 per cent. The comparison shows Alternative B to have an advantage of a present-worth cost of $1,138 over Alternative A.

Equivalent annual cost comparison. The equivalent annual cost can be obtained by multiplying the present-worth costs found above by the capital-recovery factor. The result of this method is the sum of depreciation, interest on unrecovered capital in the depreciating asset, and annual operating cost.

Equivalent annual cost for Alternative A:

Capital recovery with return, $30,000 $\overset{\text{RP 5-12}}{(0.11283)}$..............	$3,385
Annual operating cost, $2,200 × 1........................	2,200
	$5,585

Equivalent annual cost for Alternative B:

Capital recovery with return, $20,000 $\overset{\text{RP 5-12}}{(0.11283)}$..............	$2,257
Annual operating cost, $3,200 × 1........................	3,200
	$5,457

On the basis of the above comparison, the equivalent annual cost of Alternative B is less than that of Alternative A by $128 per annum.

Capitalized cost comparison. Capitalized cost can most easily be obtained by dividing the equivalent annual cost by the interest rate. This method will be used to calculate the capitalized cost of Alternative A. Capitalized cost of Alternative B will be calculated in a way that gives a clearer insight into the significance of capital-ized cost. It should be borne in mind that the capitalized cost of an alternative is the present sum that will pay for the service provided by the alternative forever. Capitalized cost may also be considered to be the present-worth cost of providing a service forever. Capitalized cost is most widely used for comparison of assets of long life, particu-larly if the annual cost associated with them is relatively low.

The capitalized cost for Alternative A is:

Equivalent annual cost $\div i$, \$5,585 $\div$ 0.05................ \$111,700

And the equivalent annual cost for Alternative B is:

Cost of initial asset..................................... \$ 20,000

RP 5-12
Capital cost of renewals, \$20,000 (0.06283) $\div$ 0.05.......... 25,140
Capital cost of annual operating cost, \$3,200 $\div$ 0.05........ 64,000
_____
\$109,140

In the calculation capitalized cost of Alternative B, it is clear that \$20,000 would have to be available to purchase the initial asset. To accumulate \$20,000 to purchase a renewal at the end of each twelve-year period,

$$\text{RS 5-12}$$
$$\$20,000(0.06283) = \$1,257$$

might be deposited at the end of each year in a sinking fund to com-pound at 5 per cent interest. A sum whose annual interest would be sufficient to provide for the annual deposit of \$1,257 would be equal to \$1,257 $\div$ 0.05 = \$25,140. An additional capital amount of \$3,200 $\div$ 0.05 = \$64,000 will be needed to earn \$3,200 each year to meet annual operating costs.

On the basis of the above comparison, the desired service can be had forever with Alternative B for a present cost \$2,560 less than the present cost of perpetual service of Alternative A.

Rate-of-return comparison. Previous comparisons have shown that Alternative A is the less desirable choice for an interest rate of 5 per cent. Alternative A also requires a higher initial investment than Alternative B. On the basis of interest at 5 per cent there is no justi-fication for making the larger investment required by Alternative A. However, at some interest rate less than 5 per cent Alternative A will be more economical than Alternative B. An insight into the situation can be gained by calculating the interest rate for which the two alternatives will have equal annual costs.

At some interest rate i, the present-worth cost of Alternative A equals the present-worth cost of Alternative B. Then

$$\$30,000 + \$2,200(\overset{\text{PR } i\text{-12}}{\quad\quad}) = \$20,000 + \$3,200(\overset{\text{PR } i\text{-12}}{\quad\quad})$$

$$\$1,000(\overset{\text{PR } i\text{-12}}{\quad\quad}) = \$10,000$$

$$\overset{\text{PR } i\text{-12}}{(10.000)} = 10,000 \div 1,000$$

From the tables,

$$\overset{\text{PR 2-12}}{(10.575)} \quad \text{and} \quad \overset{\text{PR 3-12}}{(9.954)}$$

By interpolation

$$i = 2 + (1)\frac{10.575 - 10.00}{10.575 - 9.954} = 2 + \frac{0.575}{0.621} = 2.93 \text{ per cent.}$$

Where funds are considered to earn less than 2.93 per cent interest, Alternative A will be most desirable.

Service life comparison. The service life of twelve years for Alternatives A and B is of necessity the result of estimates and may be in error. If the service for which the alternatives are under consideration were actually needed for some period other than twelve years, the advantage might pass from B to A. The service life for which the two alternatives will have equal annual costs may be calculated as follows.

For some service life of n years, the equivalent annual cost of Alternative A will equal the equivalent annual cost of Alternative B. Expressing this as an equation,

$$\$30,000(\overset{\text{RP 5-}n}{\quad\quad}) + \$2,200 = \$20,000(\overset{\text{RP 5-}n}{\quad\quad}) + \$3,200$$

$$\$10,000(\overset{\text{RP 5-}n}{\quad\quad}) = \$1,000$$

$$\overset{\text{RP 5-}n}{(0.10000)} = 1,000 \div 10,000$$

From the tables,

$$\overset{\text{RP 5-14}}{(0.10102)} \quad \text{and} \quad \overset{\text{RP 5-15}}{(0.09634)}$$

By interpolation

$$n = 14 + (1)\frac{0.10102 - 0.10000}{0.10102 - 0.09634} = 14 + \frac{0.00102}{0.00468} = 14.22 \text{ years.}$$

This result means that if the desired service will be needed for more than 14.22 years, Alternative A will be the less costly alternative.

10.3. EQUALIZING ALTERNATIVES THAT PROVIDE SERVICE OF UNEQUAL VALUE

When two or more alternatives provide unequal service, or output, monetary compensation may be made for inequalities in value of output so that comparison can be made on the basis of cost. After equalization, the alternatives may be compared by the methods presented previously.

Positive output is equal to a negative input, and conversely, a positive input is equal to a negative output. Similarly, a positive receipt is equivalent to a negative disbursement and a positive disbursement is equal to a negative receipt. This principle will be demonstrated by the following example. Suppose that two methods of insulating a boiler are under consideration. Covering Material A will reduce heat loss cost by $60 per year and its equivalent annual cost will be $22. Covering Material B will reduce heat loss cost by $48 per year and its equivalent annual cost will be $14. Since the insulating materials will provide service of unequal value, it will be necessary to equalize their outputs by adding $12 to the benefit of Covering B. In accordance with the principle above, it will be necessary to add $12 to the cost of Covering B so it may be equitably compared. The net annual benefit for each covering material may be calculated by subtracting the equalized equivalent annual cost from the equalized gross annual benefit. Thus, the net annual benefit for Covering A is $60 − $22 = $38 and ($48 + $12) − ($14 + $12) = $34 for Covering B. On the basis of the net annual benefit after equalization, Covering A would be chosen.

Alternatives that provide service of equal unit value. In some cases alternatives have outputs that are identical or equal in value per unit of time. For example, an untreated telephone pole will give just as good service while it lasts as a pole treated with a preservation to lengthen its life. Suppose that an untreated pole will cost

$16 and will last 8 years and that a treated pole will cost $21 and will last 14 years. If interest is neglected, the cost per year of service is $16 ÷ 8 = $2 for the untreated pole and $21 ÷ 14 = $1.50 for the treated pole. Here a comparison can be made on the basis of the cost per unit of output provided by the alternatives. The unit of output in either case is the service provided by a pole for a period of one year.

When a service is to be provided over a period of time by a series of renewable facilities, the outputs of alternative facilities per unit of time may be equal. If so, comparison of the alternatives can be made on the basis of the cost per unit of service.

10.4. COMPARISON OF ALTERNATIVES WITH UNEQUAL FIRST COST

As an illustration of the analysis required in the comparison of alternatives with unequal first cost consider the following example. A corporation is evaluating a proofer for balancing its daily accounts. Alternative A involves purchasing a proofer for $5,900 with the provision that the vendor will service the machine without charge for a period of 10 years. At the end of 10 years, $400 will be allowed for the old machine on the purchase of a new one. Alternative B involves leasing a proofer for $66 per month, or $792 per year. The vendor will service the machine without additional charge and will replace it when it becomes unserviceable. The corporation uses an interest rate of 6 per cent in evaluating alternatives.

Present-worth cost comparison. The present-worth cost of 10 years of service under Alternative A is:

Present worth of first cost.................................... $5,900

Present worth of receipts from salvage, $400 (0.5584)$\overset{\text{PS 6-10}}{}$.......... 223
_____
$5,677

The present-worth cost of 10 years service under Alternative B is:

Present worth of rental, $66 × 12 (7.360)$\overset{\text{PR 6-10}}{}$.................... $5,829

The economic advantage of Alternative B is $5,829 less $5,677, or $152.

Equivalent annual cost comparison. The equivalent annual cost of 10 years of service for Alternative A is:

($5,900 − $400) (0.13587)$\overset{\text{RP 6-10}}{}$ + $400 × 0.06.................... 771

For Alternative B the equivalent annual cost is the annual rental amount of $792. The advantage in favor of Alternative A is $792 less $771, or $21.

Rate-of-return comparison. On the basis of the present-worth cost comparison above, there is a positive advantage of $152 in favor of Alternative A. The problem is to find the value of i for which the advantage in favor of Alternative A is zero. For 7 per cent interest, the present-worth cost of 10 years of service is:

$$\overset{\text{PS 7-10}}{\$5,900 - \$400\ (0.5083\ )}\dots\dots\dots\dots\dots\dots\dots\dots\dots\dots\dots\ \$5,697$$

For Alternative B the present worth of 10 years of service is:

$$\overset{\text{PR 7-10}}{\$66 \times 12\ (7.024\ )}\dots\dots\dots\dots\dots\dots\dots\dots\dots\dots\dots\ 5,563$$

The advantage in favor of Alternative A at 7 per cent interest is $5,563 less $5,697, or $-$134. Let i equal the interest rate for which the advantage in favor of Alternative A is equal to zero. Then, by interpolation:

$$i = 6 + (1)\frac{152 - 0}{152 - (-134)} = 6.53 \text{ per cent.}$$

Service life comparison. When an investment is made in a unit, such as the proofer under consideration in this problem, there is always a possibility that a more desirable way of meeting the need may become available. Thus the service life of the original unit may be terminated before the end of its estimated life. An advantage of renting a service is that it may be discontinued without penalty whenever a more desirable service presents itself.

For some value of n, the present-worth cost of Alternative A will equal the present-worth cost of Alternative B. Under the assumption that the trade-in value of the purchased proofer will remain at $400,

$$\overset{\text{PS 6-}n}{\$5,900 - \$400(\qquad)} = \overset{\text{PR 6-}n}{\$66(12)(\qquad).}$$

For $n = 9$ the present-worth cost of service for Alternative A is:

$$\overset{\text{PS 6-9}}{\$5,900 - \$400\ (0.5919)}\dots\dots\dots\dots\dots\dots\dots\dots\dots\ \$5,663$$

And, for Alternative B the present-worth cost is:

$$\overset{\text{PR 6-9}}{\$66 \times 12\ (6.802)}\dots\dots\dots\dots\dots\dots\dots\dots\dots\dots\ 5,387$$

From previous calculations, the advantage in favor of Alternative A for $n = 10$ is equal to \$152. By interpolation:

$$n = 9 + (1)\frac{-276 - 0}{-276 - 152} = 9 + \frac{276}{429}$$

$$= 9.65 \text{ years.}$$

The result above shows that a slight shortening of the service life causes the advantage to pass from Alternative A to Alternative B.

10.5. COMPARISON OF ALTERNATIVES WITH UNEQUAL SERVICE LIVES

Poles for a certain telephone line may be provided by purchasing untreated poles whose average life is estimated at 12 years. These poles will cost \$15.75 each and can be installed at a cost of \$1.75 per pole. Thus, each pole in place will cost \$17.50 under Alternative A. Alternative B would involve purchasing poles suitable for treatment at \$15.25 each and applying the treatment process at a cost of \$4.25 per pole. Such treatment will impart an 18-year service life in the pole. Installation will cost \$1.75, making the installed cost \$21.25 per pole. Interest is taken at 6 per cent.

Present-worth cost comparison. Since the two alternatives provide for different periods of service, some method must be used to embrace equal periods of service in a present-worth comparison. This can be done by making the present-worth comparison on the basis of a service period of 36 years. The service period will require three poles of Alternative A — one purchased at the beginning of each 12-year period, and two poles of Alternative B — one purchased at the beginning of each 18-year period of the 36 years under consideration. The present-worth cost of 36 years of service per pole is:

Present worth of first pole, \$17.50 × 1......................	\$17.50
Present worth of second pole, \$17.50 (0.4970)................ PS 6-12	8.70
Present worth of third pole, \$17.50 (0.2470)................. PS 6-24	4.32
	\$30.52

For Alternative B the present-worth cost of 36 years of service per pole is:

Present worth of first pole, \$21.25 × 1........................	\$21.25
Present worth of second pole, \$21.25 (0.3505)................... PS 6-18	7.44
	\$28.69

These results show that 36 years of pole service is possible with Alternative A for a present-worth cost that is $1.83 less than for Alternative B. In view of the fact that the service period greatly exceeds the service life of either pole, an interpretation that might be more meaningful is that the prospective cost for pole service with Alternative A is ($28.69 ÷ $30.52) = $0.94 times, or 94 per cent of the cost of the same service with Alternative B.

Equivalent annual cost comparison. The equivalent annual cost per pole for Alternative A is:

$$\overset{\text{RP 6-12}}{\$17.50 \times (0.11928)} \dots\dots\dots\dots\dots\dots\dots\dots\dots\dots\dots\dots\dots\dots\dots \$2.09$$

For Alternative B the equivalent annual cost per pole is:

$$\overset{\text{RP 6-18}}{\$21.25 \times (0.09236)} \dots\dots\dots\dots\dots\dots\dots\dots\dots\dots\dots\dots\dots\dots\dots \$1.96$$

These results show that the prospective annual cost of Alternative B is $0.13 less per annum than that of Alternative A. It may also be useful to state the cost of service of Alternative B as a percentage of the cost of alternative A. The annual cost of service with Alternative B will be ($1.96 ÷ $2.09) = 0.94, or 94 per cent of the cost with Alternative A.

These alternatives may also be compared on the basis of their capitalized amounts, the rate of return, and the service life. These additional comparisons will assist the decision maker by giving him more viewpoints for considering the alternatives.

10.6. COMPARISON OF MULTIPLE ALTERNATIVES

Often it is necessary to make a decision from among three or more alternatives. In such cases it is usually sufficient to compare the alternatives in pairs. For example, an opportunity to invest $200,000 in a chemical processing plant or $150,000 in a manufacturing plant may come under consideration. Assuming that other alternatives have not been delineated, this situation results in at least three alternatives which may be designated as follows:

1. Invest $200,000 in a chemical processing plant.
2. Invest $150,000 in a manufacturing plant and $50,000 in an unspecified manner.
3. Invest $200,000 in undelineated alternatives.

The situation outlined presents a choice between Alternative (1) and (2), (1) and (3), and (2) and (3). Since Alternatives (1) and (2) may vary widely in the period of years they involve, activities required, equipment needed, cost of money, etc., they are difficult to compare. Each should be evaluated independently in a manner similar to that illustrated with the compressor example. When this has been done comparison should be made between (1) and (3), between (2) and (3), and finally between (1) and (2). This procedure avoids the error of selecting one of two alternatives when neither may be as desirable as the third.

Interpreting rates of return for multiple alternatives. In the example above, the level of investment was equal for each prospective investment alternative. Suppose that six investment alternatives are available that require cash inputs ranging from $150,000 to $250,000. If each alternative was calculated to yield a rate of return below that which is considered to be the minimum attractive rate of return all would be classified as unattractive for investment. However, where two or more of the alternatives show a rate of return that meets the minimum attractive rate it is necessary to compute the rate of return on the extra investment. This is in keeping with the principle that each avoidable investment of capital must measure up to the minimum standard of attractiveness.

Two types of error are often made in interpreting rates of return for multiple alternatives where the levels of investment differ. The first arises from selecting the alternative that gives the highest rate of return on the total investment. This type of error has the effect of preventing the investment of the increment of invested funds at a rate of return that may be higher than would be obtained on the total investment.

A second common error is that of choosing the largest investment on which the rate of return is equal to or greater than the minimum attractive rate of return. In so doing the investment of the extra funds may be forced to earn a rate of return lower than could be obtained if the available funds for investment were split among two or more alternatives.

10.7. BASES FOR COMPARISON OF ALTERNATIVES ARE RELATED

Since several bases for comparison of alternatives were illustrated, it may be helpful to show their relationship to each other. Each was used in the examples for a better insight into the factors involved, and because their relationships may often be shown by comparing economic alternatives on several bases.

Relationship of present-worth, equivalent annual, and capitalized amounts. The present-worth amount, equivalent annual amount, and capitalized amount bases result in equal ratios. This may be illustrated by making use of the results of these bases as computed for the compressor example. The ratios are as follows:

$$\frac{\text{present worth of receipts}}{\text{present worth of disbursements}} = \frac{\$9,497}{\$9,181} = \frac{\text{equiv. annual receipts}}{\text{equiv. annual disbursements}} = \frac{\$2,678}{\$2,589} = \frac{\text{capitalized receipts}}{\text{capitalized disbursements}} = \frac{\$58,560}{\$51,780}.$$

Rate of return and service life are related. Any given service life can be converted to a rate of return. Assume that a service life has been calculated for an asset whose salvage value is zero for an interest rate of zero, as is usually done in service life calculations. Let

l = the service life in years;

n = the estimated life of the asset in years;

$\dfrac{P}{l}$ = the estimated net average annual earnings of the asset before capital recovery with a return. (This amount is assumed to be available, for capital recovery with a return, annually for n years.) Then,

$$\frac{P}{l} = P(\overset{\text{RP } i\text{-}n}{\qquad})$$

$$\frac{1}{l} = (\overset{\text{RP } i\text{-}n}{\qquad})$$

For example, if l = five years, and n = ten years, the rate of return will be 15+ per cent. Rates of return corresponding to a number of service lives l, and estimated lives, n, appear in Table 10.1.

Table 10.1. RATES OF RETURN CORRESPONDING TO SERVICE LIFE l AND ESTIMATED LIFE n

n	l									
	2	3	4	5	6	8	10	12	15	20
2	0									
5	41	20	8	0						
10	49	31	21	15	11	4	0			
15	50	33	24	18	14	9	5	3	0	
20	50	33	25	19	16	11	8	6	3	0

10.8. ADVANTAGES AND DISADVANTAGES OF BASES FOR COMPARISON

Each of the bases for comparison that are presented have their advantages and disadvantages. Even though each is mathematically equivalent, it is important that the advantages and disadvantages be individually recognized and taken into consideration.

Present-worth basis. The present-worth basis of evaluation is an outgrowth of valuation techniques and practices mainly developed since the turn of the century. The aim of valuation is ordinarily to determine a present worth of a property. The present worth of a property is often considered to be the present worth of the difference between future receipts and disbursements associated with it at a certain interest rate. The present-worth basis of comparison often results in amounts that are quite large in comparison with the amounts encountered in the alternatives being compared. A slight change in the interest rate may result in large changes in present-worth amounts. This method of comparison is somewhat cumbersome in comparing alternatives embracing different periods of time.

Equivalent annual amount basis. The development of this basis of comparison is associated with the development and general use of cost accounting, which necessitated consideration of costs on an annual basis and therefore consideration of depreciation as an annual cost. A distinct advantage of the equivalent annual amount basis of comparison is that it conforms to thought patterns that are used in accounting practices and are therefore familiar to most people in business. A second important advantage of this method is that the period under consideration is always a unit of time, namely one year. The amounts determined with it are actually a summation of receipts and disbursements per unit of time. Since equivalent annual amounts are based on a common unit, they are easier to comprehend and compare. Most people appear to live "by the year" and tend to think in terms of annual disbursements and receipts. Thus it seems logical to make economic comparisons on the basis of yearly periods. Because of inherent advantages and its general and growing use in activities associated with engineering, the equivalent annual amount basis of comparison should be favored over either the present-worth or the capitalized amount basis.

Capitalized amount basis. The capitalized amount basis is best suited for evaluation and comparison of long-term alternatives with stable income and interest costs that are high in relation to subsequent costs. Suppose that a railway tunnel whose future upkeep will be negligible and which will reduce operating costs by $12,000 per year is under consideration. The capitalized cost method provides a ready means of determining how much may be invested in constructing the tunnel. For an interest rate of 6 per cent, the reduction in operating cost will justify investing

$$\$12,000 \div 0.06 = \$200,000$$

in the tunnel on the supposition that it will be used forever. For practical purposes, forever may be considered to be 50 years and over. In the above example the reduction of operating cost by $12,000 per year for 50 years will justify investing

$$\begin{gathered} \text{PR 6-50} \\ \$12,000(15.762) = \$189,144 \end{gathered}$$

in the tunnel. This amount differs slightly more than 5 per cent from $200,000.

An objection to the capitalized amount method is that its results are difficult to comprehend, particularly when applied to short-lived assets. In general this method is losing in favor and is now rarely applied to investments involving periods of less than 30 or 40 years.

Rate-of-return bases. The rate of return is a widely accepted measure of success. It serves equally well both for the comparison of an alternative with other alternatives that are delineated and for an alternative with other opportunities which are believed to exist but that are not delineated. The rates of return expected from different ventures are fairly well established and thus provide a standard of comparison for ventures that are being considered.

Service life bases. The service life yields a time period in which it is expected that the disbursements required by a venture will be balanced by receipts. When interpreted as a payout period, it gives a break-even point that is useful in decision making. This basis of comparison is well accepted as a means for evaluating the desirability of purchasing capital equipment and other productive assets.

PROBLEMS

1. A prospective venture is described by the following receipts and disbursements:

Year End	Receipts	Disbursements
0	$ 0	$4,000
1	$ 800	$ 600
2	$1,800	$ 600
3	$2,200	$ 400
4	$1,600	$ 200

For an interest rate of 6 per cent determine the desirability of the venture on the basis of:

(a) The present-worth cost comparison.

(b) The equivalent annual cost comparison.

(c) The capitalized cost comparison.

2. The estimated annual incomes and costs of a prospective venture are as follows:

Year End	Income	Cost
0	$ 0	$1,600
1	$700	$ 100
2	$700	$ 200
3	$900	$ 220

Determine if this is a desirable venture by the equivalent annual cost comparison if the interest rate is 5 per cent; 6 per cent.

3. What will be the rate of return of the venture described in Problem 1; the rate of return of the venture described in Problem 2?

4. A certain mine can be purchased for $187,000. On the basis of estimated production, an annual income of $18,000 is foreseen for a period of 15 years. After 15 years, the mine is estimated to be worthless. What annual rate of return is in prospect?

5. Flood damage to a certain area averages $7,000 annually. A series of coffer dams to restrain the flow will cost $25,000 and will involve annual maintenance charges of $200. With interest at 8 per cent, how many years will it take the installation to pay for itself?

6. A short conveyor costing $240 and having a life of one year is placed between Machines A and B to eliminate the necessity of hand trucking. The services of a trucker at a rate of $1.80 per hour is eliminated to the extent of 20 minutes daily. The machine rate of Machine A is $1.50 per hour and the operator receives $2.10 per hour. The convenience of the new equipment makes it possible to reduce the cycle time on the operation done by Machine A from 1.7 to 1.6 minutes. The conveyor will be used 8 hours a day during 260 days of the year. Determine the rate of return on the investment if the conveyor has a life of one year.

7. A special lathe was designed and built for $75,000. It was estimated that the lathe would result in a saving in production cost of $10,500 per year for 20 years. With a zero salvage value at the end of 20 years, what was the expected rate of return? Actually, the lathe became inadequate after 6 years of use and was sold for $20,000. What was the actual rate of return?

8. An engineering graduate estimated that his education had cost the equivalent of $14,000, as of the date of graduation, considering his increased expenses and loss of earnings while in college. He estimated that his earnings during the first decade after leaving college would be no greater than if he had not gone to college. If, by virtue of his added preparation, $1,000, $3,000, and $6,000 additional per year is earned in succeeding decades, what is the rate of return realized on his $14,000 investment in education?

9. A machine attachment that will save $0.06 per unit of product can be designed and built for $600. Maintenance cost for the attachment is estimated to be $30 per year. If interest is 7 per cent and if 3,500 units are made per year, how long will it take the attachment to pay for itself?

10. A temporary warehouse with a zero salvage value at any point in time can be built for $8,000. The annual value of the storage space less annual maintenance and operating costs is estimated to be $1,260.

(a) What rate of return is in prospect if the warehouse is used 8 years?

(b) For what life will the warehouse result in a return of 10 per cent?

11. It is estimated that a manufacturing concern's needs for storage space can be met by providing 240,000 square feet of space at a cost of $5.20 per square foot now and providing an additional 60,000 square feet of space at a cost of $18,000 plus $5.20 per square foot of space six years hence. A second plan is to provide 300,000 square feet of space now at a cost of $5.10 per square foot. If either installation will have zero salvage value when retired some time after six years, and if taxes, maintenance, and insurance costs $0.06 per square foot, and the interest rate is 6 per cent, which plan should be adopted?

12. An electronics manufacturer packages 1,000 large transmitting tubes in special cartons each year. These cartons are currently purchased for $0.35 each. In addition, 200 cartons per year are purchased at $0.40 each which the manufacturer uses to package microphones. In order to reduce cost, the electronics manufacturer is considering the purchase of a carton punching machine for $300. The plates for punching the tube cartons will cost an additional $150 and those for punching the microphone cartons will cost $200.

Two alternatives are being considered. Alternative A involves the purchase of the machine and the plates to punch the tube cartons. Alternative B involves purchasing the machine and both sets of plates. The following cost data are applicable.

	A	B
Estimated life........................	12 years	12 years
Estimated salvage value.................	$45.00	$55.00
Annual estimated maintenance...........	6.00	7.00
Annual cost of material (cardboard).......	10.00	12.00
Annual labor to punch tube cartons.......	35.00	35.00
Annual labor to punch microphone cartons.		20.00
Interest rate..........................	6%	6%

(a) Alter either Alternative A or B so that they would both provide equal service, in order that they may be compared on an equitable basis.

(b) Calculate the equivalent annual cost of each of the revised alternatives.

(c) What other alternative or alternatives should be considered?

13. An engineering student who will soon receive his B.S. degree is contemplating continuing his formal education by working toward an M.S. degree. The student estimates that his average earnings for the next six years with a B.S. degree will be $6,800 per year. If he can get an M.S. degree in one year his earnings should average $7,800 per year for the subsequent five years. His earnings while working on the M.S. degree will be negligible and his additional expenses will be $800.

The engineering student estimates that his average per year earnings in the three decades following the initial six-year period will be $8,600, $10,200, and $11,600 if he does not stay for an M.S. degree. If he receives an M.S. degree his earnings in the three decades can be stated as $8,600 + x, $10,200 + x, and $11,600 + x. For an interest rate of 6 per cent find the value of x for which the extra investment in formal education will pay for itself.

14. An industrial firm can purchase a special machine for $20,000. A down payment of $2,000 is required and the balance can be paid in 5 equal year-end installments plus 4 per cent interest on the unpaid balance. As an alternative the machine can be purchased for $18,000 in cash. For what interest rate are the two plans equivalent?

15. A needed service can be purchased for $90 per unit. The same service can be provided by equipment which costs $100,000 and which will have a salvage value of $20,000 at the end of 10 years. Annual operating expense will be $7,000 per year plus $25 per unit.

(a) If these estimates are correct, what will be the rate of return on the investment if 300 units are produced per year?

(b) What will be the rate of return on the investment if 250 units are produced per year?

16. The heat loss through the exterior walls of a building costs $206 per year. Insulation that will reduce the heat loss cost by 93 per cent can be installed for $116, and insulation that will reduce the heat loss cost by 89 per cent can be installed for $90. Determine which insulation is most desirable if the building is to be used for 8 years and if the interest rate is 10 per cent.

17. It is estimated that the annual heat loss cost in a small power plant is $310. Two competing proposals have been formulated which will reduce the loss. Proposal A will reduce heat loss cost by 60 per cent and will cost $170. Proposal B will reduce heat loss cost by 55 per cent and will cost $130. If the interest rate is 8 per cent, and if the plant will benefit from the reduction in heat loss for 10 years, which proposal should be accepted?

18. A logging concern has two proposals under consideration which will provide identical service. Plan A is to build a water slide from logging site to saw mill at a cost of $250,000. Plan B consists of building a $100,000 slide to a nearby river and allowing the logs to float to the mill. Associated machinery at a cost of $75,000 and salvage value of $25,000 after 10 years will have to be installed to get the logs from the river

to the mill. Annual cost of labor, maintenance, electricity, and insurance of the machinery will be $7,000. The life of the slides is estimated to be 30 years with no salvage value. The interest rate is 6 per cent.

(a) Compare the two plans on the basis of equivalent annual cost.

(b) Compare the two plans on the basis of thirty years of service.

19. A refinery can provide for water storage with a tank on a tower or a tank of equal capacity placed on a hill some distance from the refinery. The cost of installing the tank and tower is estimated at $82,000. The cost of installing the tank on the hill, including the extra length of service lines, is estimated at $60,000. The life of the two installations is estimated at 40 years, with negligible salvage value for either. The hill installation will require an additional investment of $6,000 in pumping equipment, whose life is estimated at 20 years with a salvage value of $500 at the end of that time. Annual cost of labor, electricity, repairs, and insurance incident to the pumping equipment is estimated at $500. The interest rate is 5 per cent.

(a) Compare the present-worth cost of the two plans.

(b) Compare the two plans on the basis of equivalent annual cost.

(c) Compare the two plans on the basis of their capitalized costs.

20. In a hydroelectric development under consideration, the question to be decided is the height of dam to be built. The function of the dam is to create a head of water. Because of the width of the proposed dam site at different elevations, heights of the dam under consideration are 173, 194, and 211 feet; costs for these heights are estimated at $1,860,000, $2,320,000, and $3,020,000, respectively. The capacity of the power plant is based on the minimum flow of the stream of 990 cubic feet per second. This flow will develop $(h \times 990 \times 62.4) \div (550 \times 0.75)$ horsepower where h equals the height of the dam in feet. A horsepower-year is valued at $31. The cost of the power plant, including building and equipment, is estimated at $180,000 for the building and $34 per hp. of capacity for the equipment.

To be conservative, the useful life of the dam and buildings is estimated at 40 years with no salvage value. Life of the power equipment is also estimated at 40 years with no salvage value. Annual maintenance, insurance, and taxes on the dam and buildings are estimated at 2.8 per cent of first cost. Annual maintenance, insurance, and taxes on the equipment are estimated at 4.7 per cent of first cost. Operation costs are estimated at $38,000 per year for each of the alternatives. Determine the rate of return for each height of dam and the rate of return on the added investment for each added height. Which height dam should be built if 10 per cent is required on all investments?

21. A firm has $50,000 to invest. Alternative A consists of investing the entire $50,000 in a venture which will yield a 6 per cent return. Alternative B involves investing $20,000 in a venture which will yield an 8 per cent rate of return and $30,000 in a venture for which the rate of return is unknown. Find the rate of return which must be realized on the $30,000 so that the aggregate return for Proposal B will equal the return for Proposal A.

22. A manufacturing plant and its equipment are insured for $700,000. The present annual insurance premium is $0.86 per $100 of coverage. A sprinkler system with an estimated life of 20 years and no salvage value at the end of that time can be installed for $18,000. Annual operation and maintenance cost is estimated at $360. Taxes are 0.8 per cent of the initial cost of the plant and equipment. If the sprinkler is installed and maintained, the premium rate will be reduced to $0.38 per $100 of coverage.

(a) What rate of return is in prospect if the sprinkler systems is installed?

(b) With interest at 8 per cent, how many years will be required for the sprinkler system to pay for itself?

23. A 100 horsepower motor is required to power a large capacity blower. Two motors have been proposed with the following engineering and cost data.

	Motor A	Motor B
Cost.	$3,600	$3,000
Life.	12 yrs.	12 yrs.
Salvage value.	0	0
Efficiency ½ load.	85%	83%
Efficiency ¾ load.	90%	89%
Efficiency full load.	89%	88%
Hours use per year at ½ load.	800	800
Hours use per year at ¾ load.	1,000	1,000
Hours use per year at full load.	600	600

Power cost per kilowatt-hour is $0.03. Annual maintenance, taxes, and insurance will amount to 1.4 per cent of the original cost. Interest is 5 per cent.

(a) What is the equivalent annual cost for each motor?

(b) What will be the return on the additional amount invested in Motor A?

24. An investor can purchase an industrial site at the present time for $30,000. If he receives no income from the land and if taxes and other disbursements incident to ownership amount to $600 per year, what is the maximum number of years he can hold the land before disposing of it for $40,000 if he desires an 8 per cent return on the investment?

CHAPTER 11

BREAK-EVEN AND
MINIMUM COST ANALYSIS

In many situations encountered in engineering economy, the cost of two alternatives may be affected by a common variable. When such a condition occurs it may be desirable to find the value of the variable that will result in equal cost for the alternatives considered. The value of the variable so designated is known as the *break-even* point.

Similarly, if the cost of a single alternative is affected by a variable that may take on a range of values it may be desirable to determine the value of the variable for which the cost of the alternative is a minimum. The value of the variable so designated is known as the *minimum cost* point.

Break-even and minimum cost analysis need not be limited to the simple cases described above. There are many instances where multiple alternatives may be successfully compared by the use of break-even or minimum cost analysis. Also, there are situations in which the cost of alternatives are a function of two or more independent variables, thus making it necessary to find the values of the variables satisfying the break-even or minimum cost criteria. Several facets of the break-even and minimum cost aspect of engineering economy analysis will be presented in this chapter.

11.1. BREAK-EVEN ANALYSIS, TWO ALTERNATIVES

When the cost of two alternatives is affected by a common variable there may exist a value of the variable for which the two alternatives will incur equal cost. The costs of each alternative can be expressed as functions of the common independent variable and will be of the form

$$TC_1 = f_1(x) \quad \text{and} \quad TC_2 = f_2(x)$$

where

$TC_1 =$ a specified total cost per time period, per project, or per piece applicable to Alternative 1;

$TC_2 =$ a specified total cost per time period, per project, or per piece applicable to Alternative 2;

$x \quad =$ a common independent variable affecting Alternative 1 and Alternative 2.

Solution for the value of x resulting in equal cost for Alternative 1 and Alternative 2 is accomplished by setting the cost functions equal, $TC_1 = TC_2$. Therefore,

$$f_1(x) = f_2(x)$$

which may be solved for x. The resulting value for x yields equal cost for the alternatives considered and is, therefore, designated the break-even point.

Break-even point, mathematical solution. Where the cost of each alternative can be mathematically expressed as functions of a common variable the break-even point may be found mathematically. For example, assume that a 20-horsepower motor is needed to drive a pump to remove water from a tunnel. The number of hours that the pump will operate per year is dependent upon the rainfall and is, therefore, uncertain. The pump unit will be needed for a period of four years.

Two alternatives are under consideration. Proposal A calls for the construction of a power line and the purchase of an electric motor, at a total cost of $1,400. The salvage value of this equipment at the end of the four-year period is estimated at $200. The cost of current per hour of operation is estimated at $0.84, maintenance is estimated at $120 per year, and the interest rate is 10 per cent. No attendant will be needed since the equipment is automatic. Let

$TC_A =$ total equivalent annual cost of Proposal A;

$D_A \quad =$ equivalent annual cost of capital recovered and return

$$\text{RP 10-4}$$
$$= (\$1,400 - \$200)\ (0.31547) + \$200\ (0.10) = \$399;$$

M = annual maintenance cost = \$120;

C = current cost per hour of operation = \$0.84;

N = number of hours of operation per year.

Then $$TC_A = D_A + M + NC.$$

Proposal B calls for the purchase of a gasoline motor at a cost of \$550. The motor will have no salvage value at the end of the four-year period. The cost of fuel and oil per hour of operation is estimated at \$0.42, maintenance is estimated at \$0.15 per hour of operation, and the cost of wages chargeable to the engine when it runs is \$0.80 per hour. Let

TC_B = total equivalent annual cost of Proposal B;

D_B = equivalent annual cost of capital recovered and return

$$\text{RP 10-4}$$
$$= \$550\ (0.31547) = \$174;$$

H = hourly cost of fuel and oil, operator, and maintenance

$$= \$0.42 + \$0.80 + \$0.15 = \$1.37;$$

N = number of hours of operation per year.

Then $$TC_B = D_B + NH.$$

There is a value of N for which the two alternatives will incur equal cost. This value may be found by setting $TC_A = TC_B$ and solving for N as follows:

$$D_A + M + NC = D_B + NH$$
$$N = \frac{D_B - (D_A + M)}{C - H}.$$

Substituting

$$N = \frac{\$174 - (\$399 + \$120)}{\$0.84 - \$1.37} = 651 \text{ hours.}$$

That the total equivalent annual cost is equal for the two alternatives is shown as follows:

$$TC_A = TC_B$$
$$D_A + M + NC = D_B + NH$$
$$\$399 + \$120 + 651(\$0.84) = \$174 + 651(\$1.37)$$
$$\$1,066 = \$1,066.$$

For the cost data given, the annual cost of the two alternatives is calculated to be equal for 651 hours of operation per year. If the equipment is used less than 651 hours per year, selection of the gasoline motor is most economical; for more than 651 hours of operation per year, the electric motor is most economical. The total annual cost for each alternative, as a function of the number of hours of operation per year is shown graphically in Figure 11.1.

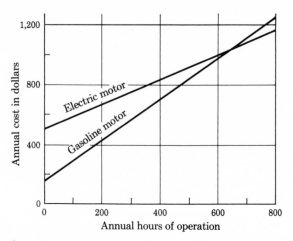

Figure 11.1. Total annual cost as a function of the number of hours of operation per year.

The difference in equivalent annual cost between the two alternatives may be calculated for any number of hours of operation. For example, suppose the equipment is to be operated 100 hours per year. Then

$$TC_A - TC_B = \Delta TC$$

$$D_A + M + NC - (D_B + NH) = \Delta TC.$$

Substituting

$$\Delta TC = \$399 + \$120 + 100(\$0.84) - \$174 - 100(\$1.37)$$

$$= \$292.$$

Break-even point, graphical solution. There are many situations in which setting up equations to represent the cost patterns of two alternatives is either too difficult or too time-consuming to be a feasible approach for the determination of a break-even point. In situations for which the cost patterns of two alternatives can be established by determining a number of points of the pattern by calculation or experiment, the break-even point may be determined graphically.

Consider the following example. Two methods, A and B, are under consideration for packing different lengths of display material in paper cartons of 24 inches in girth and 26, 36, 48, and 62 inches in length, respectively. The average times required to pack a number of cartons of the given lengths by Method A and Method B were found by time studies. The results are shown graphically in Figure 11.2.

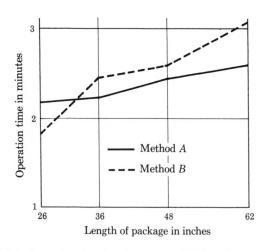

Figure 11.2. Operation time in minutes as a function of carton in inches.

The length of carton resulting in an equal operation time for the methods under consideration may be found by inspection from the graph.

11.2. MINIMUM COST ANALYSIS, SINGLE ALTERNATIVE

A single alternative may possess two or more cost components that are modified differently by a common variable. Certain cost components may vary directly with an increase in the value of the variable while others may vary inversely. When the total cost of an alternative is a function of increasing and decreasing cost components, most likely a value exists for the common variable that will result in a minimum cost for the alternative.

The general solution of the situation outlined above may be demonstrated for an increasing cost component and a decreasing cost component as follows:

$$TC = Ax + \frac{B}{x} + C$$

where

TC = a specified total cost per time period, per project, or per piece;

x = a common variable;

A, B, and C = constants.

Taking the first derivative, equating the result to zero, and solving for x results in

$$\frac{dTC}{dx} = A - \frac{B}{x^2} = 0$$

$$x = \sqrt{\frac{B}{A}}.$$

The value for x found in this manner will be a minimum and is, therefore, designated the minimum cost point.

Minimum cost point, mathematical solution. A classical example of minimum cost analysis is given by the increasing and decreasing cost components involved in the choice of the cross sectional area of an electrical conductor. Since resistance is inversely proportional to the size of the conductor, it is evident that the cost of power loss will decrease with increased conductor size. However, as the size of the conductor increases, an increased investment charge will be incurred. For some given conductor cross section, the sum of the two cost components will be a minimum.

As an example, suppose a copper conductor is being considered to transmit the daily electrical load at a sub-station, and estimates call for transmission of 800, 1,800, and 3,200 amperes for 12, 6, and 6 hours per day, respectively, for 365 days per year. The following engineering and cost data apply to the conductor installation: length of conductor, 140 feet; installed cost, $160 + $0.46 per pound of copper; estimated life, 20 years; salvage value, $0.22 per pound of copper. Electrical resistance of a copper conductor 140 feet long and of 1 square inch cross section is 0.0011435 ohm, and the electrical resistance is inversely proportional to the area of the cross section. The energy loss in kilowatt-hours in a conductor due to resistance is equal to $I^2R \times$ number of hours $\div$ 1,000, where I is the current flow in amperes and R is the resistance of the conductor in ohms. Copper weighs 555 pounds per cubic foot. The energy lost is valued at $0.007 per kilowatt-hour; taxes, insurance, and maintenance are negligible; the interest rate is 6 per cent.

The I^2R loss in dollars per year:

$$[(800)^2(12) + (1,800)^2(6) + (3,200)^2(6)]\left(\frac{365}{1,000}\right)\left(\frac{0.0011435}{A}\right)(\$0.007)$$

$$= \frac{\$258.74}{A}$$

Weight of conductor in pounds:

$$\frac{[(140)(12)(A)(555)]}{1,728} = 539.6A$$

Capital recovery plus return in dollars per year:

$$\overset{\text{RP 6-20}}{[\$160 + (\$0.46 - \$0.22)(539.6)(A)](0.08718)}$$

$$+ \$0.22(539.6)(A)(0.06) = 18.41A + 13.94.$$

The total cost per year:

$$TC = \$18.41A + \frac{\$258.74}{A} + \$13.94$$

$$\frac{dTC}{dA} = \$18.41 - \frac{\$258.74}{A^2} = 0$$

$$A = \sqrt{\frac{258.74}{18.41}} = 3.75 \text{ square inches.}$$

Therefore, the selection of a conductor with a cross-sectional area of 3.75 square inches will result in a minimum total cost. Note that this example exhibits a simple case involving an increasing and a decreasing cost component. The nature of these components may be tabulated from the expressions for I^2R loss cost and investment cost. These costs and the resulting total cost are given in Table 11.1.

It was first indicated by Lord Kelvin that the most economical

Table 11.1. TOTAL ANNUAL COST AS A FUNCTION OF CROSS SECTIONAL AREA

Cost	Cross sectional area $(in.^2)$				
	2	3	4	5	6
I^2R loss cost............	$ 50.77	$ 69.18	$ 87.59	$106.00	$124.41
Investment cost.........	$129.37	$ 86.15	$ 64.68	$ 51.75	$ 43.12
Total annual cost......	$180.14	$155.33	$152.27	$157.75	$167.53

cross sectional area for a conductor was one in which investment cost just equals the annual cost of lost energy. This is known as Kelvin's law.

Minimum cost point, graphical solution. There are many situations for which minimum cost points are sought but for which it is very difficult to set up equations that truly characterize the existing cost relationships. Since finding minimum cost points from cost equations involves differentiation, equations that only approximate true situations may result in grossly misleading results.

The graphical method for finding minimum cost points will be illustrated in the following example. The manufacturer of a pharmaceutical product plans to use an evaporative process. In this process one or several evaporators in multiple may be used. It is known that variable operating costs, of which the chief item is the cost of steam, will be approximately inversely proportional to the number of evaporators used in the installation. Fixed costs will be approximately in proportion to the number of evaporators used. Trial had demonstrated that a rather complex equation would be required to express accurately the cost relationships that existed, so a graphical solution was sought.

Estimates were made of the variable and the fixed operation costs that would be obtained if one, two, three, or four evaporators were used. Results from equipment manufacturers, experimental data, and a knowledge of the process formed the basis for estimating the costs. Table 11.2 summarizes the estimates based on 200 days'

Table 11.2. TOTAL ANNUAL COST AS A FUNCTION OF THE NUMBER OF EVAPORATORS USED

Costs	Number of evaporators used			
	1	2	3	4
Fixed costs (depreciation, insurance, taxes, etc.)	$ 860	$1,680	$2,350	$3,030
Variable costs (steam, labor, maintenance, etc.)	7,850	4,560	3,610	3,190
Total annual cost	$8,710	$6,240	$5,960	$6,220

operation per year. It is clear that, on the basis of 200 days' operation per year, the lowest annual cost of $5,960 results when three evaporators are used.

11.3. BREAK-EVEN AND MINIMUM COST ANALYSIS, MULTIPLE ALTERNATIVES

In the examples considered thus far, break-even analysis has been applied in the case where only two alternatives confront the decision maker. The application of minimum cost analysis has been illustrated for the case where only a single alternative is under consideration. The sections that follow will illustrate the application of break-even and minimum cost analysis in cases where multiple alternatives are being considered.

Break-even analysis, three or more alternatives. As an illustration of the application of break-even analysis where three alternatives are proposed, consider the following example. An architectural engineering firm has been asked to prepare preliminary plans for the construction of a three-story office building. After careful analysis, three types of construction seem feasible.

In attempting to arrive at some quantitative basis for recommending a type of construction, the engineering firm developed fixed and variable cost data. This data is given below and is assumed to represent the cost of construction and operation for a building containing between 2,000 and 6,000 basic square feet.

Concrete and Brick

First cost per square foot................................ $ 24
Annual maintenance..................................... $5,600
Annual climate control................................. $2,400
Estimated life in years................................   20
Estimate salvage value is zero.

Steel and Brick

First cost per square foot................................ $ 29
Annual maintenance..................................... $5,000
Annual climate control................................. $1,500
Estimated life in years................................   20
Estimated salvage value is 3.2 per cent of first cost.

Frame and Brick

First cost per square foot................................ $ 35
Annual maintenance..................................... $3,000
Annual climate control................................. $1,250
Estimated life in years................................   20
Estimated salvage value is 3.2 per cent of first cost.

The total cost for each type of construction will be a function of the number of basic square feet enclosed by the building. For an interest rate of 8 per cent, the total cost for each alternative is as follows:

Concrete and brick:

$$\text{RP 8-20}$$
$$TC = \$24(A)(0.10185) + \$8.000$$
$$= \$2.44A + \$8,000.$$

Steel and brick:

$$\text{RP 8-20}$$
$$TC = \$29(A)(0.968)(0.10185) + \$29(A)(0.032)(0.08) + \$6,500$$
$$= \$2.934(A) + \$6500.$$

Frame and brick:

$$\text{RP 8-20}$$
$$TC = \$35(A)(0.99)(0.10185) + \$35(A)(0.01)(0.08) + \$4,250$$
$$= \$3.658(A) + \$4,250.$$

Solution for the respective break-even points may be done mathematically by considering the alternatives in pairs. Or, by graphing the total cost of each alternative as a function of the area in square feet, it is possible to determine the break-even points by inspection. Each total cost function developed is graphed in Figure 11.3.

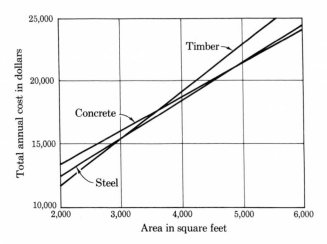

Figure 11.3. Total annual cost as a function of area in square feet.

Suppose that the client was considering a building measuring 40 feet by 100 feet. In this case, the engineering firm would recommend construction from steel and brick. However, if the client required a building of more than 5,000 square feet it would be most economical to use concrete and brick for the basic structure. For a building of less than 3,000 square feet, construction from frame and brick would be most economical. The extension of break-even analysis to cases where there are more than three alternatives follows the same reasoning.

Minimum cost analysis, two or more alternatives. As an illustration of the application of minimum cost analysis where two alternatives are proposed, consider the following example. A double track railroad bridge is to be constructed for a 1,200 foot crossing. Two girder designs have been proposed. The first will result in the weight of the superstructure per foot to be $W_1 = 22 (S) + 800$, where S is the span between piers. The second will result in a superstructure weight per foot of $W_2 = 20 (S) + 1,000$. Regardless of the girder design chosen, the piers will cost $220,000 each. The superstructure will be erected at a cost of $0.22 per pound. All other costs for the competing designs are the same.

In order to choose a girder design on the basis of minimum total cost for the superstructure and piers, it will be necessary to find the minimum cost pier spacing for each design. The general relationship that exists may be described as follows. As the number of piers increases, the amount of superstructure required decreases; and conversely, as the number of piers decreases, the amount of superstructure required increases. Therefore, this situation involves increasing and decreasing cost components, the sum of which will be a minimum for a certain number of piers.

The total cost for the superstructure and piers for girder Design 1 is as follows:

$$TC_1 = [22(S) + 800]($0.22)(1,200) + \left(\frac{1,200}{S} + 1\right)$220,000$$

$$= 5,810(S) + \frac{264,000,000}{S} + 431,000.$$

The minimum cost span between piers is

$$\frac{dTC}{dS} = 5,810 - \frac{264,000,000}{S^2} = 0$$

$$S = \sqrt{\frac{264,000,000}{5,810}} = 213 \text{ feet.}$$

And the minimum total cost for the superstructure and piers is

$$TC_1 = 5,810(213) + \frac{264,000,000}{213} + 431,000$$

$$= $2,908,000.$$

The total cost for the superstructure and piers for girder Design 2 is as follows:

$$TC_2 = [20(S) + 1,000]($0.22)(1,200) + \left(\frac{1,200}{S} + 1\right)$220,000$$

$$= 5,280(S) + \frac{264,000,000}{S} + 484,000.$$

The minimum cost span between piers is

$$\frac{dTC}{dS} = 5{,}280 - \frac{264{,}000{,}000}{S^2} = 0$$

$$S = \sqrt{\frac{264{,}000{,}000}{5{,}280}} = 224 \text{ feet.}$$

And the minimum total cost for the superstructure and piers is

$$TC_2 = 5{,}280(224) + \frac{264{,}000{,}000}{224} + 484{,}000$$

$$= \$2{,}846{,}000.$$

On the basis of this analysis, the designer would choose girder Design 2 as the design that will result in a minimum total cost for the bridge. The pier spacing chosen for the design would be as approximate to 224 feet as possible. In this case, $1200 \div 224 = 5.36$ spans so 6 piers would be used for a span between piers of 240 feet. The nature of the increasing and decreasing cost components is given for various numbers of piers in Table 11.3.

Table 11.3. TOTAL COST AS A FUNCTION OF THE NUMBER OF PIERS FOR TWO COMPETING BRIDGE DESIGNS

Piers	Cost of piers	Superstructure cost design 1	Superstructure cost design 2	Total cost design 1	Total cost design 2
4	$ 880,000	$2,534,000	$2,376,000	$3,414,000	$3,336,000
5	1,100,000	1,953,600	1,848,000	3,053,600	2,948,000
6	1,320,000	1,605,120	1,531,000	2,925,120	2,851,000
7	1,540,000	1,372,800	1,320,000	2,912,800	2,860,000
8	1,760,000	1,210,176	1,172,160	2,970,176	2,932,160
9	1,980,000	1,082,400	1,056,000	3,062,400	3,036,000

The extension of minimum cost analysis to cases where there are more than two alternatives should be obvious.

PROBLEMS

1. A certain assembly requires rods 0.10 inches square and varying in length from 0.25 to 4 inches. The rods may be made from either brass or steel. The machining cost of brass rods is $0.0054 + $0.006L per piece, where L is the length of the rod in inches. For steel the machining cost may be expressed as $0.0072 + $0.010L per piece. Brass costs $0.60 per pound and steel costs $0.20 per pound. The weight of brass and steel is 0.309 and 0.283 pounds per cubic inch, respectively. What length will equalize the cost of producing the brass and steel rods?

2. The oil well pumping unit now being used must be repaired every four years at a cost of $1,200. A replacement which will cost $2,860 is being considered. Operating and maintenance costs for the units are equal and their salvage values are assumed to be zero. If an interest rate of 8 per cent is used, how many years must the more expensive unit last in order to break even in equivalent annual cost?

3. A certain part is positioned on a metal table by hand and welded at the rate of one part every 4 minutes. It is estimated that the use of a special positioner will increase the rate to one part every 2 minutes. The welder receives $2 per hour. It will cost $3,000 to design and fabricate a suitable positioner. The positioner will be used for 10 years, 250 days per year, after which time it will be scrapped. Annual maintenance is estimated at $200. If the interest rate is 5 per cent, how many parts per day must be welded for the positioner to pay for itself in welding time saved?

4. An engineering firm wishes to make a decision as to the economic desirability of leasing instead of owning company automobiles. The firm has been offered the needed automobiles for a flat rate of $0.14 per mile. Automobiles can be purchased for $3,000 with a guaranteed trade-in value of $1,000 at the end of 3 years. Fuel, oil, and maintenance is estimated at $0.03 per mile. Storage, taxes, insurance, and license is estimated at $10 per month. If the interest rate is 10 per cent, how many miles must be driven per automobile per year for the cost of the two plans to break even?

5. In considering the purchase of an automobile with an overdrive, it is estimated that the mileage without overdrive will be 14.5 per gallon and the mileage with overdrive will be 16.3 per gallon. The overdrive will add $70 to the first cost of the automobile and will increase its trade-in value by $5 after a service life of 9 years. The overdrive will be used 60 per cent of the time and will add approximately $25 per year to the maintenance of the automobile. If gasoline costs $0.30 per gallon and if the interest rate is 4 per cent, how many miles per year must be driven for the overdrive to pay for itself?

6. An engineering consulting firm can purchase a small electronic computer for $25,000. It is estimated that the life and salvage value of the computer will be 12 years and $4,000, respectively. Operating expenses are estimated to be $50 per day, and maintenance will be performed under contract for $3,000 per year. As an alternative, sufficient computer time can be rented at an average cost of $100 per day. If the interest rate is 6 per cent, how many days per year must the computer be needed to justify its purchase?

7. An electronic manufacturer is considering two methods for producing a required circuit board. The board can be hand wired at an estimated cost of $0.98 per unit and with an annual equipment cost of $200. A printed equivalent of the required circuit can be produced with an investment of $3,000 in printed circuit processing equipment which will have an expected life of 9 years and a salvage value of $100. It is estimated that labor cost will be $0.32 per unit and that the processing equipment will cost $150 per year to maintain. If all other costs are assumed equal, and if the interest rate is 5 per cent, how many circuit boards must be produced each year for the two methods to break even in equivalent annual cost?

8. A contractor can purchase a heavy-duty truck with a 12-cubic-yard dump body for $13,000. Its estimated life is 7 years and its estimated salvage value is $2,000. Maintenance is estimated at $1,100 per year. Daily operating expenses are estimated at $23, including the cost of the driver. The contractor can hire a similar unit and its driver for $53 per day. If the interest is taken at 8 per cent, how many days per year must the services of a dump truck be required to justify the purchase of a truck?

9. Two brands of a protective coating are being considered. Brand A costs $4.50 per gallon. Past experience with Brand A has revealed that it will cover 350 square feet of surface per gallon, will give satisfactory service for 3 years, and can be applied by a workman at the rate of 70 square feet per hour. Brand B, which costs $7.60 per gallon, is estimated to cover 400 square feet of surface per gallon and can be applied at the rate of 80 square feet per hour. The wage rate of the workman is $1.92 per hour. If an interest rate of 10 per cent is used, how long should Brand B last to provide service at equal cost with that provided by Brand A?

10. A certain area can be irrigated by piping water from a nearby river. Two competing installations are being considered for which the following engineering and cost data apply.

	Six-Inch System	Eight-Inch System
Size motor required..............	25	10
Energy cost per hour of operation...	$ 0.22	$ 0.07
Cost of motor installed...........	$ 360	$ 160
Cost of pipe and fittings..........	$2,050	$2,640
Salvage value at end of 10 years...	$ 80	$ 100

On the basis of a 10 year life with an interest rate of 5 per cent, determine the number of hours of operation per year for which the two systems will break even.

11. A dam is being planned for a certain river of erratic flow. The greater the mass of the dam, the less will be the danger that it will be destroyed by flood. It has been determined by past experience that a dam of sufficient capacity to withstand flows whose probability of being exceeded in any one year is 0.10, 0.05, 0.025, 0.0125, and 0.00625 will cost $142,000, $154,000, $170,000, $196,000, and $220,000, respectively; will require annual maintenance amounting to $4,600, $4,900, $5,400, $6,500, and $7,200, respectively; and will suffer damage of $122,000, $133,000, $145,000, $170,000, and $190,000, respectively if subjected to flows exceeding its capacity. The life of the dam will be 40 years with no salvage value.

For an interest rate of 4 per cent calculate the annual cost of the dam including probable damage for each of the five proposed plans and determine the dam size that will result in a minimum cost.

12. In Frederick Taylor's famous metal cutting experiments, he found that metal is removed at a minimum cost if feeds and speeds are such that a lathe tool will endure for T hours between changes for sharpening where $T = 7t$. In this expression, t multiplied by the sum of the lathe operator's and the lathe's hourly cost is equal to all costs incident to a single change of tools. The costs incident to a change of tools include the time of the lathe operator and the lathe during a change of tools, and all costs related to sharpening the tool.

(a) Calculate T in hours when the lathe's rate is $1 per hour. The lathe operator receives $2.10 per hour. The lathe is stopped 6 minutes to change tools. Time consumed by the tool grinder and tool grinder operator at rates $0.80 and $2.25 per hour, respectively, is 9 minutes per regrind. The tool is purchased ready for use for $3.30 and may be reground 12 times before scrapping.

(b) Calculate T in hours when the lathe's rate is $1.75 per hour. The lathe operator receives $2.10 per hour. The lathe is stopped for 5 minutes to change tools. Time consumed by the tool grinding machine and its operator, at rates of $1 and $2.50 per hour, respectively, is 8 minutes per regrind. The tool is purchased ready for use for $4 and may be reground 15 times before scrapping.

13. Ethyl acetate is made from acetic acid and ethyl alcohol. Let x = pounds of acetic acid input, y = pounds of ethyl alcohol input, and z = pounds of ethyl acetate output. The relationship of output to input is

$$\frac{z^2}{(1.47\ x - z)\ (1.91\ y - z)} = 3.91.$$

(a) Determine the output of ethyl acetate per pound of acetic acid, where the ratio of acetic acid to ethyl alcohol is 2, 1.5, 1, 0.67, and 0.50 and graph the result.

(b) Graph the cost of material per pound of ethyl acetate for each of the ratios given and determine the ratio for which the material cost per pound of ethyl acetate is a minimum if acetic acid costs $0.08 per pound and ethyl alcohol costs $0.06 per pound.

14. An hourly electric load of 1,600 amperes is to be transmitted from a generator to a transformer in a certain power plant. A copper conductor 150 feet long can be installed for $160 + $0.46 per pound, will have an estimated life of 20 years, and can be salvaged for $0.26 per pound. Power loss from the conductor will be a function of the cross-sectional area and may be expressed as $25,875 \div A$ kilowatt-hours per year. Energy lost is valued at $0.008 per kilowatt-hour; taxes, insurance, and maintenance are negligible; the interest rate is 8 per cent. Copper weighs 555 pounds per cubic foot.

(a) Plot the total annual cost of capital recovery with a return and power loss cost for conductors for cross sections of 1, 2, 3, 4, and 5 square inches.

(b) Find the minimum cost cross section mathematically and check the result against the minimum point found in (a).

15. An overpass is being considered for a certain railroad crossing. The superstructure design under consideration will be made of steel and will have a weight per foot depending upon the span between piers in accordance with $W = 32(L) + 1,850$. Piers will be made of concrete and will cost $185,000 each. The superstructure will be erected at a cost of $0.36 per pound. If the number of piers required is to be one less than the number of spans, find the number of piers that will result in a minimum total cost for piers and superstructure if $L = 1275$ feet.

16. It has been found that the heat loss through the ceiling of a building is 0.13 Btu per hour per square foot of area per degree Fahrenheit. If the 2,200-square-foot ceiling is insulated, the heat loss in Btu per hour per

degree temperature difference per square foot of area is taken as being equal to

$$\frac{1}{\dfrac{1}{0.13} + \dfrac{t}{0.27}}$$

where t is the thickness in inches. The in-place cost of insulation 1, 2, and 3 inches thick is $0.08, $0.11, and $0.15 per square foot, respectively. The building is heated to 75 degrees 3,000 hours per year by a gas furnace with an efficiency of 50 per cent. The mean outside temperature is 45 degrees and the natural gas used in the furnace costs $0.60 per 1,000 cubic feet and has a heating value of 2,000 Btu per cubic foot. What thickness of insulation, if any, should be used if the interest rate is 6 per cent and the resale value of the building 6 years hence is enhanced $200 if insulation is added, regardless of the thickness?

17. A contractor is offered his choice of either a gasoline, diesel, or butane engine to power a bulldozer he is to purchase. The gasoline engine will cost $1,600, will have an estimated maintenance cost of $105 per year, and will consume $3.60 worth of fuel per hour of operation. The diesel engine will cost $2,200, will cost an estimated $95 per year to maintain, and will consume $2.40 worth of fuel per hour. The butane engine will cost $2,400, will cost $80 per year to maintain, and will consume $1.80 worth of fuel per hour of operation. Since the salvage value of each engine will be identical, it may be neglected. All other costs associated with the three engines are equal and the interest rate is 6 per cent. The service life of each engine is 4 years.

(a) Plot the total annual cost of each engine as a function of the number of hours of operation per year.

(b) Find the range of number of hours of operation for which it would be most economical to specify the gasoline engine; the diesel engine; the butane engine.

18. The daily electrical load to be transmitted by a conductor in a power plant is 6,000 amperes per day for 365 days per year. Two conductor materials are under consideration, copper and aluminum. The following information is available for the competing materials.

	Copper	*Aluminum*
Length.........................	120 ft.	120 ft.
Installed cost..................	$150 + $0.46/lb.	$150 + $1.40/lb.
Estimated life.................	20 yrs.	20 yrs.
Salvage value..................	$0.22/lb.	$0.70/lb.
Electrical resistance of conductor 120 feet by 1 sq. in. cross section.................	0.000982 ohms	0.001498 ohms
Density.......................	555 lb./ft.^{3}	162 lb./ft.^{3}

The energy loss in kilowatt-hours in a conductor due to resistance is equal to I^2R times the number of hours divided by 1,000, where I is the current flow in amperes and R is the resistance in the conductor in ohms. The electrical resistance is inversely proportional to the area of the cross section. Lost energy is valued at $0.007 per kilowatt-hour.

(a) Plot the total annual cost of capital recovery and return plus power loss cost for each material for cross sections of 2, 3, 4, 5, and 6 square inches.

(b) Solve mathematically for the optimum cross section of each material.

(c) Recommend the minimum cost conductor material and specify the cross sectional area.

CHAPTER 12

EVALUATION OF REPLACEMENTS

Mass production has been found to be the most economical method of satisfying human wants. However, mass production necessitates the employment of large quantities of producer goods which become consumed, inadequate, obsolete, or in some way become candidates for replacement. Decisions concerning the replacement of an asset would be simple if the future could be correctly predicted. If such were the case, the choice between an existing asset and its challenger would be based upon the differences in future receipts and disbursements as indicated by analysis that is directed toward reducing the differences to an equivalent basis for comparison. Unfortunately, there is no general rule that will yield accurate information about the future. Each situation must, therefore, be evaluated in the light of experience, knowledge, and judgment available at the time a decision is to be made.

It is not surprising to find many engineers actively engaged in replacement analysis. By virtue of their training, experience, familiarity with equipment, and objectivity, engineers are particularly well qualified to make recommendations concerning the replacement of physical assets. Engineers not directly engaged in replacement analysis will be interested in the methods employed since physical assets are an essential element in the process of want satisfaction.

12.1. REPLACEMENT SHOULD BE BASED UPON ECONOMY

When the success of an economic venture is dependent upon profit, replacement should be based upon the economy of future operation.

Although production facilities are, and should be, considered as a means to an end; that is, production at lowest cost, there is ample evidence that motives other than economy often enter into analysis concerned with the replacement of assets.

The idea that replacement should occur when it is most economical rather than when the asset is worn out is contrary to the fundamental concept of thrift possessed by many people. In addition, existing assets are often venerated as old friends. People tend to derive a measure of security from familiar old equipment and to be skeptical to change, even though they may profess a progressive outlook. Replacement of equipment requires a shift of enthusiasm. When a person initiates a proposal for new equipment, he must ordinarily generate considerable enthusiasm to overcome inertia standing in the way of its acceptance. Later, enthusiasm may have to be transferred to a replacement. This is difficult to do, particularly if one must confess to having been overenthusiastic about the equipment originally proposed.

Part of the reluctance to replace physically satisfactory but economically inferior units of equipment has roots in the fact that the import of a decision to replace is much greater than that of a decision to continue with the old. A decision to replace is a commitment for the life of the replacing equipment. But a decision to continue with the old is usually only a deferment of a decision to replace that may be reviewed at any time when the situation seems clearer. Also a decision to continue with old equipment that results in a loss will usually result in less censure than a decision to replace it with new equipment that results in an equal loss.

The economy of scrapping a functionally efficient unit of productive equipment lies in the conservation of effort, energy, material, and time resulting from its replacement. The unused remaining utility of an old unit is sacrificed in favor of savings in prospect with a replacement. Consider, by way of illustration, a shingle roof. Even a roof that has many leaks will have some utility as a protection against the weather and may have many sound shingles in it. The remaining utility could be made use of by continual repair. But the excess of labor and materials required to make a series of small repairs over the labor and materials required for a complete replacement may exceed the utility remaining in the roof. If so, labor and materials can be conserved by a decision to replace the roof.

12.2. BASIC REASONS FOR REPLACEMENT

There are two basic reasons for considering the replacement of a physical asset; physical impairment and obsolescence. Physical impairment refers only to changes in the physical condition of the asset itself. Obsolescence is used here to describe the effects of changes in the environment external to an asset. Physical impairment and obsolescence may occur independently or they may occur jointly in regard to a particular asset.

Physical impairment may lead to a decline in the value of service rendered, increased operating cost, increased maintenance cost, or a combination. For example, physical impairment may reduce the capacity of a bulldozer to move earth and consequently reduce the value of the service it can render. Fuel consumption may rise, thus increasing its operating cost, or the physical impairment may necessitate increased expenditure for repairs.

Little useful data are available relative to how such costs occur in relationship to length of service of assets. A storage battery may render perfect service and require no maintenance up to the moment it fails. Water pipes, on the other hand, may begin to acquire deposits on installation, which reduce their capacity in some proportion to the time they have been in service. Many assets are composites of a number of elements of different service lives. Roofs of buildings usually must be replaced before side walls. The basic structure of bridges ordinarily outlasts several deck surfacings.

Obsolescence occurs as a result of the continuous improvement of the tools of production. Often, the rate of improvement is so great that it is an economy to replace a physical asset in good operating condition with an improved unit. In some cases, the activity for which a piece of equipment has been used declines to the point that it becomes advantageous to replace it with a smaller unit. In either case, replacement is due to obsolescence and necessitates disposing the remaining utility of the present asset in order to allow for the employment of the more efficient unit. Therefore, obsolescence is characterized by changes external to the asset and is used as a distinct reason in itself for replacement where warranted.

12.3. THE PRESENT ASSET AND ITS REPLACEMENT

Two assets must be evaluated at the time replacement is being considered; the present asset and its challenger. The economic future of the present asset can be represented by a column of estimated receipts and disbursements headed by its present value. Since the economic future of a possible replacement can be represented in the same way, methods of analysis applicable to one asset are applicable to the other. However, the future of a present asset is less cause for concern than that of a possible replacement because of its shorter remaining life, lower value, and the fact that a decision not to replace can be reviewed and reversed at any time in the future. If, for example, decisions are reviewed at annual intervals, a decision not to replace is in reality a commitment to continue with the present asset for one year.

Present assets should not be considered for retirement on the basis of the life estimated for them that led to their purchase. Likewise, the value of an asset that should be used in a study of replacement is the value that it will have if it is retired.

New assets characteristically have high capital costs and low operating costs. The reverse is usually true for assets which are being considered for retirement. Thus, capital costs for an asset for replacement may be expected to be low and decreasing while operating costs are usually high and increasing.

Since the remaining life of an asset being considered for replacement is usually short, the future of the asset can be estimated with relative certainty. There is also the advantage that a decision not to replace it now may be reversed at any time in the future. Thus a decision may be made on the basis of next year's cost of the old asset, and if it is not replaced, a new decision can be made on the basis of next year's cost a year later and so forth.

The capital costs of an asset being considered for retirement are likely to be small or nil. Where this is the case the decision to replace will be principally or entirely based on next year's or a shorter period of operating cost.

The method of treating data relative to a present asset should be the same as that used in treating data relative to a possible replacement in an economy study. In both cases only the future of the assets should be considered.

12.4. CONSIDERATIONS LEADING TO REPLACEMENT

The main considerations leading to replacement may be classified as inadequacy, excessive maintenance, declining efficiency, and obsolescence. Any of the above may lead to replacement, but usually two or more are involved when replacement is considered. In the sections that follow, examples illustrating an approach to replacement analysis for each of these considerations will be presented. More general methods of analysis will be presented later in the chapter.

Replacement because of inadequacy. A physical asset that is inadequate in capacity to perform its required services is a logical candidate for replacement. For example, a boring mill used almost exclusively to face and bore pulleys has a maximum capacity of machining pulleys 54 inches in diameter. At the time the mill was purchased, the largest pulley ordered was well below the capacity of the mill, but at the present time orders are being received for pulleys up to 72 inches in diameter and these orders seem to be on the increase.

Orders for pulleys between 54 and 72 inches are subcontracted to another concern. Not only is this costly but it occasions delays that are detrimental to the reputation of the company. The factor entering into consideration of replacement in this example is inadequacy. Although the present boring mill is up to date, efficient, and in excellent condition, consideration of its replacement is being forced by the need for a boring mill of greater capacity.

Where there is inadequacy, a usable piece of equipment, often in excellent condition, is on hand. Often, as in the case of the boring mill, the desired increased capacity can be met only by purchasing a new unit of equipment of the desired capacity.

In many cases, such as with pumps, motors, generators, and fans, the increased capacity desired can be met by purchasing a unit to supplement the present machine, should this alternative prove more desirable than purchasing a new unit of the desired capacity.

The method of comparing alternatives where inadequacy is the principal factor will be illustrated by the following example. One year after a 10 h.p. motor has been purchased to drive a belt coal conveyor, it is decided to double the length of the belt. The new belt requires 20 h.p. The needed power can be supplied either by adding a second 10 h.p. motor or by replacing the present motor with a 20 h.p. motor.

The present motor cost $420 installed and has a full load efficiency of 88 per cent. An identical motor can now be purchased and installed for $440. A 20 h.p. motor having an efficiency of 90 per cent can be purchased and installed for $780. The present 10 h.p. motor will be accepted as $270 on the purchase price of the 20 h.p. motor. Current costs $0.02 per kw-hr., and the conveyor system is expected to be in operation 2,000 hours per year.

Maintenance and operating costs other than for current of each 10 h.p. motor are estimated at $35 per year and for the 20 h.p. motor at $50 per year. Taxes and insurance are taken as 1 per cent of the purchase price. Interest will be at the rate of 6 per cent. The service lives of the new motors in the present application are taken as 10 years, with a salvage value of 20 per cent of their original cost at that time. The present motor will be considered to have a total life of 11 years, an approximation that will introduce little practical error in the analysis. Most likely all motors will outlast the period of service they will have in the application under consideration.

Alternative A will involve the purchase of the 20 h.p. motor for $780 and the disposal of the present motor for $270. The annual cost for this alternative is computed as follows:

Capital recovery and return, ($780 − $156) $\overset{\text{RP 6-10}}{(0.13587)}$
+ $156 × 0.06 .... $ 94.22

Current cost, $\dfrac{20 \text{ h.p.}}{0.90 \text{ eff.}} \times \dfrac{0.746 \text{ kw}}{\text{h.p.}} \times \dfrac{\$0.02}{\text{kw-hr.}} \times 2{,}000 \text{ hr}$ 663.11

Maintenance and operating cost 50.00
Taxes and insurance, $780 × 0.01 .... 7.80

Total equivalent annual cost $815.13

Alternative B will involve the purchase of an additional 10 h.p. motor for $440. The annual cost for this alternative is computed as follows:

Present 10 h.p. Motor:

Capital recovery and return, ($270 − $84) $\overset{\text{RP 6-10}}{(0.13587)}$
+ $84 × 0.06 .... $ 30.31

Current cost $\dfrac{10}{0.88} \times 0.746 \times \$0.02 \times 2{,}000$ 339.08

Maintenance and operating cost 35.00
Taxes and insurance, $420 × 0.01 .... 4.20

New 10 h.p. motor:

Capital recovery and return, ($440 − $88) $\overset{\text{RP 6-10}}{(0.13587)}$
+ $88 × 0.06 .... 53.11

Current cost, $\dfrac{10}{0.88} \times 0.746 \times \$0.02 \times 2{,}000$ 339.08

Maintenance and operating cost 35.00
Taxes and insurance, $440 × 0.01 .... 4.40

Total equivalent annual cost $840.18

On the basis of the analysis above, the advantage of replacing the 10 h.p. motor rather than supplementing it is equivalent to $840.18 less $815.13, or $25.05 per year. Because of the incorrect decision to purchase a 10 h.p. motor a year ago, a sunk cost equal to its present book value less $270 is incurred. This sunk cost has been revealed, rather than caused, by the present analysis. Since engineering economy analyses are concerned with the future, this sunk cost must not enter into the analysis embracing the future. This principle will be given detailed treatment in Section 12.6.

The trade-in value of $270 was taken as the present value of the original 10 h.p. motor because if it is replaced $270 will be received for it. Thus, its value is a necessary element in the comparative analysis. The annual charge for taxes and insurance was based on the original cost, because taxes and insurance charges are usually based upon book values; but for simplicity no reduction was made in these items to correspond to the expected decline in book values.

The alternative to supplement the present motor will require an investment of $270 in the present motor plus $440 in a new 10 h.p. motor or a total investment of $710. The second alternative can be implemented by an investment of $780.

The fact that $270 can be realized from the sale of a capital asset and applied upon the purchase price of the 20 h.p. motor does not reduce the expenditure necessary to acquire the motor or the amount invested in it. Thus the analysis above reveals that an additional investment of $780 − $710 = $70 will result in a return of 6 per cent on the additional investment plus $25.05 per annum.

Replacement because of excessive maintenance. A machine rarely has all of its elements wear out at one time. Experience has proven that it is economical to repair many types of assets in order to maintain and extend their usefulness. Some repairs are of a current nature and minor in extent. Others are periodic and extensive.

An extensive periodic repair is not usually contemplated until it becomes necessary to extend the life of the unit of equipment in question. Usually, for example, an engine is not overhauled until its failure to provide acceptable service has occurred or is believed to be imminent. Thus the cost of an extensive periodic repair may be considered to be an expenditure to purchase additional service by extending the life of a unit of equipment. This view holds even when a program of preventative maintenance is in effect.

Before an expenditure for major repairs is made to extend the service life of a machine or structure, analysis should be made to determine if the needed service might be more economically provided by other alternatives.

In this connection consider the following situation. The main roadway through an oil refinery, six-tenths of a mile long and twenty feet wide and made of concrete, is badly in need of repair to continue in service. The maintenance department of the refinery estimates that repairs which will extend the life of the roadway for three years can be made for $4,600. A contractor has offered to replace the present roadway with a type of pavement estimated to have a life of 20 years for $18,400.

Current maintenance cost on the repaired pavement is estimated to average $160 per year and that on the replacing pavement is estimated to average $80 per year. Other items are considered to be equal or negligible. The company has no difficulty in borrowing funds at 4 per cent, so this rate of interest is used in the comparison. The salvage value of the present pavement is considered to be nil if it is replaced. The annual cost comparison for the two alternatives follows:

Repair Pavement to Extend Its Life 3 Years

RP 4-3

Capital recovery and return, $4,600 (0.36035)	$1,657
Average annual repair cost	160
Total	$1,817

Replace with Pavement with Estimated Life of 20 Years

RP 4-20

Capital recovery and return, $18,400 (0.07358)	$1,354
Average annual repair cost	80
Total	$1,434
Annual advantage of replacing over repairing	$ 383

In some classes of equipment current repairs increase with age. Maintenance may be slight at first but increases at a progressive rate. Thus, a point in time is ultimately reached where it is more economical to replace than to continue maintenance. To illustrate the economy of this situation, consider the following example.

A piping system in a chemical plant was installed at a cost of $32,000. This system deteriorated by corrosion until it was replaced at the end of six years. The salvage value of the system was nil.

Maintenance records show that maintenance costs in the past have been as given in Column B of Table 12.1. It may be noted that annual cost of maintenance increases with lapse of time. This is typ-

Table 12.1. ANALYSIS OF MAINTENANCE COSTS

Year A	Cost of maintenance for year B	Sum of maintenance cost to end of year, ΣB C	Cost of n years of service, $32{,}000 + C$ D	Average annual cost of service to end of year, $D \div A$ E
1	\$ 1,260	\$ 1,260	\$33,260	\$33,260
2	3,570	4,830	36,830	18,415
3	6,480	11,310	43,310	14,437
4	9,840	21,150	53,150	13,287
5	14,230	35,380	67,380	13,476
6	19,820	55,200	87,200	14,533

ical of many classes of equipment and may be the primary reason for replacement. Total expenditures for repairs are given to the end of any year in Column C. The sum of the maintenance costs given in Column C and the original cost of the equipment is equal to the cost of providing the number of years' service designated in Column A.

The piping system could have been scrapped at the end of any year. Column E gives the average annual cost of service that would have resulted from scrapping the system at the end of any year. Thus if the system had been scrapped at the end of the first year, the cost for a year of service would have been \$33,600. If it had been scrapped at the end of the second year, the two years of service would have cost \$36,830, as given in Column D, and the average annual cost would have been \$18,415.

The least average annual cost, \$13,287, occurs for a four year life. If interest had been considered and equivalent annual costs had been used, the quantities in Column E would have been somewhat larger than those given. But the general pattern would have been much the same. Although the lowest annual cost in the example above occurs for a four year life, it does not necessarily follow that greatest economy would have resulted from scrapping the system after four years of service. The economy of replacement depends upon a number of additional factors such as the need for services of a piping system in the future, changes in levels of maintenance cost, and the characteristics and cost of a replacement. A decision to replace the present equipment should be based on an analysis of costs in prospect with the present equipment and with a possible replacement.

Replacement because of declining efficiency. Equipment usually operates at peak efficiency initially and suffers a loss of efficiency with usage and age. A gasoline engine usually reaches its maximum efficiency after a short run-in period after which its efficiency declines as cylinder walls, pistons, piston rings, and carburetors wear and the ignition system deteriorates.

When loss of efficiency is due to the malfunctioning of only a few parts of a whole machine, it is often economical to replace them periodically and in this way maintain a high level of efficiency over a long life.

There are a number of facilities that decline in efficiency with use and age but which it is not feasible to repair. Pipes that carry hot water, for example, often fill with scale. As their internal diameter decreases, the amount of energy required to force a given quantity of water through them increases. Pipe lines often decline in efficiency as carriers of fluid or gas because of increasing loss by leakage due to external or internal corrosion with age. When it is not economical to restore efficiency by maintenance, the entire system should be replaced at intervals on the basis of economy. Consider the following example. The buckets on a conveyor are subject to wear that reduces the capacity of the conveyor in accordance with the data given in Table 12.2.

As the capacity of the buckets becomes smaller, it is necessary to run the conveyor for longer periods of time, thus increasing operating costs. When the buckets are in new condition, the desired annual quantity of material can be handled in 1,200 hours of operation. The hours of operation required for various efficiency levels are shown in Column D. At $6.40 per hour of operation the annual cost of operation is given in Column E. The average annual cost in Column G is based on a bucket replacement cost of $960.

The example above is typical of many kinds of equipment whose efficiency declines progressively when it is not feasible to arrest the

Table 12.2. ANALYSIS OF DECLINING EFFICIENCY

Year number A	Efficiency at beginning of year B	Average efficiency during year C	Annual hour of operation 1200 ÷ C D	Annual cost of operation exclusive of replacement of buckets, D × \$6.40 E	Sum of operation costs to end of year, ΣE F	Average annual cost of service to end of year, (\$960 + F) ÷ A G
1	1.00	0.97	1,237	\$7,917	\$ 7,917	\$8,877
2	0.94	0.91	1,319	8,442	16,359	8,659
3	0.88	0.86	1,395	8,928	25,287	8,749
4	0.84	0.82	1,463	9,363	34,650	8,903
5	0.80					

decline with maintenance. In the example the least cost of operation occurs when efficiency is permitted to decline to 88 per cent, corresponding to a life of two years before replacement takes place.

Although least cost of operation occurs for a life of two years in the example above, this is not conclusive evidence that least cost of operation will result from a policy to replace buckets at two-year intervals unless the replacing buckets will duplicate the buckets being replaced in first and subsequent costs. But determination of a least-cost life for a unit of equipment and casual consideration of subsequent replacement is often sufficient and as far as it is practical to go in many situations. The problem of the optimum replacement interval will be treated in detail in Section 12.8.

Replacement due to obsolescence. As an illustration of the analysis involving replacement because of obsolescence, consider the following example. A manufacturer produces a hose coupling consisting of two parts. Each part is machined on a turret lathe purchased thirteen years ago for \$3,700 including installation. The lathe has been depreciated on the basis of a 15 year life and a salvage value of \$250 and now has a book value of \$710. A new turret lathe is proposed as a replacement for the old. Its installed cost will be \$6,800.

The production times per 100 sets of parts with the new and old machine are as follows:

Part	Present Machine	New Machine
Connector	2.92 hours	1.98 hours
Swivel	1.84 hours	1.14 hours
Total	4.76 hours	3.12 hours

The company's sales of the hose couplings average 40,000 units per year and are expected to continue at approximately this level. Machine operators are paid $1.42 per hour. The old and the proposed machine require equal floor space. The proposed machine will use power at a greater rate than the present one, but since it will be used fewer hours, the difference in cost is not considered worth figuring. This is also considered true of general overhead items. Interest is to be taken at 8 per cent. The salesman for the new machine has found a small shop that will purchase the old machine for $900. The prospective buyer estimates the life of the new machine at 10 years and its salvage value at 10 per cent of its installed cost of $6,800. The old turret lathe is estimated to be physically adequate for 10 more years and to have a salvage value of $250 at the end of that time.

The equivalent annual cost of operation if the present turret lathe is retained will be as follows:

RP 8-10

Capital recovery and return, ($900 − $250) (0.14903)
+ $250(0.08) .... $ 117
Direct labor, (4.76 ÷ 100) (40,000) ($1.42) $2,704

$2,821

The equivalent annual cost of operation if the new turret lathe is purchased will be as follows:

RP 8-10

Capital recovery and return, ($6,800 − $680) (0.14903)
+ $680(0.08) .... $ 968
Direct labor, (3.12 ÷ 100) (40,000) ($1.42) $1,772

$2,740

The annual amount in favor of the new machine is $81. The prospective buyer does not feel that the annual saving is sufficient to warrant replacement. This conclusion may be interpreted as a decision to incur additional cost of $81 per year in order to be in a position to accept a more advantageous alternative in the future.

In the situation above the old machine could be sold for more than its book value. This is not unusual in a period of inflation. The amount that will be realized for an old machine if replacement takes place is the correct one to use in a comparative analysis. It should be noted that the new machine will be used $(3.12 \div 100) \times 40,000 =$ 1,248 hours per year. No cognizance is taken of the fact that it is available for use many more hours per year; the unused capacity is of no value until used. Since, however, the overcapacity is potentially of value and may prove a safeguard against inadequacy, it should be considered an irreducible in favor of the new machine.

Replacement because of a combination of causes. In most situations, a combination of causes rather than a single cause leads to replacement consideration. As an item of equipment ages, its efficiency may be expected to decline and its need for maintenance to increase. More efficient units of equipment may become available. Moreover, it frequently happens that changes in activities result in a unit being either too large or too small for maximum economy.

Regardless of the cause or combination of causes that lead to consideration of replacement, analysis and decision must be based upon estimates of what will occur in the future. The past is irrelevant in the contemplated analysis.

12.5. EVALUATION OF REPLACEMENTS ON THE BASIS OF A SELECTED STUDY PERIOD

Replacement studies consist of comparing the economic desirability of continuing certain activities with a present asset or continuing the same or similar activities with a replacement for the present asset. These alternatives are definable in terms of their future receipts and disbursements and the time of their occurrence. Where the receipts for the alternatives are identical, comparison may be made on the basis of disbursement or cost. Where receipts of alternatives differ, adjustment for the difference may be made by considering the greater income to be a negative cost.

It is usually presumed that each event in history is dependent upon previous events. Thus in theory it is necessary, for accurate comparison of a pair of alternatives, to consider the entire future or a period from the present to a point in the future when the effect of both alternatives will be identical. It is rarely feasible to consider all links in the chain of events in the future. It also is frequently impossible to be able to discern a point in the future at which the selection of one of a pair of alternatives in the present will have the same effect as the selection of the other.

In the paragraphs that follow, a general method for placing alternatives on a comparative basis involving the selection of more or less arbitrary study periods will be illustrated. With this method, comparison of alternatives is made on the basis of costs and income that occur during a selected period in the future. The effect of values occurring after the selected study period is eliminated by suitable calculations. Study periods for all alternatives in a given comparison should be equal.

As an illustration of the use of a selected study period, consider the following example. A certain operation is now being carried on with Machine A whose present salvage value is estimated to be $2,000. The future life of Machine A is estimated at five years, at the end of which its salvage value is estimated to be zero. Operating costs with Machine A, exclusive of depreciation and interest, are estimated at $1,200 per year. It is expected that Machine A will be replaced by Machine B whose initial cost, life, final salvage value, and annual operating costs are estimated to be, respectively, $9,000, 15 years, zero, and $800. It should be realized that estimates relating to Machine B may turn out to be grossly in error.

The desirability of replacing Machine A with Machine C is being considered. Machine C's estimated initial cost, life, final salvage value, and annual operating costs are estimated to be, respectively, $8,000, 15 years, zero, and $900. The interest rate is taken to be 6 per cent. Detailed investment and cost data for Machines A, B, and C are given in Table 12.3.

Analysis based on a 15-year study period, recognizing unused value. Because of the difficulty of making further estimates into the future, a study period of 15 years coinciding with the life of Machine C is selected. This will necessitate calculations that will bring both plans to equal status at the end of 15 years.

Under Plan I, the study period embraces five years of service with Machine A and ten years of service with Machine B, whose useful life extends five years beyond the study period. Thus, an equitable allocation of the costs associated with Machine B must be made for

Table 12.3. ANALYSIS BASED ON A SELECTED STUDY PERIOD

Year end number	PLAN I		PLAN II	
	Machine investment	Operating costs	Machine investment	Operating costs
0	Machine A, $2,000		Machine C, $8,000	
1		$1,200		$900
2		1,200		900
3		1,200		900
4		1,200		900
5	Machine B, $9,000	1,200		900
6		800		900
7		800		900
8		800		900
9		800		900
10		800		900
11		800		900
12		800		900
13		800		900
14		800		900
15		800		900
16		800		
17		800		
18		800		
19		800		
20		800		

(The left margin is labeled "15 years selected study period" spanning years 0 through 15.)

the period of its life coming within and after the study period. In assuming that annual costs associated with this unit of equipment are constant during its life, the present-worth cost of service during the study period may be calculated a follows.

The equivalent annual cost for Machine B during its life is equal to

$$\overset{\text{RP 6-15}}{\$9,000(0.10296)} + \$800 = \$1,726.64.$$

The present-worth cost of 15 years of service in the study period is equal to

$$\$2,000 + \overset{\text{PR 6-5}}{\$1,200(4.212)} + \overset{\text{PR 6-10}}{\$1,726.64(7.360)}\overset{\text{PS 6-5}}{(0.7473)} = \$16,551.14.$$

The calculations above assume that Machine B will depreciate in accordance with the sinking-fund method. On this basis the value remaining in Machine B at the end of the study period may be calculated as a matter of interest as follows:

$$\overset{\text{RS 6-15}}{\$9,000} - \overset{\text{SR 6-10}}{\$9,000}(0.04296)(13.181) = \$3,903.70.$$

Under Plan II, the life of Machine C coincides with the study period. The present-worth cost of 15 years service in the study period is equal to

$$\$8,000 + \overset{\text{PR 6-15}}{\$900}(9.712) = \$16,740.80.$$

On the basis of present-worth costs of Plans I and II for a study period of 15 years of $16,551.14 and $16,740.80 respectively, Plan I should be chosen.

Analysis based on a 15-year study period, not recognizing unused value. Values remaining in assets at the end of a selected study period are sometimes disregarded in order to simplify the calculations necessary for making a comparison. The effect of disregarding values remaining in an asset at the end of a study period is to assume that the asset will be retired at the end of the study period.

On the basis of this assumption the present-worth cost of 15 years of service for Plan I may be calculated as follows. The equivalent annual cost for Machine B during the study period is equal to

$$\overset{\text{RP 6-10}}{\$9,000}(0.13587) + \$800 = \$2,022.83$$

and the present-worth cost of 15 years of service in the study period is equal to

$$\$2,000 + \overset{\text{PR 6-5}}{\$1,200}(4.212) + \overset{\text{PR 6-10}}{\$2,022.83}(7.360)\overset{\text{PS 6-5}}{(0.7473)} = \$18,175.82.$$

This result should be compared with that calculated for 15 years of service for Plan I, where cognizance was taken of value remaining in Machine B at the end of the study period.

The practice of disregarding values remaining in an asset at the end of a study period introduces error equivalent to the actual value of the asset at that time. This practice is difficult to defend for it does not greatly reduce the burden of making comparisons, nor does it necessarily produce results in the direction of conservatism.

Analysis on the basis of a five-year study period. Lack of information often makes it necessary to use rather short study periods.

For example, the characteristics of the successor to Machine A in Table 12.3 might be vague. In that case a study period of five years might be selected to coincide with the estimated retirement date of Machine A.

The equivalent annual cost of continuing with Machine A during the next five years is

$$\overset{\text{RP 6-5}}{\$2,000 \times (0.23740)} + \$1,200 = \$1,674.80.$$

The equivalent annual cost of Machine C based on a life of 15 years is

$$\overset{\text{RP 6-15}}{\$8,000(0.1096)} + \$900 = \$1,723.68.$$

These results suggest continuing with Machine A. If Machine C's equivalent cost had been less than that of Machine A, some consideration should be given to the characteristics of the possible replacement for Machine A before the latter is replaced.

In general, the longer the study period, the more significant the results. But the longer the study period, the more likely that estimates are in error. Thus, the selection of a study period must be based on estimate and judgment.

12.6. EVALUATION OF REPLACEMENTS WHERE SUNK COSTS ARE INVOLVED

The following example will be used to illustrate correct and incorrect methods of evaluating replacements where sunk costs are involved. Suppose that Machine A was purchased in 1958 for $2,200. It was estimated to have a life of ten years and a salvage value of $200 at the end of its life. Its operating expense had been found to be $700 per year, and it appeared that the machine would serve satisfactorily for the balance of its estimated life. It had been depreciated by the straight-line method and its book value in 1962 was $2,200 − (4 × $200) = $1,400. In 1962 a salesman offered Machine B for $2,600. Its life was estimated at ten years and its salvage value at the end of its life was estimated to be $300. Operating costs were estimated at $400 per year.

The operation for which these machines are used will be carried on for many years in the future. Equipment investments are expected to justify 8 per cent interest, in accordance with the policy of the company concerned. The salesman offers to take the old machine in on trade for $600. This appears low to the company, but the best offer received elsewhere is $450. All estimates relative to both machines above have been carefully reviewed and are considered sound.

The "outsider" viewpoint. As an aid to analysis from the correct viewpoint in similar situations, the analysis may be undertaken from the standpoint of a person who has a need for the service that Machine A or Machine B will provide but owns neither. In attempts to purchase a machine he finds that he can purchase Machine A for $600 and Machine B for $2,600. This analysis of which to buy will not be biased by the past since he was not part of the original transaction for Machine A and, therefore, will not be forced to admit a sunk cost. With this "outsider" viewpoint, the analysis is given below.

Comparison based on salvage value. If Machine A is traded in for $600, a sunk cost of $1,400 − $600 or $800 is revealed. Also, if Machine B is purchased, Machine A will be "sold" for $600. The logical alternatives then are (1) to consider Machine A to have a value of $600 and to continue with it for six years and (2) to purchase Machine B for $2,600 and use it for ten years.

The equivalent annual cost to continue with Machine A for six years is calculated as follows:

Annual Capital Recovery and Return, ($600 − $200)(0.21632) [RP 8-6]
  + $200 × 0.08 .... $102.53
Annual Operating Cost 700.00
                                                                 ————
                                                                 $802.53

The equivalent annual cost to dispose of Machine A, purchase Machine B and use it for ten years is calculated as follows:

Annual Capital Recovery and Return, ($2,600 − $300)(0.14903) [RP 8-10]
  + $300 × 0.08 .... $366.77
Annual Operating Cost 400.00
                                                                 ————
                                                                 $766.77

If the latter alternative is adopted the annual saving in prospect for the next six years is equal to $802.53 − $766.77 = $35.76. For the next four years after that time the amount of savings will be dependent upon the characteristics of the machine that might have been purchased six years from the present to replace Machine A.

This is a question that cannot be answered, and in not answering it the assumption is made that costs will be the same during this period as with Machine B.

Calculation of comparative use value. A second method of comparison, which is particularly good for demonstrating the correctness to skeptical people of the comparison above, is to calculate the value of the machine to be replaced which will result in an annual cost equal to the annual cost of operation with the replacement. In this calculation, let X equal the present value of Machine A for which annual cost with Machine A equals annual cost with Machine B. Then

$$\overset{\text{RP 8-6}}{(X - \$200)(0.21632)} + \$200 \times 0.08 + \$700$$

$$= \overset{\text{RP 8-10}}{(\$2,600 - \$300)(0.14903)} + \$300 \times 0.08 + \$400.$$

Solving for X results in

$$X = \$435.$$

Machine A has a comparative use worth in comparison with Machine B of only $435. Thus it is obvious that it should be replaced if it can be disposed of for $600. Compare this result with that obtained in the previous section. Note that $600 - \$435 = \$165$ is equivalent to $\overset{\text{PR 8-6}}{\$35.76 \times (4.623)} = \$165$.

Fallacy of adding sunk cost to a replacement. In spite of the fact that sunk cost cannot be recovered, a face saving practice of charging the sunk cost of a machine to the cost of its contemplated replacement is often employed. This practice, human but unrealistic, will be illustrated by the following situation.

Three years ago A, who authorizes machine purchases in a manufacturing concern, was approached by B for authorization to purchase a machine. B pleaded his cause in glowing terms and with enthusiasm. He had many figures and arguments to prove that an investment in the machine he proposed would easily pay out. A was at first skeptical, but he also became enthusiastic about the purchase as the profits in prospect were calculated, and authorized the purchase. After three years B realized that the machine was not coming up to expectations and would have to be replaced, at a loss of $1,200.

B was well aware of the necessity of admitting this sunk cost when he went to A to get authorization for a replacement. He realized the difficulty of trying to establish confidence in his arguments for the replacement and at the same time admit an error in judgment that had resulted in a loss of $1,200. But he hit on the expedient of focusing attention on the proposed machine by emphasizing that the $1,200 unrecovered balance could be added to the cost of the new machine and that the new machine had such possibilities for profit that it would pay out shortly, even though burdened with the unamortized balance of the previous machine. Such improper handling of sunk cost is merely deception designed to make it appear that an error in judgment has been corrected.

As a numerical example of the fallacy of adding sunk cost of an old machine to the cost of a replacement, consider the following replacement situation. Machine C, purchased for $3,400 a year ago, had an estimated life of six years and a salvage value of $400. Its operating cost is $3,200 per year. At the end of the first year a salesman offers Machine D for $4,600. This machine has an estimated life of five years, a salvage value of $600, and, owing to improvements it embodies, an operating cost, as shown by trial, of only $2,200. The salesman offers to allow $1,400 for Machine C on the purchase price of Machine D.

At the end of the first year, the book value of Machine C on the basis of straight-line depreciation is equal to $2,900; thus the sunk cost is $1,500.

Annual cost with Machine C, on the basis of its present trade-in value and estimated salvage value five years hence is

Annual Capital Recovery and Return, ($1,400 − $400)(0.25046) [RP 8-5]
+ $400 × 0.08.. $ 282
Annual Operating Cost.................................... 3,200

                                                                      $3,482

Annual cost with Machine D, as incorrectly calculated when sunk cost of $1,500 of Machine C is added to the cost of Machine D, is

Annual Capital Recovery and Return, ($6,100 − $600)(0.25046) [RP 8-5]
+ $600 × 0.08.. $1,426
Annual Operating Cost.................................... 2,200

                                                                      $3,646

On the basis of this *incorrect* result, Machine C is continued for the next year on the erroneous belief that $3,646 less $3,482, or $164 is being saved annually. Annual cost with Machine D as correctly calculated is

$$
\begin{array}{lr}
\text{Annual Capital Recovery and Return, } (\$4,600 - \$600)\overset{\text{RP 8-5}}{(0.25046)} & \\
\quad + \$600 \times 0.08\dots\dots\dots\dots\dots\dots\dots\dots\dots\dots\dots\dots\dots\dots\dots & \$1,050 \\
\text{Annual Operating Cost}\dots\dots\dots\dots\dots\dots\dots\dots\dots\dots\dots\dots\dots\dots & 2,200 \\
\hline
& \$3,250
\end{array}
$$

On this correct basis, purchase of Machine D should result in an annual saving of $3,482 less $3,250, or $232.

Comparison based on future receipts and disbursements.
For a different viewpoint, the alternatives of continuing five years with Machine C and of replacing Machine C with Machine D and using the latter for the next five years can be compared on the basis of receipts and disbursements associated with them. The receipts and disbursements if Machine C is retained for the next five years are

Receipts and Disbursements	Year 0	Year 1	Year 2	Year 3	Year 4	Year 5
Disbursements (considered to come at end of year)..	...	$3,200	$3,200	$3,200	$3,200	$3,200
Receipts at end of year...	...	...	...	...	...	$ 400

The present worth of the net cost of five years of service with Machine C is equal to

$$
\overset{\text{PR 8-5}}{\$3,200(3.993)} - \overset{\text{PS 8-5}}{\$400(0.6806)} = \$12,506.
$$

The receipts and disbursements if Machine D is purchased and used for 5 years are

Receipts and Disbursements	Year 0	Year 1	Year 2	Year 3	Year 4	Year 5
Disbursements (considered to come at end of year)..	$4,600	$2,200	$2,200	$2,200	$2,200	$2,200
Receipts at end of year...	$1,400	...	...	...	...	$ 600

The present worth of the net cost of five years of service if Machine C is sold and Machine D is purchased and used for 5 years is equal to

$$
\$4,600 - \$1,400 + \overset{\text{PR 8-5}}{\$2,200(3.993)} - \overset{\text{PS 8-5}}{\$600(0.6806)} = \$11,577.
$$

The net present worth of the advantage of accepting the latter alternative is \$12,506 less \$11,577, or \$929. This is equivalent to

$$\text{RP 8-5}$$
$$\$929 \times (0.25046) = \$232$$

and is equal to the annual saving resulting from the previous correct comparison made above.

If the incorrect calculation had been the one used, the decision would have been to retain Machine C with the thought that this action would result in an annual saving of \$164. Actually this action would have resulted in an annual loss of \$232.

12.7. PATTERNS OF MAINTENANCE COSTS

The replacement problem may be further understood by considering the relationship of maintenance costs to capital costs for an asset. In order to simplify the discussion, maintenance costs will be classified as sporadic, constant, and constantly increasing.

Table 12.4. ECONOMIC HISTORY OF A MACHINE WITH SPORADIC MAINTENANCE COSTS

End of year number A	Maintenance cost for end of year given B	Summation of maintenance costs, ΣB C	Average cost of maintenance through year given, $C \div A$ D	Average capital cost if retired at year end given, $\$400 \div A$ E	Average total cost through year given, $D + E$ F
1	\$100	\$ 100	\$100	\$400	\$500
2	100	200	100	200	300
3	300	500	167	133	300
4	100	600	150	100	250
5	100	700	140	80	220
6	100	800	133	67	200
7	100	900	129	57	186
8	300	1,200	150	50	200
9	100	1,300	144	44	188
10	100	1,400	140	40	180

Sporadic maintenance cost. Assume that a machine is puchased for \$400, and that its salvage value is zero at any age at which it may be retired. Assume that the interest rate is zero. Then the pertinent facts related to Machine A may be set down as in Table 12.4. Table 12.4 brings out the fact that capital costs decrease in some inverse proportion to the length of life. This is also true for interest rates other than zero and for any pattern of salvage value normally encountered.

The fact that maintenance costs are averaged in Column D, tends to smooth out the effect of sporadic large maintenance costs. In the example, the ratio of the cost of the asset and its maintenance cost is relatively high. In spite of this, the average total cost in Column F is generally downward. Unless there is a rising trend in sporadic maintenance cost, there will be no "minimum" cost in a given year that will not be bettered in a future year. But it is clear that if replacement is to be made, it is desirable to do so immediately prior to a large expenditure for maintenance.

Constant maintenance costs. Where maintenance costs are constant in succeeding years they will never justify replacement. Where no interest or salvage value is involved an equation for the average cost of a year of service can be written as follows:

$$C_A = \frac{P}{n} + m_c$$

where

C_A = average annual cost of capital recovery and maintenance;

P = initial cost of asset;

m_c = constant yearly cost of maintenance;

n = life of asset in years.

It is apparent that the value of C_A will never reach a minimum value.

For a case where interest and salvage value are involved, an expression for equivalent annual cost, C, may be written as follows:

$$C = (P - L)(\overset{\text{RP } i\text{-}n}{}) + Li + m_c.$$

A glance at a table of values for $(\overset{\text{RP } i\text{-}n}{})$ shows that C will decrease with an increase in n. This trend will be emphasized if L, the salvage value, also decreases with n.

Constantly increasing maintenance costs. An understanding of the replacement problem may also be gained from considering situations in which maintenance costs increase constantly with the age of an asset. Assume that a machine has been purchased for $800, that its salvage value is zero at any age, that its maintenance cost is zero the first year and rises at a constant rate of $100 per year thereafter. If it is assumed that the interest rate is zero the facts concerning the machine may be represented by Table 12.5.

Table 12.5. ECONOMIC HISTORY OF A MACHINE WITH CONSTANTLY INCREASING MAINTENANCE COSTS

End of year number A	Maintenance cost for end of year given B	Summation of maintenance costs, ΣB C	Average cost of maintenance through year given, $C \div A$ D	Average capital cost if retired at year end given, $800 \div A$ E	Average total cost through year given, $D + E$ F
1	$ 0	$ 0	$ 0	$800	$800
2	100	100	50	400	450
3	200	300	100	267	367
4	300	600	150	200	350
5	400	1,000	200	160	360
6	500	1,500	250	133	383

Because there is a rising trend in maintenance cost, there will be a minimum average total cost at some point in the life of the asset. This point occurred in the fourth year in the example presented.

12.8. THE OPTIMUM REPLACEMENT INTERVAL

If the future could be predicted with certainty, it would be possible to accurately predict the optimum replacement interval for an asset at the time of its purchase. The analysis would simply involve the calculation of the total equivalent annual cost at the end of each year in the life of the asset. Selection of the total equivalent annual cost that is a minimum would specify a minimum cost life for the asset.

As mathematically attractive as it may be to determine a minimum cost life of assets, this end is primarily an ideal toward which to strive. There are several reasons for this. An important one is that even reasonably good necessary data are rarely available for an asset at the time of its purchase. A second reason is that a decision to retire an asset is rarely made at the time of its purchase. Decisions to retire assets almost always result from consideration of factors in existence shortly before the time of retirement.

Minimum cost life, increasing maintenance cost. Where a rising trend in maintenance cost exists, it is possible to formulate an idealized model that will express the minimum cost life for an asset. Neglecting interest, the average annual cost for an asset with increasing maintenance cost may be expressed as follows:

$$C = \frac{P}{n} + Q + (n - 1)\frac{m'}{2}$$

where

C = average annual cost;

P = initial cost of asset;

Q = annual constant portion of operating cost of asset (is equal to first year operation cost, of which maintenance is a part);

m' = the amount by which maintenance costs increase each year;

n = life of asset in years.

This expression, if differentiated with respect to n, set equal to zero and solved for n, results in the following:

$$\frac{dC}{dn} = -\frac{P}{n^2} + \frac{m'}{2} = 0$$

$$n = \sqrt{\frac{2P}{m'}}.$$

For the example presented in Table 12.5, $P = \$800$, $Q = 0$, and $m' = \$100$. Therefore, the minimum cost life is

$$n = \sqrt{\frac{2(\$800)}{\$100}} = 4 \text{ years}$$

as is shown in the Table. The minimum cost shown in Table 12.5 may be verified as follows:

$$C = \frac{\$800}{4} + 3\left(\frac{100}{2}\right) = \$350.$$

The economic history of an asset whose first cost is $5,000, whose salvage value at any time is zero, and whose cost of maintenance is zero the first year and increases at a constant rate of $100 for an interest rate of 6 per cent, is shown in Table 12.6.

Table 12.6. EQUIVALENT ANNUAL COST OF MAINTENANCE PLUS CAPITAL RECOVERY WITH A RETURN OF AN ASSET FOR CONSTANTLY INCREASING MAINTENANCE

End of year number A	Maintenance cost at end of year designated B	Present-worth factor for year designated, $\mathrm{PS}_{i\text{-}n}$ C	Present-worth as of beginning of year No. 1, of maintenance for year designated, $B \times C$ D	Summation of present worths of maintenance through year designated, ΣD E	Capital-recovery factor for year designated, $\mathrm{RP}_{i\text{-}n}$ F	Equivalent annual cost of maintenance through year designated, $E \times F$ G	Equivalent annual cost of capital recovery and return through year designated, $F \times \$5{,}000$ H	Total equivalent annual cost through year designated, $G + H$ I
1	$ 0	0.9434	$ 0	$ 0	1.06000	$ 0	$5,300	$5,300
2	100	0.8900	89	89	0.54544	48	2,727	2,775
3	200	0.8396	167	256	0.37411	96	1,870	1,966
4	300	0.7921	237	494	0.28859	142	1,442	1,585
5	400	0.7473	298	793	0.23740	188	1,187	1,375
6	500	0.7050	352	1,145	0.20336	233	1,016	1,249
7	600	0.6651	399	1,545	0.17914	276	895	1,172
8	700	0.6274	439	1,984	0.16104	319	805	1,124
9	800	0.5919	473	2,457	0.14702	361	735	1,096
10	900	0.5584	502	2,960	0.13587	402	679	1,081
11	1,000	0.5268	526	3,487	0.12679	442	633	1,076
12	1,100	0.4970	546	4,033	0.11928	481	596	1,077
13	1,200	0.4688	560	4,593	0.11296	518	564	1,083
14	1,300	0.4423	574	5,168	0.10758	556	537	1,094

Note: Cents have been omitted after having been carried through final computations.

This table illustrates a method for determining the equivalent annual cost of maintenance and the equivalent annual cost of capital recovery and return for lives ranging from one to fourteen years. The sum of these costs is a minimum for a life of eleven years. The quantities in Columns G, H, and I have been plotted to reveal trends in Figure 12.1.

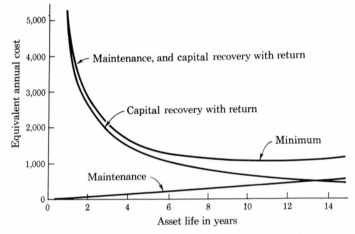

Figure 12.1. Minimum cost life of an asset with constantly increasing maintenance costs.

Study of the total equivalent annual cost curve reveals that it is rather flat in the region of the minimum. It may, therefore, be concluded that a deviation of one or two years from the minimum cost life will result in relatively small increases in total equivalent annual cost.

The model above assumed an interest rate of zero. For the example of Table 12.6, with an interest rate of zero, the minimum cost life is

$$n = \sqrt{\frac{2P}{m'}} = \sqrt{\frac{2(\$5,000)}{\$100}} = 10 \text{ years.}$$

Therefore, this equation may be used to approximate the optimum life of an asset for cases involving interest.

Minimum cost life, increasing obsolescence cost. If it is assumed that obsolescence takes place at a uniform rate, it may be treated mathematically in a way that gives an insight into its effect. For simplicity, assume zero salvage value and that an improved replacement becomes available at the beginning of each succeeding year. Assume that the installed costs of the original asset and each possible replacement are equal and are represented by P. Assume that the original asset is purchased in the year 19x1, its annual operating cost is Q, and the annual operating cost of possible future replacements is as given in Table 12.7.

Table 12.7. EFFECT OF CONSTANTLY INCREASING OBSOLESCENCE ON ANNUAL OPERATING COSTS

Beginning of year in which asset is purchased	*Comparative year-end operating costs of assets acquired in year designated*						
	19x1	19x2	19x3	19x4	19x5	19x6	19x7
19x1	Q	Q	Q	Q	Q	Q	Q
19x2		$Q - b$	$Q - b$	$Q - b$	$Q - b$	$Q - b$	$Q - b$
19x3			$Q - 2b$	$Q - 2b$	$Q - 2b$	$Q - 2b$	$Q - 2b$
19x4				$Q - 3b$	$Q - 3b$	$Q - 3b$	$Q - 3b$
19x5					$Q - 4b$	$Q - 4b$	$Q - 4b$
19x6						$Q - 5b$	$Q - 5b$

In Table 12.7, Q represents the actual operating cost of the original asset purchased at the beginning of 19x1. The term b represents a net improvement in comparative performance of succeeding assets. The improvement represented by b consists of a reduction of operating costs and increases in value of services of a succeeding asset as compared to the original acquired in 19x1. It should be recalled that an increase in income has the same effect as a decrease in cost and that neither Q nor b includes physical impairment.

From the standpoint of capital costs an asset purchase in 19x1 should be used forever as a means of approaching a minimum capital recovery with return cost. But assets should be replaced yearly to take advantage of reduced operating costs. Thus, it appears that there is an optimum interval of replacement for the conditions given, and this optimum can be found as follows. Consider the two plans of replacement shown in Table 12.8. Under Plan A the assets are replaced annually, and under Plan B a single asset is used indefinitely. The costs of the two plans may be tabulated as given in Columns K and L.

Table 12.8. REPLACEMENT ALTERNATIVES INVOLVING OBSOLESCENCE

Year J	Plan A K	Plan B L	Plan A minus Plan B M
19x1	$P + Q$	$P + Q$	$P - (P)$
19x2	$P + Q - b$	Q	$P - (+b)$
19x3	$P + Q - 2b$	Q	$P - (+2b)$
. . .	. . . .	. . .	. . . .
19xn	$P + Q - (n - 1)b$	Q	$P - [+(n - 1)b]$

The differences of Plan A and Plan B may be expressed as shown in Column M. Plan A minus Plan B will be a maximum for the interval of years for which the equivalent annual amount of the right-hand quantities in Column M will be a minimum. Except for P, the pattern of the right-hand quantities in Column M is identical with that in Column B in Table 12.6. The equivalent annual amount of all the right-hand quantities in Column M of the tabulation may be found by following the method used to obtain Column I in Table 12.6.

The optimum life span may be obtained from a counterpart of Column I by inspection. The life span so found is the interval at which assets should be replaced for the established conditions: namely, constant asset costs, constantly rising obsolescence, and no physical impairment. The left-hand quantities in Column M of the tabulation have no effect on determining the life span as may be determined by applying them. Care should be exercised to realize that costs designated by b, $2b$, and so forth, in this analysis are not real costs but merely comparative costs.

Although they are useful in determining the interval of replacement, they will not become apparent as year to year disbursements of the asset whose optimum life they are used to determine.

Minimum cost life, physical impairment and obsolescence costs in combination. For an illustration of the combined effect of physical impairment and obsolescence, consider a situation in which physical impairment increases at a rate m' per year and obsolescence increases at a rate b per year. The first year's operating cost is Q. The first costs of assets are equal to P, and their salvage values at the end of any life are equal to zero. To analyze this situation, consider two plans: Plan A in which assets are replaced annually, and Plan B in which a single asset is used. The costs of the two plans are given in Columns K and L of Table 12.9.

Table 12.9. REPLACEMENT ALTERNATIVES INVOLVING PHYSICAL IMPAIRMENT AND OBSOLESCENCE

Year J	Plan A K	Plan B L	Plan A minus Plan B M
19x1	$P + Q$	$P + Q$	$P - P$
19x2	$P + Q - b$	$Q + m'$	$P - (b + m')$
19x3	$P + Q - 2b$	$Q + 2m'$	$P - 2(b + m')$
...	....	....	....
19xn	$P + Q - (n-1)b$	$Q + (n-1)m'$	$P - (n-1)(b + m')$

The optimum life to keep the asset purchased under Plan B in 19x1 for the conditions outlined may be found by finding the life for which the equivalent annual amount of the right-hand quantities in Column M in Table 12.9 is a minimum by the method suggested for the case of constantly increasing maintenance. The life so found is the one which will result in minimum disbursements in the future for the conditions given, but it should be realized that quantities designated with b are not real costs of the asset in question but are comparative costs of the asset in question and a succession of future assets.

For situations of constantly increasing maintenance and obsolescence, with no salvage value and zero interest rate, the following equation applies:

$$C = \frac{P}{n} + Q + (n - 1)\frac{m' + b}{2}$$

from which

$$n = \sqrt{\frac{2P}{m' + b}}.$$

Let $b = rm'$

Then

$$n = \sqrt{\frac{2P}{m'(1 + r)}} = \frac{1}{\sqrt{1 + r}}\sqrt{\frac{2P}{m'}}.$$

Values of $\dfrac{1}{\sqrt{1 + r}}$ for selected values of r are given in Table 12.10.

Table 12.10. EFFECT OF OBSOLESCENCE AND INCREASING MAINTENANCE ON OPTIMUM LIFE

Value of r	0.25	0.5	1	2	3
Value of $\dfrac{1}{\sqrt{1+r}}$	0.89	0.82	0.71	0.59	0.50

The tabulation shows that the optimum life decreases as obsolescence, in proportion to maintenance, increases. For example, inclusion of an obsolescence rate equal to the maintenance rate corresponding to $r = 1$ reduces the optimum life by $1 - 0.71$, or 0.29 per cent.

Additional considerations concerning the optimum replacement interval of an asset are presented in Appendix B.

12.9. INSTALLATION AND REMOVAL COSTS

When a new unit of equipment is purchased, a number of additional expenses beyond its purchase price may be incurred to put the unit into operation. Such expense items may embrace freight, cartage, construction of foundations, special connection of wiring and piping, guard rails, and personal services required during a period of run-in or adjustment. Expenses for such of the items above as apply are first-cost items and for all practical purposes represent an investment in a unit of equipment under consideration. For this reason all first-cost items necessary to put a unit of equipment into operation should be depreciated as part of the total original investment in the unit.

When a unit of equipment is replaced, its removal may entail considerable expense. Some of the more frequently encountered items of removal expense are dismantling, removal of foundations, haulage, closing off water and electrical connections, and replacing floors or other structural elements. The sum of such costs should be deducted from the amount received for the old unit to arrive at its net salvage value. It is clear that this may make the net salvage value a negative quantity. When the net salvage value of an asset is less than zero it is mathematically correct to treat it as a negative quantity in depreciation calculations.

The replacement of an existing asset with new equipment is worthwhile only when it results in a true reduction in cost. For this reason consideration of the costs of installation and removal is necessary if the value of a replacement is to be accurately evaluated and compared with the value of the existing asset.

PROBLEMS

1. A 1,200 kilowatt steam electric plant was constructed 14 years ago at a cost of $220 per kilowatt. The original estimate of a 20-year life and a 5 per cent salvage value is still expected to be correct. Annual demand has been 5,400,000 kilowatt-hours and annual operating expenses have been $31,000. It is estimated that the annual demand for current and the annual operating expenses will remain the same. Taxes and insurance have been 2.3 per cent of the first cost of the plant.

A diesel electric plant is being considered for a replacement and will cost $245 per kilowatt to construct. The steam electric plant can be sold for $75,000. The diesel electric plant will have a life of 25 years with a 10 per cent salvage value and will cost $23,000 annually to operate. Taxes and insurance will be 2.3 per cent of the first cost. If the interest rate is 6 per cent per annum, should the steam electric plant be replaced?

2. A chemical processing plant secures its water supply from a well which is equipped with a 6-inch, single-stage centrifugal pump that is currently in good condition. The pump was purchased 3 years ago for $1,350 and has a present book value of $1,005, having been depreciated on the basis of an expected life of 10 years. Due to design improvements, the demand for a pump of this type is such that its present value is only $500. It is anticipated that the pump will have a trade-in value of $200 seven years from now. An improved pump of the same type can now be purchased for $1,700 and will have an estimated life of 10 years with a trade-in value of $200 at the end of that time.

The pumping demand is 225 cubic feet per minute against an average head of 200 feet. The old pump has an efficiency of 75 per cent when furnishing the demand above. The new pump has an efficiency of 81 per cent when furnishing the same demand. Power costs $0.026 per horsepower-hour and either pump must operate 2,400 hours per year. Do the improvements made in design justify the purchase of a new pump if interest of 6 per cent is required?

3. A gasoline motor driven pump unit is used 6 hours per day 120 days per year at full load capacity to pump irrigation water from a lake. The pump delivers 450 cubic feet per minute against a head of 18 feet. Fuel

is consumed at the rate of 4.4 gallons per hour and costs $0.32 per gallon.

An equipment dealer offers to sell a similar unit and states that the fuel consumption will be not more than 3.5 gallons per hour. The unit will be purchased for an installed cost of $720 if, after a month's trial, it demonstrates that its fuel consumption will conform to the claims of the dealer. At the end of the trial period, it is found that fuel consumption has been 3.58 gallons per hour. The dealer then offers to sell the unit at a 20 per cent reduction in price and will accept the old unit as $60 in payment for the new unit. It is estimated that the old unit will be usable for 2 more years and will then be scrapped for no salvage value. The new unit is estimated to have a life of 5 years with no salvage value. The interest rate is 6 per cent.

(a) Should the dealer's offer at the discounted price be accepted on the basis of equivalent annual cost?

(b) What discount on the quoted price will just compensate for the difference in claimed and actual fuel consumptions, on the assumption that the latter will continue throughout the expected life of the unit?

4. A manufacturer is considering the purchase of an automatic lathe to replace one of two turret lathes. The turret lathes were purchased 12 years ago at a cost of $3,400 and were depreciated 2 years ago to $400. The automatic lathe can be purchased for $8,600 and the turret lathe can be sold for $700. Other pertinent data are as follows:

	Turret Lathes	Automatic Lathe
Annual output, Part A.............	40,000 each	80,000
Annual use other than on Part A....	400 hours each	0
Production, units of Part A per hour	34 each	82
Labor (one man per machine)......	$2.20 per hour	$2.60 per hour
Estimated annual maintenance.....	$80 each	$120
Power cost per hour of operation....	$0.06 each	$0.11
Taxes and insurance, 1.6% of.......	Present value	Original cost
Space charges per year............	$24 each	$32

The turret lathes are in good mechanical condition and may be expected to serve an additional 10 years before maintenance rises appreciably. Their salvage value will probably never drop below $300 each. If one of the turret lathes is replaced by the automatic lathe, it is assumed that the automatic lathe will be used to produce the entire 80,000 units of Part A and that the remaining turret lathe will be used 800 hours per year. If the interest rate is 8 per cent, how many years will be required for the automatic lathe to pay for itself?

5. Two years ago, a centrifugal pump driven by a direct-connected induction motor was purchased to meet a need for a flow of 2,000 gallons of water per minute for an industrial process. The unit cost $2,100 and had an estimated salvage value of $300 at the end of 6 years of use. It consumed electric power at the rate of 43 kw and was used 16 hours per day for 300 days a year. The process for which the water is required has been changed and in the future a flow of only 800 gallons per minute is needed 3 hours per day for 300 days a year. At the decreased flow both pump and motor are relatively inefficient and the current consumption is 36 kw.

A new unit of a capacity conforming to future needs will cost $1,180. This new unit will have an estimated life of 8 years with an estimated salvage value of $180 at the end of that time. Its current consumption will be 19 kw. The present unit has a book value of $1,100 and can be sold for $600. The original estimates of useful life and salvage value are still believed to be reliable. Insurance, taxes, and maintenance are estimated at 6 per cent of the original cost for both units. The cost of power is $0.022 per kilowatt-hour and the interest rate is 7 per cent.

(a) Should the old unit be retained or should the new unit be purchased?

(b) At what number of hours per day for 300 days a year with a requirement of 800 gallons of water per minute will the future equivalent annual cost of the two units be equal?

6. Five years ago a milling machine was installed in a manufacturing plant at a cost of $27,000. It was estimated that the machine which is still in good condition, would have a useful life of 20 years. Annual operating costs excluding depreciation and interest charges are $1,250. The number of parts to be processed have doubled and will continue at the higher rate for the rest of the life of the machine. Another identical machine can be installed for $22,000 or a machine with double the capacity can be installed for $31,000. Annual operating cost is expected to be $1,800. The present machine can be sold for $6,800. Either of the three machines will have a salvage value at retirement of 10 per cent of original cost. The interest rate is 8 per cent. Compare the two alternatives for obtaining the required services on the basis of equivalent annual cost over a 15-year study period, recognizing any unused value remaining in the machines at the end of that time.

7. Four years ago an ore-crushing unit was installed at a mine at a cost of $81,000. Annual operating costs for this unit are $3,540, exclusive of charges for interest and depreciation. This unit was estimated to have a useful life of 10 years and this estimate still appears to be substantially

correct. The amount of ore to be handled is to be doubled and is expected to continue at this higher rate for at least 20 years. A unit that will handle the same amount of ore and have the same annual operating cost as the one now in service can be installed for $75,000. A unit with double the capacity of the one now in use can be installed for $112,000. Its life is estimated at 10 years and its annual operating costs are estimated at $4,936. The present realizable value of the unit now in use is $26,000. All units under consideration will have an estimated salvage value at retirement age of 12 per cent of the original cost. The interest rate is 10 per cent. Compare the two possibilities of providing the required service on the basis of equivalent annual cost over a study period of 6 years, not recognizing unused value remaining in the unit at the end of that time.

8. A hydroelectric plant utilizing a continuous flow of 11 cubic feet of water per second with an absolute head of 860 feet was built 4 years ago. The 18-inch pipeline in the system cost $92,000 for pipe, installation, and right of way and has a loss of head due to friction of 81 feet. Additional water rights have been acquired which will result in a total of 22 cubic feet per second of water flow. The following plans are under consideration for utilizing the total flow. Plan A: Use the present pipeline. This will entail no additional expense but will result in a total loss of head due to friction of 346 feet resulting from the increased velocity of the water. Plan B: Add a second 18-inch pipeline at a cost of $68,000. The loss of head for this line will be 81 feet. Plan C: Install a 26-inch pipeline at a cost of $91,000 and remove the existing line, for which $3,800 can be realized. The loss of head due to friction for the 26-inch pipeline will be 63 feet.

The energy of the water delivered to the turbine is valued at $64 per horsepower year, where horsepower = $h \times F \times 62.4 \div 550$. In this equation, h is the net head in feet, and F is the flow in cubic feet per second. Insurance and taxes amount to 2 per cent of first cost. Operating and maintenance costs are essentially equal for all three plans. The interest rate is 7 per cent. If all lines, including the one now in use, will be retired in 30 years with no salvage value, what is the comparable equivalent annual costs of the three alternatives?

9. A small manufacturing company leases a building for machining of metal parts used in their final product. The annual rental of $10,000 is paid, in advance, on January 1. The present lease runs until December 31, 1968 unless terminated by mutual agreement of both parties. The owner wishes to terminate the lease on December 31, 1964 and offers the company $2,000 if it will comply with the request. If the company does not

agree, the lease will remain in effect at the same rate until the 1968 termination date. The company owns a suitable building lot and has a firm contract for construction of a building for a total cost of $170,000 to be completed in one year. These figures are firm whether the building is constructed in 1964 or 1968.

If the company elects to stay in the leased building, it will spend $8,000, $6,500, and $7,000 in 1965, 1966, and 1967, respectively, on the facility with no salvage value resulting. It is estimated that operating expenses will be $3,500 less per year in the new building for a comparable level of output. Taxes, insurance, and maintenance will cost 3.5 per cent of the first cost of the building per year. The life of the building is estimated to be 25 years with no salvage value and the interest rate is 6 per cent. The decision is to be made on January 1, 1964 on the basis of the present worth of the two plans as of December 31, 1964.

(a) What is the present worth of the two plans as of December 31, 1964 if the prospective difference is recognized in the lengths of service provided?

(b) What is the present worth of the two plans as of December 31, 1964 if the prospective difference is ignored in the length of service provided?

(c) The company considers the privilege of waiting 4 years to build to have a present worth of $5,000. On the basis of this fact, and the results of part (a), which plan should be adopted?

10. Machine A was purchased in 1960 for $2,500 and was estimated to have a life of 10 years with a salvage value of $300. Its operating expense has been $1,100 per year. In 1964, a salesman offered Machine B for $4,200. Its life was estimated at 8 years and its salvage value at the end of its life was estimated at $500. The annual operating costs were estimated at $840. The salesman offers to take the old machine in on trade for $700. The company estimates that Machine A will continue to have an annual operating cost of $1,100 and the original estimates of service life and salvage value for Machine A are still the best that can be made. A used machinery dealer has offered to pay $800 for Machine A. Equipment investments are expected to justify 8 per cent compounded continuously, and the purpose served by either machine is expected to continue for many years. Determine the annual cost of retaining Machine A and compare it with the annual cost of buying Machine B.

11. Two bridge designs proposed for the crossing of a small stream are to be compared by the present-worth method for a period of 40 years. The wooden design has a first cost of $500 and an estimated life of 8 years.

The steel design has a first cost of $1,000 and an estimated life of 20 years. Each structure has zero salvage value at the end of the given period and it is estimated that the annual expenditures will be the same regardless of which design is selected. Using an interest rate of 6 per cent, does the increased life of the steel design justify the extra investment?

12. A gear manufacturer purchased a beveled gear cutting machine one year ago for $8,400. At that time, it was estimated to have a service life of 6 years with no salvage value. Annual operating cost of the machine amounted to $2,200. A new gear cutting machine is being considered which would cost $10,000 but would match the output of the old machine for an annual operating cost of $900. The new machine's service life is 5 years with no salvage value. An allowance of $2,000 would be made for the old machine on the purchase of the new machine. The interest rate is 6 per cent.

(a) List the receipts and disbursements for the next five years if the old machine is retained; if the new machine is purchased. Compare the present worth of receipts and disbursements.

(b) Take the "outsider's viewpoint" and calculate the equivalent annual cost for each of the two alternatives.

(c) What is the use value of the old machine in comparison with the new machine?

(d) Should the new machine be purchased? Why?

13. A 5-ton dump truck to haul crushed stone from a crusher to storage, a distance of 0.5 mile, was purchased two years ago for a cost of $9,000. At that time, it had an estimated life of 10 years and an estimated salvage value of $500. Depreciation was determined by the straight-line method. Annual operating costs, including maintenance and taxes, but exclusive of depreciation and interest on the investment on the truck, have averaged $4,200 and will probably continue at this rate. A belt conveyor system is under consideration as a replacement for the truck. The installed cost of the system will be $6,000, and it has an estimated life and salvage value of 5 years and $700, respectively. Annual operating costs are estimated at $2,100. The truck can be sold for $5,000. The interest rate is 6 per cent.

(a) What is the present book value of the truck?

(b) What will be the sunk cost if the truck is sold for $5,000?

(c) If the salvage value of the truck is now estimated at $400, eight years hence, should it be replaced?

14. A manufacturer is now using Machine A, whose annual operating cost is expected to continue at $1,000. This machine is expected to continue to operate satisfactorily for five additional years, at which time it may be ·expected to have negligible salvage value. The manufacturer has an opportunity to purchase Machine B for $2,000. Machine B is estimated to have a life of 5 years, negligible salvage value at the end of its life, and an annual operating cost of $400. If Machine B is purchased, Machine A will be sold for $100 and a sunk cost of $1,200 on it will be revealed. The interest rate is 6 per cent.

(a) What error in equivalent annual costs will result if the manufacturer erroneously adds the sunk cost he has suffered to the cost of Machine B in making a comparison of the financial desirability of the two machines?

(b) Calculate the comparative use value of Machine A.

15. Plot the data in Columns D, E, and F of Table 12.5. If an interest rate had been used the data would be slightly different. Indicate with a superimposed dashed line the change that interest would make.

16. At the end of the seventh year, replacement of the asset described in Table 12.4 is being considered. The salvage value of the asset has been determined to be zero at the end of the seventh year. What will be the average yearly cost to operate the asset one, two, or three years more?

17. At the end of the ninth year, replacement of the asset described in Table 12.6 is being considered. At that time, the salvage value of the asset was estimated to be zero. What will be the equivalent annual cost of operating the asset one, two, or three years more?

18. The maintenance cost of a certain machine is zero the first year and increases by $100 per year for each year thereafter. The machine costs $1,000 and has no salvage value at any time. Its annual operating cost is $2,000 per year. If the interest rate is zero and straight-line depreciation is used, what life will result in minimum average annual cost? Solve by trial and error showing yearly costs in tabular form.

19. Same data as Problem 18 except that the interest rate is 6 per cent and sinking-fund depreciation is used. Solve by trial and error.

20. A special-purpose machine was installed 8 years ago at a cost of $4,800. The following table shows a record of its annual operating cost, maintenance cost, book value, and scrap value. If interest is neglected, what is the average annual cost for each service life in years? For what service life was the average age annual cost at a minimum?

Year of Service	Operation Cost for Year	Maintenance Cost for Year	Book Value at End of Year	Scrap or Salvage Value at End of Year
1	$5,140	$ 30	$4,300	$200
2	5,170	38	3,800	200
3	5,215	54	3,300	200
4	5,263	82	2,800	200
5	5,240	108	2,300	200
6	5,370	196	1,800	200
7	5,565	316	1,300	200
8	5,782	575	800	200

21. A special milling machine is being installed at a first cost of $4,000. Maintenance cost is estimated to be $6,000 for the first year and will increase by 2 per cent each year. The book value will decrease at the rate of $200 per year. If interest is neglected and the salvage value is $200 at any time, for what service life will the average annual cost be a minimum?

22. Use the same data given in Problem 21, but assume that the interest rate is 8 per cent compounded continuously.

CHAPTER 13

ECONOMY IN THE
UTILIZATION OF PERSONNEL

Up to this point most of the analysis presented has been concerned with the economy of material resources. However, material resources are of no value in the satisfaction of human wants until they are transformed by human action. A critical element in the development of the forces and materials of nature is human effort. Since engineers are directly concerned with the development of material resources they should also be concerned with the characteristics and economical use of human input as it relates to this development process.

As with material resources, human resources can be wasted through misuse or they can be used with economy. The key to the success of many activities within the engineering process is the economic and efficient utilization of human effort. The purpose of this chapter will be to present selected concepts and methods of analysis useful in engineering economy studies involving the utilization of personnel.

13.1. HOW LABOR IS SAVED

Although great improvements have been made in the effectiveness of labor utilization, labor continues to be an important factor in the cost of production of goods and services. Individuals and organizations seem characteristically motivated to obtain their desired goals with a minimum expenditure of effort. The innovations which result in less labor being expended per unit of output of product are quickly adopted. These innovations may be classified as labor-saving organizations, labor-saving equipment, labor-saving materials, and labor-saving methods.

Many aspects of these innovations are studied in such formal courses as industrial organization and management, machine design, tool design, mechanics of materials, metallurgy, work analysis, and methods engineering. The paragraphs that follow will be devoted to a detailed discussion of how these labor-saving innovations contribute to economy.

Labor-saving organization. Perhaps the most important labor-saving innovation utilized by mankind is organization. Organizations consist of the coordinated effort of individuals, and have existed since the beginning of time. Through organizations, man can either attain ends that no one can achieve by individual effort or he can attain certain ends more economically.

Organized effort is often a means to economy in accomplishment through labor saving. Suppose, for example, that two men adjacent to each other are each confronted with the task of lifting a box onto a loading platform, and that each of the two boxes is too heavy for one man to lift but not too heavy for two men to lift. Assume that the only practical way for one man to accomplish his task is to obtain a hand winch with which the task can be accomplished in 30 minutes' time. If there is no coordination of effort the cost of getting the two boxes onto the platform will be 60 man-minutes.

Suppose that the two men had coordinated their efforts to lift the two boxes in turn and that the time consumed was one minute per box. The two tasks would have been accomplished at the expense of four man-minutes, or about 7 per cent as much as if there had been no coordination of effort.

Coordination of human effort is so effective a means of labor saving that it may be economical to pay for effort to bring about coordination of effort. In the example above, effort directed to bring about coordination would result in a net labor saving of 56 man-minutes of effort.

For further illustration of the creativeness of coordination of human effort, suppose that a water well would have a value of $100 to each of 100 families in a village. The head of each of the families in turn recognizes this and on inquiry finds that a well will cost $1,000 and each head of a family, being oblivious of the opportunities for coordination, abandons the well drilling project as unprofitable. If an entrepreneur could bring about a coordination of effort in the village, the picture might be as follows:

Total benefit of well, 100 families × $100....................	$10,000
Total cost of well.......................................	1,000
Net benefit...	$ 9,000

Labor-saving equipment. An outstanding phenomenon has been the rapid change in the relationship of the cost of labor and the cost of equipment in terms of accomplishment. Consider, for example, the cost of transporting a person one mile about 50 years ago as compared to the present century. The comparative cost of transporting a person one mile 50 years ago is approximately as follows:

Man Walking:
  Labor cost (20 min. ÷ 60 min.) $0.20 per hr.................. $0.067
Man Using Automobile at 20 m.p.h.:
  Labor cost (3 min. ÷ 60 min.) $0.20 per hr.................... $0.01
  Automobile cost at $0.20 per mile............................ $0.20

The ratio of cost for a man alone and cost for man and machine is approximately 1 to 3. At present, the comparative cost of transporting a person one mile is approximately as follows:

Man Walking:
  Labor cost (20 min. ÷ 60 min.) $2.25 per hr................... $0.75
Man Using Automobile at 40 m.p.h.:
  Labor cost (1.5 min. ÷ 60 min.) $2.25 per hr................. $0.056
  Automobile cost at $0.10 per mile............................ $0.100

The ratio of cost for a man alone and cost for man and machine is approximately 1 to 0.2.

Although the illustration above was based on approximate cost data, the analysis does illustrate a trend. Experience since the Industrial Revolution indicates that real wages increase as labor-saving equipment is employed. Also, labor-saving equipment tends to decrease in cost in terms of accomplishment, because improved labor-saving machines are used in their manufacture.

Labor-saving materials. The approach to evaluation of labor-saving materials is frequently through experimentation. When more elaborate methods of comparison are needed, the patterns suggested in earlier chapters may be applied. Ordinarily, the greatest difficulty is not evaluation but awareness of the existence of labor-saving materials.

A nurseryman was irked by the necessity for spending large sums to remove ties from grafts a few days after they were made. As a result, he had ties made from a material that deteriorated from the desired number of days' exposure to sunlight. The ties were much more expensive than ordinary cord, but as a labor-saving means they were an economy.

Examples of other labor-saving materials are quick-drying lacquers, ready-mixed paints, degreasers, stationery with carbon paper attached, use of identifying colors, and chemical weed killers. In general, materials that minimize repair and replacement save labor.

Labor saving methods. Labor-saving methods are the outgrowth of the pioneering work of F. W. Taylor, F. B. Gilbreth, and others who formalized methods analysis.

Most proposed labor-saving methods can be tried either with no equipment changes or with makeshift devices to investigate their potentialities; ordinarily their evaluation is not difficult. The limiting factors to economies from labor-saving methods are the conception and development of an improved method and the difficulty of getting the improved method adopted. Economy studies showing the comparative costs of the old and new methods are often effective in directing attention to the desirability of the new method and overcoming resistance to it.

13.2. THE ECONOMY OF ORGANIZATION

Organizations are a means for creating and exchanging utilities. The fact that they are creative may be inferred from the following example of a business organization. A person who is employed by a business organization may be presumed to value the wages and other benefits he gets more highly than the efforts he contributes to gain them. The person who sells material to the organization must value them less than the money he receives for them or he would not sell. The same may be said of the seller of equipment. Similarly, a person who loans money to an organization will in the long run receive more in return than he advances or he will cease to loan money. The customer who comes with money in hand to exchange for the products of the organization may be expected to part with his money only if he values it less than he values the products he can get for it. This situation is illustrated in Figure 13.1.

In order that the organization illustrated be successful, not only must the total of the satisfactions exceed the total of contributions, but also each contributor's satisfactions must exceed his contribution as he evaluates them. In other words, each contributor must realize his aspirations to a satisfactory degree or he ceases to contribute. Organizations are essentially devices to which people contribute

Figure 13.1. Illustration of the economy of organization.

what they desire less to gain what they desire more. Unless people receive more than they put into an organization they withdraw from it. For an organization to endure, its efficiency — output divided by input — must exceed unity.

The function of a manager is to maintain a system for pooling the activities of people so that each person, including the manager himself, gains more than he contributes and so that individual contributors do not believe that superior alternatives are open to them elsewhere.

Communication is the means whereby ideas are transmitted. Ideas that are not transmitted in some way can have no effect on organizational achievement. The ability to communicate effectively has high economic value in organized effort.

But communication is costly and so much planning of organizations is based upon reducing the need for communication and its cost. The need for communication can be reduced in numerous ways, such as by specializing people as to type of work, geographical location, standardization of product and terminology, by employing people such as engineers, physicists, and accountants — who have been trained in communication in special fields, and by employing people because of special abilities to communicate.

13.3. THE ECONOMY OF HUMAN RESOURCE INPUT

In order for organizations to remain active, they must receive inputs in the form of human resources. To reach a decision relative to the economic desirability of a proposed input, a relationship between the cost of input and the value of expected output should be established in terms of a comparable measure such as money.

The cost of human resource input in terms of wages, supervision, fringe benefits, and the like can usually be obtained without great difficulty. But the value of output is often very difficult, if not impossible, to obtain. In such cases, a worthwhile analysis is necessary to determine the increment of human resource output that must be obtained for an increment of human resource input. For example, suppose that the desirability of providing a workman with a hoist is being considered. Under the present set-up the annual cost of wages and fringe benefits is $5,280 per year. Under the proposed arrangement, the annual cost would be increased by the equivalent annual cost of the hoist. If a hoist can be provided for an equivalent annual cost of $60, the annual cost of the workman and hoist will be $5,340. Let

μ = the number of units of utility produced per workman per year without the hoist;

x = fractional increase in utility of the workman if the hoist is provided.

Then

$$\frac{\$5,280}{\mu} = \frac{\$5,340}{\mu(1 + x)}$$

$$x = \frac{\$5,340 - \$5,280}{\$5,280} = 1.1 \text{ per cent.}$$

The decision is now reduced to consideration of the estimated increase in utility with the minimum increase needed to pay for the hoist.

As a variation of the analysis above suppose that the purchase of either a standard typewriter for $200 or an electric typewriter for $400 is under consideration. The annual service maintenance charge for the former is estimated at $15 and that of the latter is estimated at $30. The life of each machine is estimated at five years. One or the other of these machines will be used 60 per cent of the working time by a person whose direct and indirect labor cost is estimated at $2 per hour. What percentage increase in effectiveness, E, must result to justify the electric typewriter? If interest and trade-in value are neglected, an analysis may be made as follows.

$$\left(\frac{\$400}{5} + \$30\right) - \left(\frac{\$200}{5} + \$15\right) = (0.60 \times 2{,}000 \text{ hr.} \times \$2)E$$

$$E = 0.023, \quad \text{or} \quad 2.3 \text{ per cent.}$$

In the calculation above only the estimate of the percentage of time the typewriter would be used was subject to much error. The analysis reduces the choice between the two machines to a judgment of whether or not the more costly machine would result in an increase in productivity of 2.3 per cent or more.

When the effectiveness of a unit of equipment is known, but the amount that it will be used per year is unknown, the amount of use to justify the purchase of equipment may be calculated as in the following example. An engineer does some calculating which, according to an estimate, could be performed with a calculator in one third the time that is required with a slide rule. He works 2,000 hours per year, his annual salary is $6,400, and, it costs $400 per year to provide office facilities for him. The calculator will cost $700. Maintenance of the machine will cost $45 per year, and the life of the machine is estimated to be 10 years. What is the minimum number of hours, N, of use per year that will justify the purchase of the machine on the basis of time saved at an interest rate of 6 per cent?

RP 6-10
$$\$700(0.13587) + \$45 = [(\$6{,}400 + \$400) \div 2{,}000](1 - \tfrac{1}{3})N$$

$$N = 62 \text{ hours.}$$

In the previous examples, the objective was to expose the desirability of supplementing a given human resource input with a non-human resource input. Consider an example in which the objective will be to evaluate the desirability of supplementing a given human resource input with an increased human resource input. Suppose that at present a foreman with an annual salary of $6,000 supervises 8 workmen, each of whom receives an annual wage of $5,000. It is proposed that the foreman's salary be increased to $6,800 per year, that he be given the assistance of a clerk at an annual salary of $4,000, and that he be required to supervise 12 workmen. Fringe benefits amount to 10 per cent of all direct salaries. What increase in output per worker will be necessary to justify the new organization? Let

μ = average number of units of utility produced per worker per year at present;

x = per cent increase in utility of the workers if the new organization is adopted.

Then, if it is assumed that the efforts of the foreman and clerk have no significance except as they result in worker output, the per cent increase required is

$$\frac{1.10(8 \times \$5,000 + \$6,000)}{8\mu} = \frac{1.10(12 \times \$5,000 + \$6,800 + \$4,000)}{12(1 + x)\mu}$$

$$x = \frac{\$5,900 - \$5,750}{\$5,750} = 2.6 \text{ per cent.}$$

The question is now reduced to a decision concerning the probable increase in output per worker and its comparison with a break-even increase of 2.6 per cent.

13.4. THE NATURE OF OUTPUT AT DIFFERENT ORGANIZATIONAL LEVELS

Observation leads to the conclusion that most of the concrete aspects of products and services produced by an organization are the result of the activities of those on its lowest level. For example, it is not the orchestra leader, the sales manager, or the foundry superintendent who makes the music, the sale, or the castings. These are made by the men on the lowest level of organization.

This fact in no way minimizes the importance of the functions performed by those of the upper levels or organization. The function of much if not most of the activities of the upper hierarchy of organization is to facilitate the work of those on the lower levels. This is particularly clear in regard to the work of the methods engineer. His work has no significance except that it enables those on the lowest levels to make a product with less effort. Although not as apparent, this seems equally true of the functions of design, production control, stores control, industrial relations, and cost accounting.

Persons in organizational levels above the lowest are for the most part concerned with the determination of objectives and the means for attaining them. The higher the level, the greater the emphasis on general objectives, and the less the emphasis on means. Thus, top levels are concerned predominantly with objectives and the lower levels with the means for accomplishing objectives.

The exception to the rule that concrete aspects of production are performed by persons on the lowest organizational levels is sometimes found in procurement. Negotiation for funds, the purchase of principal items of raw material and equipment, and bargaining for labor are often carried on by persons on high organizational levels. Also, important sales are often made on high levels.

The results of upper-level activities to facilitate the work of those on lower levels are communicated to the point of use in the form of policies, specifications, and directions and are effective only to the extent that they can be communicated.

13.5. SPAN OF CONTROL AND NUMBER OF ORGANIZATIONAL LEVELS

In considering organizational structure from the standpoint of economy, the first aspect to note is the relationship of span of control and the number of organizational levels. When all levels are complete and the span of control is constant throughout the organization, the relationship between the number of levels, the span of control, and the total number of persons in an organization may be established. Let

N = the total number of persons in an organization;

S = the span of control;

L = the number of levels of organization.

Then $$N = 1 + S + S^2 + \ldots + S^{L-1}.$$

This result is shown graphically for a number of spans of control and levels of organization in Figure 13.2. From the graph it may be found, for example, that 10,000 people can be organized with a span of control of 6 or 20 and that the number of levels would be 6 and 4, respectively.

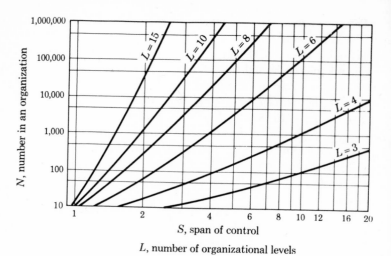

Figure 13.2. Span of control, number of organizational levels, and the number in an organization.

It is recognized that the difficulty of communication is increased by the number of levels. In an organization of a given size the number of levels can be decreased by increasing the span of control. But there are economical limits to the span of control. Thus, one problem in the design of an organization's structure is to determine the most economical compromise between number of organization levels and span of control.

Because of the difficulty of measuring the effect of either the number of organizational levels or the span of control, the thinking about them has been predominantly in qualitative terms. The fact that effective span of control varies widely for different persons and classes of work further complicates the problem. But quantitative analyses can be made of some aspects that will be helpful in improving judgments in regard to the number of organizational levels and the span of control.

13.6. RELATIONSHIP OF SPAN OF CONTROL AND ECONOMY

It has been pointed out that the primary function of leadership is to facilitate the accomplishment of subordinates. Assuming that this is true, one question that may be considered is the ratio of input of leadership to that of those on the lowest level of an organization through whose efforts the concrete aspects of production are accomplished.

On the basis of the development in the previous section

$$N = 1 + S + S^2 + \ldots + S^{L-1}.$$

Of N employees, $1 + S + S^2 + \ldots + S^{L-2}$ are on levels of organization above the lowest. The number on the lowest level equals S^{L-1}. The ratio r_L of these two groups is expressed by

$$r_L = \frac{1 + S + S^2 + \ldots + S^{L-2}.}{S^{L-1}}$$

As the number of levels L increases, the ratio r_L approaches $1/(S-1)$. For example, for a span of control S of six, the following values are obtained.

Number of Levels L	Number in Upper Levels $1 + S + \ldots + S^{L-2}$	Number in Lowest Level S^{L-1}	Ratio r_L
1	0	1	0
2	1	6	0.167
3	7	36	0.194
4	43	216	0.199
5	259	1,296	$\frac{1}{5}$ nearly

Leader and subordinate relationships. There are a number of relationships that a leader must take into consideration in dealing with his subordinates. These are known as direct single, direct group, and cross relationships. Consider a leader, s, who has two subordinates, a and b. The span of control S is equal to two. The leader has direct single relationships with a and b when he deals with them individually. He has a group relationship with them when he deals with a and b together. Between a and b the cross relationship of a to b and b to a can exist. The number of these relationships may be calculated on a minimum basis. For the direct single relationships, X

Span	Relationships	Number
1	s to a	1
2	s to a and b	2
3	s to a, b, and c	3
4	s to a, b, c, and d	4
S	s to a, b, $\ldots$, and S	S

For the direct group relationships, Y

Span	Relationships	Number
1		0
2	s to ab	1
3	s to abc, ab, ac, and bc	4
4	s to $abcd$, abc, abd, acd, bcd, ab, ac, ad, bc, bd, and cd	11
S	s to $(ab \ldots S) \ldots$ etc.	$(2^s - S - 1)$

And, for the cross relationships, Z

Span	Relationships	Number
1		0
2	ab	1
3	ab, ac, and bc	3
4	ab, ac, ad, bc, bd, and cd*	6
S	ab, ac, ad, ae, $\ldots$ etc.	$\dfrac{S}{2}(S-1)$

The number of organizational relationships that may exist between a leader and his subordinates may be calculated from the general expressions developed above. These are tabulated for a span of control up to 20 in Table 13.1.

The success of a leader depends in large measure upon his effectiveness in giving proper consideration to the relationships that are pertinent to effective direction and employment of his subordinates. It will be noted that the number of relationships that a leader must consider increases more rapidly than the span of control. Many students of leadership hold that the span of control should be limited to 3 to 6 or 8 persons, depending upon the nature of work, because for a greater number of subordinates the number of relationships exceeds that with which a leader can cope efficiently. Certainly the number of relationships confronting a leader are a quantitative aspect of leadership. Let

$$Q = X + Y + Z = S + 2^s - S - 1 + \frac{S}{2}(S - 1).$$

Ratio of leadership to subordinate input. The number of subordinates assigned to a leader for the accomplishment of a given task may be varied. Such variation may be thought of as a variation

---

*Others that could be considered are a to bcd, b to acd, c to abd, d to abc, a to bc, a to bd, a to cd, b to ac, etc., and their reverse.

Table 13.1. MINIMUM NUMBER OF ORGANIZATIONAL RELATIONSHIPS AS A FUNC-
TION OF THE SPAN OF CONTROL

Span of control, S	X	Y	Z	Q
1	1	0	0	1
2	2	1	1	4
3	3	4	3	10
4	4	11	6	21
5	5	26	10	41
6	6	57	15	78
7	7	120	21	148
8	8	247	28	283
9	9	502	36	547
10	10	1,013	45	1,068
11	11	2,036	55	2,102
12	12	4,083	66	4,161
13	13	8,178	78	8,269
14	14	16,369	91	16,474
15	15	32,752	105	32,872
16	16	65,519	120	65,655
17	17	131,054	136	131,207
18	18	262,125	153	262,296
19	19	524,268	171	524,458
20	20	1,048,555	190	1,048,765

in the ratio of leader to subordinate input on a man-to-man basis.
Compensation may be considered and the ratio of leader to subordinate input may be obtained in terms of cost.

A function of leadership activities is to utilize the effort of subordinates in such a manner that their output will be greater than it
would be without leadership. Thus, the amount by which the output
of unsupervised workers must be increased by leadership to justify
an expenditure for leadership can be calculated. Let

S = number of workers per leader, that is, span of control;

W = average daily wage per worker;

W_1 = average daily wage per leader;

P = ratio of leader's to subordinate's wage rate = $W_1 \div W$;

U = average daily output per unsupervised worker;

R = ratio of daily output of supervised subordinate to daily output of unsupervised worker;

RU = average daily output per supervised subordinate;

T = leader's time per worker per 480-minute day.

The daily wage cost per supervised group of S subordinates and one leader is equal to $SW + W_1 = SW + PW$. The daily output per supervised group of S subordinates and one supervisor is equal to SRU, and the cost per unit output for a supervised group of S subordinates and one supervisor is equal to $(SW + PW)/SRU$.

Let cost per unit output for a supervised group of S subordinates and one leader equal the cost per unit output of unsupervised workers; then

$$\frac{SW + PW}{SRU} = \frac{W}{U}.$$

Solving for R,
$$R = 1 + \frac{P}{S}.$$

Also
$$T = \frac{480}{S}.$$

Values for R and T corresponding to values of S from 1 to 20 and for values of P from 1 to 3 are given in Figure 13.3.

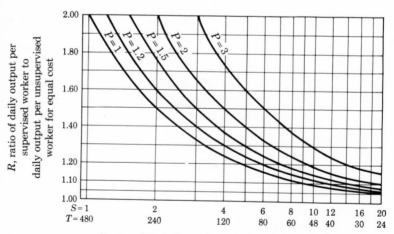

S, span of control
T, leaders time per subordinate in minutes per 480 min. day
P, ratio of leaders to subordinates wage rate

Figure 13.3. Supervision, span of control, and worker output.

Suppose that the question under consideration is whether 6 or 8 is the better span of control on the basis of which to organize a function, and that the ratio of leader's to subordinate's wage considered desirable is 1.2. From Figure 13.3 the value of R for a span of 6 is 1.20 and for a span of 8 is 1.15 when $P = 1.2$. To justify a span of 6 as against a span of 8, one would have to be satisfied that the output per subordinate would be increased to the extent that R would be increased from 1.15 to 1.20 or by

$$\frac{1.20 - 1.15}{1.15} = 0.043, \quad \text{or 4.3 per cent.}$$

Supervision per worker can be increased from 60 to 80 minutes per subordinate per day or

$$\frac{80 - 60}{60} = 0.33, \quad \text{or 33 per cent.}$$

Reference to Table 13.1 reveals that a reduction of the span of control from 8 to 6 will reduce the number of organizational relationships from 283 to 78 or

$$\frac{283 - 78}{283} = 0.72, \quad \text{or 72 per cent.}$$

The question of whether to use a span of control of 6 or of 8 has been reduced to a decision whether a span of control of 6, which permits 33 per cent more time for leader activities per subordinate and which reduces the number of organizational relationships the leader must consider by 72 per cent, will result in an increase in output per subordinate of 4.3 per cent.

13.7. SELECTION OF PERSONNEL

Viewed objectively, subordinates are merely their leader's means for reaching ends. Of the several productive factors used in industry, none has such a variety of characteristics as personnel. Characteristics of both body and mind are of concern. One individual may accomplish several times as much of a task requiring physical strength, dexterity, or acuteness of vision as another. The range of mental proficiencies for given tasks is even wider.

The physical and mental endowments of people appear to be subject only to limited change by training and leadership. For this reason it is important that personnel be selected that have inherent characteristics as nearly compatible as possible with the work they are to perform and the position they are to occupy. Contrasted with the meticulous care with which materials are selected, the selection of personnel in most concerns is given but superficial attention.

The range of human capacities. In an experiment conducted by T. R. Turnbull, 500 persons were instructed in the method of tossing thirty-two ⅜ in. × ⅜ in. × 2 in. blocks, pre-positioned in 4 rows on a work table into a 2 in. × 4 in. hole, 4½ inches from the edge of the table. Each person was asked to perform the task as rapidly as possible. The results of the experiment are shown in Figure 13.4.

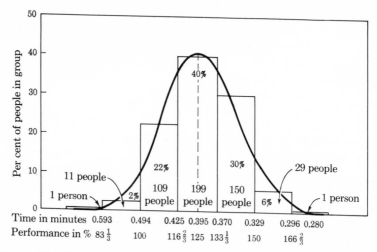

Figure 13.4. Frequency distribution of time taken by 500 people to perform block-tossing operation based on 0.395 minutes = 125% performance. [Reproduced with permission from Table XXII and Figure 243, Ralph M. Barnes, *Motion and Time Study* (New York: John A. Wiley & Sons, Inc., 1948)].

The frequency distribution is typical of those for many physical or mental tasks. The ratio of the poorest to the best performance time is 0.60 ÷ 0.28 = 2.14. It is apparent that the cost of labor input per unit of output might be materially reduced by selecting only employees capable of better than average performance. In many cases superior employees recieve little or no greater compensation than less capable employees. This is particularly true where performance is measured with difficulty. Superior managerial ability, for example, may go unrecognized and therefore unrewarded for long periods of time because it cannot be measured. But even where superior ability is proportionally compensated for, savings may still result.

Superior ability that remains unused is not an advantage and may often be a disadvantage because of the resulting frustration and dissatisfaction of the employee. Generally speaking, the work assignment should require the workman's highest skill.

For many tasks, tests can be devised for selection of prospective employees with superior ability. Representative of these are a battery of three tests for the selection of mail distributors for the Postal Service. It was found, from extensive experimental trials, that of those making the highest 25 per cent of scores on these tests, over 93 per cent would be above average in proficiency. The economic desirability of having most employees above average in ability for the task under consideration (even though compensation be in proportion to ability, which it rarely is) can hardly be overestimated.

In this relatively new field, results of the installation of a program of selection practices are most difficult to estimate. Since the input cost of a program can usually be estimated with reasonable accuracy, it may be helpful in arriving at a decision to calculate the benefits necessary to justify a contemplated selection program.

Suppose that a certain plant employs 40 operators. The average output is 28 pieces per hour, the average spoilage is 1.7 per cent, and each rejected piece results in a loss of $0.60. Records reveal that average spoilage for the best 20 operators is 1.1 per cent, whereas that for the poorest 20 operators is 2.3 per cent. A consultant agrees to prepare a set of tests and administer them for a year for $1,800. Administration subsequent to the first year is expected to cost $3 per operator hired or $140 per year based upon the estimated turnover.

Let P equal the percentage reduction in spoilage during first year to justify expenditure of $1,800. Then

$$P \times 40 \text{ operators} \times 28 \text{ pieces per hr.} \times 2,000 \text{ hr. per year} \times$$
$$\$0.60 \text{ per reject} = \$1,800$$
$$P = 0.00134 \text{ or } 0.134 \text{ per cent.}$$

This percentage reduction in spoilage seems attainable in view of the fact that a program that will reject applicants of less than average

ability in relation to spoilage will result in an average reduction of
1.7 − 1.1 or 0.6 per cent. Moreover, it is reasonable to expect other
benefits from the program.

By tending to place people in work for which they are best fitted,
sound selection is generally beneficial. Even those who are rejected
will generally be benefited; for, if continually rejected for work for
which they are unfitted, they must eventually find a job that will
permit them to work at their highest skill.

The economy of education. All discernible human activity is
of a physical nature. Man achieves his ends by manipulation of his
physical environment. This is as true of the administrator as it is of
a machinist, for whatever thoughts the former may have, he cannot
transmit them except as they are manifested in physical ways which
can be perceived by the sense organs of others.

Knowledge of what must be done to achieve a given end often
saves much labor and thus has utility. In nearly all situations, appropriate knowledge will increase the abilities of persons to achieve
ends.

The manipulation of the physical environment necessary to
produce a desired result can be learned only as the result of experience
or of instruction. Experience is often very costly, but the knowledge
that a single person has gained may often be transmitted through the
processes of instruction at relatively little cost. For example, the
ingredients and the method of heat-treating a useful alloy may be
learned only after years of costly experimentation, but the knowledge gained may be taught and become useful to other persons at
relatively little cost.

Instruction is an economical method of transmitting useful knowledge and therefore an economical means of increasing the abilities of
persons to achieve ends not otherwise attainable or at less cost.
Through instruction, the best knowledge of the most capable persons
can be made available to all.

Industrial and business organizations are making increasing use of
instructional programs to improve the competence of employees.
The worth of such programs is often difficult to evaluate. However,
the cost of an instructional program can usually be estimated with a
fair degree of accuracy. Based on the cost, the increase in the outputs
of participants necessary to justify a program of instruction can be

calculated. Consider the following example.

A program of instruction consisting of 80 hours is provided for a class of ten engineers at a cost of $20 per hour plus salary costs of participants. Assume that average salary of participants is $6,000 for a 40 hour, 50 week year. Let

μ = average number of units of utility of output per man per year;

x = the average increase in utility of output per man per year to justify the instructions.

$$\frac{10 \times \$6,000}{10\mu} = \frac{10 \times \$6,000 + \$20 \times 80}{(1+x)\mu}$$

$$x = 0.0267, \quad \text{or} \quad 2.67 \text{ per cent.}$$

For further insight into the problem, let y equal the increase in the average output of the engineers per unit of time to justify the instruction and the company time they gave to it during one year.

$$\frac{10 \times \$6,000}{\dfrac{(50 \times 40)}{2,000} \times 10\mu} = \frac{10 \times \$6,000 + \$20 \times 80}{\dfrac{48 \times 40}{2,000} \times (1+y) \times 10\mu}$$

$$y = 0.0694, \quad \text{or} \quad 6.94 \text{ per cent.}$$

Calculations such as those presented above often contribute insight and may be expected to enhance the sureness of judgment.

Leadership attention and performance. The value of a person to an organization may be considered to be the difference between the worth of his output and the cost of the input that he requires in terms of leadership attention and material incentives. The output of a person in an organization consists of his performance that contributes (1) to the attainment of the organization's objectives, and (2) to the establishment and maintenance of a system of cooperative effort.

Examples of the former contributions are such outputs as negotiating a loan on which to base plant expansion, closing a sale for 600 units of product with XYZ Company, designing a new water pump, planning a transformer production layout, turning out 800 motor frame castings, typing a letter to John Doe and Company, helping an electrician install a motor. The value of such contributions depends upon their volume, quality, and timeliness. They are usually concrete and easily observable and are generally quite well understood.

Most things are accomplished in cooperation with others. This necessitates the coordination of several persons' activities in such a way that their joint effort is specialized in a system of cooperation in a way that will accomplish the desired result. An individual may contribute to the establishment and the maintenance of effective cooperative effort; such persons are integrating influences. Those who tend to destroy effective cooperative effort are disruptive influences. Maintenance of effective cooperation is so important in many situations that a member of an organization may be valued primarily for his integrating influence rather than for his concrete output. On the other hand, some star performers, whether on athletic teams or in industrial organizations, are dropped because their disruptive influence outweighs their concrete performance.

A variety of inputs are associated with the utilization of personal service. Among the more tangible are wages and allied compensation, cost of recruitment, and the maintenance of comfort facilities such as heat, light, furniture, and rest rooms. An important additional input is what may conveniently be called leadership attention. Leadership attention to a subordinate takes the form of directions, instructions, encouragement, discipline, transfer to more suitable work, and compensation for a shortcoming in ability or performance.

It is observable that there is a great difference in the amount of leadership attention required to secure satisfactory performance from individuals. Some individuals require so little leadership that they need only be given general directions. Some have shortcomings requiring so much leadership attention that the cost of this input exceeds the value of their output.

The economy of dependability. There is an economy of each of the innumerable personal qualities, but few transcend dependability in importance. Dependability in relation to organized action means behaving as agreed upon or as expected. For example, the chairman of an industrial committee has called a meeting of twelve persons but arrives fifteen minutes after the specified time. If the average salary rate of committee members is $4 per hour the lack of dependability of the chairman may have resulted in a loss of time of $12 \times 0.25 \times \$4$, or $12. This direct loss points up the value of dependability, but it probably is not as great as the frustration and loss of confidence that the lack of dependability engenders in the persons affected by it.

Dependability rests upon ability, consideration for others, willingness to cooperate, and honesty. Lack of dependability in one person, regardless of the reason for it, invariably results in the need for increased vigilance and effort on the part of others. People in supervisory positions are keenly aware of the costs of deviation from dependability, and they thus prize dependability highly.

Willful undependability and dishonesty are particularly difficult to cope with because even infrequent dishonesty leads to the necessity for a supervisor to be continually prepared against the entire range of defections that a dishonest person may cause. Thus, for many positions, even extremely limited dishonesty may outweigh the honest services a person may render.

13.8. ECONOMY AND THE ASSIGNMENT OF PERSONNEL

As an illustration of the economy of personnel assignment, consider the fact that some sales effort must be applied to dispose of nearly all products, particularly those to be purchased by the ultimate consumer. The level of sales effort to apply for optimum results is an important consideration in economy. Level of sales effort applied to a product or a group of products may be expressed in terms of the amount of advertising purchased, the number of dealer outlets, the number of calls by salesmen, and so forth, or a combination of these.

In general there is a level that produces more favorable results than any other. This optimum level is continually being sought for through research, experimentation, and the exercise of reason and opinion. The effect of different levels of sales effort in the disposal of a truck accessory is illustrated in Table 13.2.

The first column gives the number of trucks in each salesman's territory. The second column gives values taken from a smooth curve drawn to represent average number of units sold per salesman per year. In the third column the cost of sales effort per unit of product is given. These values are found by dividing $14,200 by the number of sales per year. $14,200 represents the average cost per salesman per year and is independent of the number of trucks per salesman.

Table 13.2. EFFECT OF SALES EFFORT ON COST OF SALES

Number of trucks per salesman	Number of units sold per salesman per year	Cost of sales effort per unit
30,000	1,240	$11.45
40,000	1,570	9.04
50,000	1,740	8.16
60,000	1,760	8.07
70,000	1,690	8.40
80,000	1,580	8.99
90,000	1,410	10.07

Where only the cost of sales effort is pertinent, one salesman per 60,000 trucks is most economical. The relationship of total sales to output and plant capacity must also be considered. Thus, if the plant's normal capacity cannot be sold by assigning one salesman to each 60,000 trucks, greater profit may result from decreasing the number of trucks per salesman, even though sales cost per unit of product is increased thereby.

13.9. ECONOMY OF SPECIALIZATION

To specialize is to restrict a person or thing to a particular activity, place, time, or situation. Specialization in this sense results when there is a division of labor, as for example, when operations in a process performed by a single person are divided among a number of persons. It is clear that machines can also be specialized in this sense, that is, specialized as to activity.

Persons or things can also be specialized as to use, place, or time. Thus a person whose assignments require that he report to work in St. Louis is specialized as to place. A passenger train that operates on a schedule is specialized as to time and place; so is a person who works in one place from nine to five o'clock, five days a week.

Specialization is of interest in relation to economy studies because it is often a means whereby the cost of accomplishing a given result can be reduced. In any design or planning effort the desirability of specialization should be considered as a routine matter. It is widely recognized that specialization, particularly as it relates to people, may result in improved performance.

Specialization usually requires pre-planning and specialized arrangements, the cost and maintenance of which may more than offset the advantage gained. The gains of a specialization of one kind may require specialization of another that is too costly. For instance, it might be desirable to have two men perform one each of two activities that must be performed one after the other, *unless* the new arrangement would also require the men to be specialized as to time. The latter specialization might easily result in one man's being idle while the other works.

Specialization is subject to the law of diminishing returns. It is apparent that it would not be economical to specialize to such an extent, for example, that one truck driver made only right turns and another made only left turns.

Generalization, the reverse of specialization, may also be a factor in economy. Thus in machine design it is often desirable to have one part serve several purposes; the crankcase of an engine, for instance, serves as a base for the engine, a container for oil, and a support for the crankshaft and cylinder. The term "all-around man" is evidence of generalization with respect to personnel.

13.10. ECONOMY OF PROFICIENCY

Value of proficiency is not necessarily directly proportional to degree of proficiency. Thus, a baseball player whose batting average is 0.346 will ordinarily command more than twice as much salary as one whose average is 0.173, if they are equal in other respects. In some activities the compensation of those with unusually high proficiencies is extremely high, but those with ordinary abilities can find no market for their services. Consider acting; the motion picture industries pay fabulous salaries for those whose box office appeal is high when they undoubtedly could cast all their productions with volunteer actors of fair ability without cost.

The cost of human effort is a considerable portion of the total cost of carrying on nearly all business activities. People are employed with the idea of earning a profit on the skills they possess. In general, the higher a person's proficiency in any skill, be it manual dexterity, creativeness, leadership, inventiveness, or physical ability, the greater his value to his employer. Consider a machine operation for which a workman is paid $2 per hour for producing 10 pieces per hour on a machine whose rate is $6 per hour. (The machine rate embraces all costs incident to operating the machine.) In this example the cost per piece is equal to

$$\frac{\$2 + \$6}{10} = \$0.80.$$

If a second worker of less proficiency completes 9 pieces per hour, his relative worth to his employer (as compared with that of the first workman) is calculated as follows: Let W equal the hourly pay of the second workman to result in a cost per piece of \$0.80. Thus,

$$\frac{W + \$6}{9} = \$0.80$$

and $\qquad\qquad W = \$1.20.$

It will be noted in this example that a 10 per cent reduction in the ability of the workman to turn out pieces results in his services being worth 60 per cent as much per hour to his employer as the services of the first workman, all other things being equal.

If the second workman also received \$2 per hour, the cost per piece of the 9 pieces he turns out in an hour will be as follows:

$$\text{cost per piece} = \frac{\$2 + \$6}{9} = \$0.888.$$

It is conceivable that the resulting cost per piece may be so high that the employer cannot profit if he must pay the second workman \$2 per hour.

The comparative worth of a third workman, who produces only 7 pieces per hour, is calculated as follows: Let W equal the hourly pay of the third workman to result in a cost per piece of \$0.80.

$$\frac{W - \$6}{7} = \$0.80$$

and $\qquad\qquad W = -\$0.40.$

The negative result is illustrative of the fact that there are levels below which proficiencies have little or no economic value. Thus, the fixing of wage rates by minimum wage laws or other artificial limitations may result in unemployment for persons of low output and increased demand for persons of high proficiency.

13.11. THE ECONOMY OF INCENTIVES

A person will accept and continue to work in a situation he believes to hold a net advantage for him in comparison with other opportunities that he knows to be open to him. The advantages of a situation may be considered to be positive incentives and the disadvantages may be considered to be negative incentives. People are induced to act on the basis of net incentives. Incentives are personal. A thing prized highly by one person may be regarded with indifference, or even with disgust, by another.

The following are representative of the incentives considered to be effective in inducing people to contribute their services to organized activities.

1. Material incentives
2. Nonmaterial incentives
    (a) Social considerations
    (b) Opportunity for advancement
    (c) Opportunity for enlarged participation
    (d) Opportunity for creativeness

Much of the effort of supervisors and managers is directed toward providing maximum net incentives for minimum cost.

Material incentives. Material incentives offered to induce people to work in free enterprise are wages; wage supplements such as contributions to insurance, savings, and housing programs; and the physical condition of the plant and its locale. Up to the point where it is sufficient to provide the basic necessities of life, material compensation is one of the strongest incentives. But even wages must be paid out in certain ways for greatest effectiveness. Recognition of this fact at one time led to some very complex incentive wage plans. But, today with our more advanced techniques and greater experience, the trend is to keep the plan itself as simple as possible. Merit rating and job evaluation are other techniques that are being used to secure greater output for an input of wages.

Although material incentives as represented by compensation are emphasized, they have limited effectiveness, particularly after the individual receiving them is provided with physical necessities. This may be inferred from the fact that it is generally recognized that such valuable qualities as devotion, dependability, loyalty, initiative, industry, and honesty can be purchased for money in only a small degree. High rates of absenteeism often accompany high rates of compensation. Productivity per man does not necessarily increase with an increase in wages, and it has been known to fall. Ordinarily, doubling of wages cannot be expected to incite people to work twice as hard, if for no other reason than their physical limitations.

The overemphasis on material incentives stems, no doubt, in some measure from the sales effort, most readily discernible in modern advertising, directed at inculcating a desire for material things. The latter is a means for increasing output so that advantage may be taken of the economies of mass production. It has also resulted in demands for higher wages for a given service, or in other words, has resulted in a decrease in the value of wages as an incentive.

There are a number of material incentives that do not result in enlarged employee earnings. These are embodied in the objective plant conditions and involve such things as cleanliness, quality of buildings and equipment, maintenance, lighting, heating, ventilation, rest rooms, provision of parking space, and recreational facilities. These incentives seem to have more or less universal appeal and are evaluated in comparison with the conditions existing in other plants. They can be applied on an impersonal basis. Good physical conditions are often an important factor in inducing a favorable response, particularly in conjunction with other incentives of more personal nature, but alone their effectiveness appears to be very limited.

Nonmaterial incentives. There seems to be a wide individual divergence in the effectiveness of nonmaterial incentives. Some people are greatly influenced by the companionship afforded by fellow workers. Others can be induced to perform superlatively by a knowledge that such performance will result in praise or prestige. An important incentive for ambitious people is the opportunity a situation affords for advancement. The opportunity for enlarged participation in the affairs of the organization with which they are associated is a very strong incentive for many. For some this takes the form of being able to have a hand in directing the activities of the group; others will consider being "in the know" a reward for faithful service.

One of the strongest incentives is the opportunity for self-expression through creativeness in work that is in accord with natural aptitudes of the person concerned. This incentive is not feasible in work requiring strict obedience to specifications, policies, and superiors.

Leaders should strive to organize their subordinates in relation to the work to be done, so that each worker may receive the greatest satisfaction in doing that which contributes most toward reaching the objectives to be accomplished. When the work itself provides an incentive for doing it in whole or in part, there is true economy.

Nonmaterial incentives are not provided without cost, and they can easily be more costly for the beneficial motivation they provide than material incentives. They must, to a large extent, be applied upon a personal basis, for their effectiveness depends upon the characteristics of the persons to whom they are offered. For example, the prestige of a private office might be a great incentive to some employees, but not to others.

A peculiarity of nonmaterial incentives is that they often affect others beside the person to whom they are directed. Thus, giving one employee a private office might prove to be a negative incentive to several others and result in a net loss. On the other hand, if all employees of a group were given private offices, the beneficial motivation might be very slight.

Because of their personal nature, the successful and extensive offering of nonmaterial incentives depends upon the selection of personnel who are easily pleased and upon leaders who have an aptitude for distributing incentives to their subordinates in such a way that each feels he has received favorable individual attention. The selection of employees who are easily and favorably motivated is an economy, since such employees require less input of leadership attention.

The cost and effectiveness of nonmaterial incentives rests almost entirely upon the personal attributes of leaders. Nonmaterial incentives that are offered to a subordinate are controlled in large measure by leaders. Thus, the selection of leaders is an important factor in economy, although it appears not to receive the attention it warrants.

PROBLEMS

1. An appliance manufacturer leases 10,000 square feet of usable warehouse space with a ceiling height of 12 feet. The lease rate is $0.70 per square foot per year. The appliances are stored in boxes 2.9 feet in height and

are stacked two high. If a fork truck is purchased to handle the appliances, they could be stacked four high, with a saving of 1,200 man-hours per year in handling. The fork truck will cost $4,800 and will have an annual operating cost of $360. If each man employed is paid $2.10 per hour, how long will it take to justify the investment in the fork truck from the saving in space and labor if the interest rate is 5 per cent?

2. A small amount of collating is done in an office. A collating device which permits assembly of papers to be accomplished in about one-half the time required without it can be purchased for $125. On the basis of a service life of five years, an employee wage rate of $1.65, and a 50 per cent time saving, calculate the number of hours of use per year to justify the purchase of the device if the interest rate is 8 per cent.

3. Assume that N units of product can be made manually by one man in a year of 2,000 working hours, that the man's wage rate is W dollars per hour, and that a labor saving machine whose annual capital and operating cost is equivalent to $R \times 2,000$ hours of labor, will, if used throughout the year, reduce the amount of labor needed to produce the N units by $S \times 2,000$ hours. Write equations for the unit cost of product when manually made and when made with the aid of the machine. Determine the ratio of R to S when the costs are equal.

4. A pneumatically operated wrench costing $31 will permit the installation of a certain bracket 75 per cent faster than with a manual wrench. On the basis of a service life of 5 years, an employee wage rate of $1.75 per hour, and an interest rate of 8 per cent compounded continuously, calculate the number of hours of use per year that will justify the purchase of the automatic wrench.

5. Two typewriters are under consideration costing $250 and $310, respectively. A secretary will use a typewriter 70 per cent of her working time. The annual direct and indirect cost of the secretary is $5,100. What per cent increase in effectiveness will be necessary to justify the price of the higher priced typewriter if each machine has a service life of 4 years and the interest rate is 9 per cent?

6. An architect has been using a consulting engineer for the mechanical planning of buildings. His average annual fees have been $120,000 per year. Annual office expenditures have averaged $80,000, leaving a net profit of $40,000 per year.

To hire a mechanical engineer in the office would cost $1,000 per month. This would increase the architect's fees by 20 per cent each year. If these estimates remain constant and interest is taken as 7 per cent, what will be the present worth of the increase in profit for a 3-year period?

7. A manufacturing concern has sales offices in five states in addition to the main plant and offices. Each branch sales manager is paid $12,000 per year and the vice-president for sales receives $18,000 per annum. At the present time, average annual sales amounts to $2,300,000. An annual sales conference is being considered which will meet at the main plant for 2 days each year.

(a) If each branch sales manager is paid $280 for travel and other expenses, what is the total cost of the conference on the basis of a 240-day work year?

(b) What percentage increase in sales attributable to the conference is necessary to justify the annual meeting if the gross profits are 12 per cent of sales?

8. A foreman receiving a salary of $7,200 per year supervises the work of 18 men whose average annual salary is $4,200 per year. It is proposed that the employment of a second foreman will improve the total situation.

(a) Assuming that the two foremen would have to spend 2 hours each day coordinating their work, what will be the average increase in the time spent in supervision per day per man?

(b) What average percentage increase in output is necessary to justify the employment of the second foreman?

9. Foreman A directs the work of 12 men. He plans his work "as he goes" during the eight-hour work period. Foreman B also directs the work of 12 men, but spends two hours per day in planning the work to be done, thus reducing the time available for active supervision. What percentage more effective must his supervision be per unit of time so that his supervisory effectiveness equals that of Foreman A?

10. An engineer can do certain required computations in 3 hours or he can delegate the work to an engineering aid. If the work is delegated, it will take 0.75 hour to explain the computational procedure and 0.50 hour to check the results The actual calculations will take 4 hours to do if done by the aid. If the engineer receives a salary of $10,800 per year and the aid receives $4,200 per year, what are the comparative costs for each of the methods for a working year of 2,080 hours?

11. A foreman is in charge of a construction crew of eight men and takes great pride in the amount of work he personally performs on the job. Observation shows that the accomplishment of the men is impaired by lack of direction as a result of the foreman's active participation in the work to be done. The foreman receives $3.10 and his men $2.55 per hour. If the foreman does one-third as much work as the average of his men

would do if they were properly directed, what loss in the effectiveness of the crew will just be compensated for by the actual work performed by the foreman?

12. A group of 60 employees, whose average salary is $4,600 per year, is directed by 5 foremen, whose average salary is $6,200 per year. It is suggested that the number of foremen be increased to 6.

(a) What per cent increase in average output per man must result for the two plans to incur equal cost?

(b) If the suggested plan is adopted, what will be the percentage increase in average time that can be spent in supervision per worker and the percentage decrease in the number of organizational relationships with which each foreman will have to deal?

13. A manufacturer of a special purpose precision machine conducts a 2-week course for machine operators employed by its customer companies. It is generally accepted that the output of operators attending such a course is increased by 5 per cent. A company employing operators at a salary of $175 per week is considering the 2-week course.

(a) What is the total cost of training per operator if the fee is $250 and the operator is paid 15 per cent extra for attending the course?

(b) What would be the annual rate of return on the investment in the training program?

14. A machine tool operator produces 46 units per hour of which an average of 6 are defective. He is paid on a straight piecework basis at the rate of $5 per 100 satisfactory units. The firm sustains a loss of $0.02 per defective unit produced. The machine used in the process has a total operating cost of $3 per hour which includes depreciation, return on investment, and overhead. The operator works 1,800 hours per year. If a training program is initiated, it is anticipated that the production rate will increase to 52 units per hour only 2 of which will be defective.

(a) What is the maximum amount that the firm can spend on the training program per year?

(b) What would be the effect of the training program on the hourly wage of the operator?

15. A foreman supervises the work of Mr. A, Mr. B, and eight other men. The foreman states that "Mr. A requires twice as much and Mr. B requires half as much of my time as the average of my men." Mr. A's output is 8 units per day and Mr. B's output is 7 units per day. On the basis of equal cost per unit, what monthly salary is justified for Mr. B if the foreman receives $400 per month and Mr. A receives $320 per month?

16. An employee of a manufacturing concern has a total retirement credit of $27,000 applicable at a retirement age of 65. He may elect to receive this credit as a lump sum and invest it in a savings and loan association, yielding 5 per cent compounded quarterly, or he may elect to receive year end payments of $1,950 for the remainder of his life. Which alternative should be chosen for an expected life of 15 years after retirement?

17. The retirement plan in operation for the employees of a certain state operates as follows. Four per cent of the employee's salary is deducted and placed in a retirement fund to accumulate at 3 per cent interest compounded annually. At the age of 65 years, the employee has available in a fund to his credit, the amount above plus an equivalent amount that has been contributed by the state. What will be the amount available for retirement payments if an employee was hired at the age of 25 for an annual salary of $3,000 which has increased at the rate of $100 each year.

18. In a die-casting shop, the workers are paid on a piecework basis at the rate of $6 per 100 castings. Inspection reveals that for every 100 good castings produced, there are 9 defectives produced. Each defective represents a loss to the firm of $1.10. The methods department suggested two alternatives for producing the castings which would reduce the number of defectives but will also reduce the output of each worker.

	Defectives (Per 100 Good Ones)	Average Hourly Output Per Worker
Present Plan A	9	20
Alternate Plan B	6	15
Alternate Plan C	3.6	10

(a) Determine the piece rates per hundred units that should be paid under Plans B and C in order that the workers' earnings will remain unchanged?

(b) Determine the piece rates per hundred units that will make the total costs under Plans B and C equal to that under Plan A.

19. A manufacturer has been awarded a contract to make 6,500 mechanisms for a 50-cap blasting machine. Assembly of the mechanism can be performed by highly skilled operators working individually or by workmen of lesser skill working as a team, if they are provided with specialized assembly equipment and given special supervision. It is estimated that the highly skilled workmen, whose wage rate is $4.15 per hour, will require an average of three hours per assembly.

An assembly line that will permit specialization of labor can be set up for an initial cost of $9,500. The assembly can then be performed by four men whose individual wage rate is $3.10 per hour supervised by a foreman whose wage rate per hour is $4.35. It is estimated that the average time for this crew to complete an assembly will be 30 minutes per unit. If the assembly line equipment will be worthless after completion of the contract which method should be used?

20. In a certain manufacturing activity, 40 employees are engaged in identical activities. The average output of the group as a whole is 46.4 units per hour. The average output of the less productive half is 40.2 satisfactory and 1.4 unsatisfactory units per hour and the average of the more productive half is 52.6 satisfactory and 0.8 unsatisfactory units per hour. The employees work on a straight piecework plan and receive $3.30 per hundred satisfactory units. The firm sustains a loss of $0.07 for each unsatisfactory unit. One machine is required for each employee. Each machine has an annual fixed cost of $320 and a variable cost of $0.18 per hour. Supervision and other overhead costs are estimated at $560 per employee per year. The average employee works 1,900 hours per year. How much could be paid annually for a selection, training, and transfer program which would result in raising the average productivity of the entire group to 52.6 satisfactory and 0.8 unsatisfactory units per hour?

CHAPTER 14

THE EVALUATION
OF PUBLIC ACTIVITIES

The standards by which private enterprise, which must have profits to survive, evaluates its activities are markedly different from those that apply in the evaluation of public activities. In general, private activities are evaluated in terms of profit whereas public activities are evaluated in terms of the general welfare. The general welfare, as collectively and effectively expressed, is the primary basis for evaluating public activities with economy in terms of cost, income, and profit (a secondary basis). Economic analysis of governmental activity is, therefore, applicable only where monetary considerations are pertinent and have an influence on the general welfare.

A basis for evaluating public activities is necessary for an understanding of the characteristics of the governmental agencies that sponsor them. This chapter will present concepts and methods of analysis applicable to the evaluation of such activities.

14.1. THE FUNCTION OF GOVERNMENT

A national government is a super-organization to which all agencies of the government and all organizations in a nation, including lesser political subdivisions such as states, counties, cities, townships, and school districts as well as private organizations and individuals, are subordinate. In some of its aspects the government of the United States may be likened to a huge corporation. Its one hundred eighty million citizens play a role similar to that of stockholders. Each, if he chooses, may have a voice in the election of the policy-making group; the latter, the Congress of the United States, may be likened to a board of directors.

In the United States the lesser political subdivisions, such as states, counties, cities, and school districts, carry on their functions in much the same way as does the United States, for in them each citizen may have a voice in determining their policy. Each of these lesser political subdivisions has certain freedom of action, although each is in turn subordinate to its superior organization. The subdivisions of the government are delineated for the most part as continuous geographical areas that are easily recognized.

It is a basic tenet that the purpose of government is to serve its citizens. The chief aim of the United States as stated in its Constitution is the *national defense* and the *general welfare* of its citizens. For convenience in discussion, these aims may be considered to be embraced by the single term — general welfare. This simply stated aim is, however, very complex. To discharge it perfectly requires that the desires of each citizen be fulfilled to the greatest extent and in equal degree with those of every other citizen.

Since the general welfare is the aim of the United States, the superorganization to which the lesser political subdivisions are subordinate, it follows that the latter's aims must conform to the same general objective regardless of what other specific aims they may have.

The nature of public activities. The government of the United States and its several subdivisions engage in innumerable activities — all predicated upon the thesis of promotion of the general welfare. So numerous are the services available to individual citizens, associations, and private enterprises that books are required to catalog them.

Governmental activities may be classified under the general headings of protection, enlightenment and cultural development, and economic benefits. Included under protection are such activities as the military establishments, police forces, the system of jurisprudence, flood control, and health services. Under enlightenment and cultural development are such services as the public school system, the Library of Congress and other publicly supported libraries, publicly supported research, the postal service, and recreation facilities. Economic benefits include harbors and canals, power development, flood control, research and information service, and regulatory bodies.

The list above, although incomplete, shows that there is much overlapping in classification. For example, the educational system is considered by many to contribute to the protection, the enlightenment, and the economic benefit of people. Consideration of the purposes of governmental activities as suggested by the classification above is necessary in considering the pertinency of economic analysis to public activities.

Following World War II, approximately one-fourth of the national income was collected as taxes and expended for governmental activities. In point of expenditure, protection, particularly as represented by the military establishment, is of greatest importance. Other leading activities, as judged by the expenditure they require, are the public educational system, maintenance and construction of the highway system, and old-age benefits.

14.2. THE ENGINEERING PROCESS IN PUBLIC ACTIVITIES

Engineering is a factor in nearly all public activities because of the physical facilities these activities require. Most activities will at least have to be housed in some type of structure. The success of many activities is largely dependent upon the science and art of engineering.

Our system of highways embodies much engineering. The curves and grades of highways must be laid out in relation to the physical requirements of the vehicles that are to use them. Plans for their construction must encompass the physical characteristics of the soil on which they are to be built and the materials of which they are made. Engineering also comes into play in the design and usage of equipment required for highway construction.

The military might of nations is expressed largely now in terms of their industrial potential. Modern military establishments, if effective, are highly mechanized. Such military weapons as the tank and its gyroscopic gun stabilizer, proximity fuses, and atomic weapons are in large measure products of the application of engineering abilities.

A large percentage of expenditures on all governmental levels involves engineering directly or indirectly; many engineers find an outlet for their talents as employees or consultants of governmental agencies. Thus, public activities are a concern of all engineers as citizens and of many engineers as an outlet for their talents.

The plan for engineering economy analysis presented in Chapter 8 embraced the creative step which emphasized the direction of analysis toward (1) the discovery of opportunities for the employment of resources or (2) the discovery of means to circumvent factors limiting the success of present activities.

Suppose that a municipality has under consideration two projects, one a swimming pool and the other a library. The municipality has resources for one or the other, but not for both. The selection cannot be made on the basis of profit, since no profit is in prospect for either venture. The selection must be made on the basis of which will contribute most to the general welfare as expressed by the citizens of the community, perhaps by a vote. There is no superior basis for evaluating the contribution of each alternative to the general welfare.

The creative step as outlined for an economy study is useful and applicable to public activities if interpreted in terms of the objective of public activities, namely, the general welfare. The definitive, conversion, and decision steps are also directly applicable to the analysis of public activities when interpreted in terms of the public welfare objective.

The analyst who wishes to serve the public well will take particular pains with the conversion step. Suppose that a proposal to install equipment to soften the water in a community is to be decided by a vote of the taxpayers. Since the average taxpayer has little understanding of technical matters, a detailed analysis of the hardness of the water and the chemical treatment necessary to soften it will help him little to understand the proposal. What he will be interested in is how it will affect him from day to day and what it will cost. Benefits at the point of use should be explained. For example, it might be shown that soft water will not stain fixtures, will permit better results in laundering and shampooing, will be easier on the hands in dishwashing, and will reduce expenditures for soap, water tanks, and plumbing repair.

It should be noted that evaluations of public activities in terms of the general welfare encompass both the benefits to be received from and the cost of the proposed activity. No matter how subjective an evaluation of the contribution of an activity to the general welfare may be, its cost may often be determined quite objectively. It may be fairly simple to determine the immediate and subsequent costs in prospect if either the swimming pool or the library in the example above is constructed. A knowledge of the costs in prospect for benefits to be gained may be expected to result in sounder selection of public activities.

14.3. THE GENERAL WELFARE OBJECTIVE AS SEEN BY THE CITIZENRY

Since each citizen may have a voice, if he will excercise it, in a government, the objectives of the government stem from the people. For this reason the objectives taken by the government must be presumed to express the objectives necessary for attainment of the general welfare of the citizenry as perfectly as they can be expressed. This must be so, for there is no superior authority to decide the issue.

Thus, when the United States declares war, it must be presumed that this act is taken in the interest of the general welfare. Similarly, when a state votes paving bonds, it also must be presumed to be in the interest of the general welfare of its citizens. The same reasoning applies to all activities undertaken by any political subdivision; for, if an opposite view is taken, it is necessary to assume that people collectively act contrary to their wishes.

Broadly speaking, the final measure of the desirability of an activity of any governmental unit is the judgment of the people in that unit. The exception to this is when a subordinate unit attempts an activity whose objective is contrary to that of a superior unit, in which case the final measure of desirability will rest in part in the people of the superior unit. Also, it must be clear that governmental activities are evaluated by a summation of judgments of individual citizens whose basis for judgment has been the general welfare as each sees it. The objectives of most governmental activities appear to be primarily social in nature, although economic considerations are often a factor. Public activities are proposed, implemented, and judged by the same group, namely, the people of the governmental unit concerned.

The situation of the private enterprise is quite different. Those in control of private enterprise propose and implement services to be offered to the public, which judges whether the services are worth their cost. To survive, a private business organization must, at least, balance its income and costs; thus profit is of necessity a primary objective. For the same reason a private enterprise is rarely able to consider social objectives except to the extent that they improve its competitive position.

Thus, profit must be a first consideration in evaluating an activity of private enterprise. But when a public activity is being considered, the question to be decided is: Will it result in the greatest possible enhancement of the general welfare (in terms of economic, social, cultural, and other satisfactions) as judged by the people in the governmental unit concerned?

14.4. THE GENERAL-WELFARE OBJECTIVE AS SEEN BY THE INDIVIDUAL

In the previous section it was stated that public activities are evaluated by a summation of judgments of individual citizens, each of whose basis for judgment has been the general welfare as he sees it. Each citizen is the product of his unique heredity and environment; his home, cultural patterns, education, and aspirations differ from those of his neighbor. Because of this and the additional fact that human viewpoints are rarely logically determined, it is rare for large groups of citizens to see eye to eye on the desirability of proposed public activities.

The father of a family of several active children may be expected to see more point to expenditures for school and recreational facilities than to expenditures for a street-widening program planned to enhance the value of downtown property. It is not difficult for a person to extol the value of aviation to his community if a proposed airport will increase the value of his property or if he expects to receive the contract to build it. Many public activities have no doubt been strongly supported by a few persons primarily because they would profit handsomely thereby.

But it is incorrect to conclude that activities are supported only by those who see in them opportunity for economic gain. For example, schools and recreational facilities for youth are often strongly supported by people who have no children. Many public activities are directed to the conservation of national resources for the benefit of future generations.

It is clear that the benefits of public activities are very complex. Some that are of great general benefit may spell ruin for some persons and vice versa. Lack of knowledge of the long-run effect of proposed activities is probably the most serious obstacle in the way of the selection of those activities that can contribute most to the general welfare.

14.5. THE FINANCING OF PUBLIC ACTIVITIES

Funds to finance public activities are obtained through the assessment of various types of taxes and charges for services. Governmental receipts are derived chiefly from income, property, and excise taxes and duties on imports. Considerable income on some governmental levels is derived from fees collected for services. Examples of such incomes on the national level are incomes from postal services, and on the city level, incomes from supplying water service and from levies on property owners for sidewalks, pavements, and sewers adjacent to their property.

Two basic philosophies in the United States greatly influence the collection of funds and their expenditure by governmental subdivisions. These are collection of taxes on the premise of *ability to pay* and the expenditure of funds on the basis of *equalizing opportunity* of citizens. Application of the ability-to-pay viewpoint is clearly demonstrated in our income and property tax schedules. The equalization-of-opportunity philosophy is apparent in federal assistance to lesser subdivisions to help them provide improved educational and health programs, highway systems, old-age assistance, and the like. This philosophy is also manifested in the federal farm subsidy program.

14.6. IMPEDIMENTS TO EFFICIENCY IN GOVERNMENTAL ACTIVITIES

There are two serious impediments to efficiency in governmental activities. First, the person who pays taxes has no practical way of evaluating what he receives in return for his tax payment. His tax payments go into a common pool and lose their identity. The taxpayer, with few exceptions, receives nothing in exchange at the time or place at which he pays his taxes on which to base a comparison of the worth of what he pays in and what benefits he will receive as the result of his payment.

Since governmental units are exclusive franchises, the taxpayer has no choice as to which unit he must pay taxes. Thus, he does not have an opportunity to evaluate the effectiveness of tax units on the basis of comparative performance nor an opportunity to patronize what he believes to be the most efficient unit.

The second deterrent to efficiency in governmental activities is the fact that recipients of the products of tax supported activities cannot readily evaluate the products in reference to what they cost. Where no direct payment is exchanged for products, a person may be expected to accept them on the basis of their value to the recipient only. Thus, the products of governmental activities will tend to be accepted even though their value to the recipient is less than the cost to produce them.

14.7. CONSIDERATION OF INTEREST IN EVALUATION OF PUBLIC ACTIVITIES

The purpose of economic analysis of prospective public activities is to select and carry out activities that will result in the greatest satisfaction to the people concerned at the least cost.

Public activities financed through taxation require payments of funds from citizens. Broadly speaking, the funds expended for public activities should result in benefits comparable with those which the same funds would bring if expended in private ventures. It is almost universal for individuals to demand interest or its equivalent as an inducement to invest their private funds. To maintain public and private expenditures on a comparative basis, it seems logical to consider interest in economic evaluation of public activities that are financed through taxation.

Some public activities are financed in whole or in part through the sale of services or products. Examples of such activities are power developments, irrigation and housing projects, and toll bridges. Many such services could be carried on by private companies and are in general in competition with private enterprise. Again, since private enterprise must of necessity consider interest, it seems logical to consider interest in the economic analysis of public activities that compete in any way with private enterprise in order that both may be on a comparable basis.

Expenditures for capital goods are made on the promise that they will ultimately result in more consumer goods than can be had for a

present equal expenditure. Interest represents the expected difference. Not to consider interest in the evaluation of public activities
is equivalent to considering a future benefit equal to a present similar
benefit. This appears to be contrary to human nature.

The interest rate to use in an economy study of a public activity is
a matter of judgment. The rate used should not be less than that
paid for funds borrowed for the activity. In many cases, particularly
where the activity is comparable or competitive with private activities, the rate used should be comparable with that used in private
evaluations.

14.8. CONSIDERATION OF TAXES IN EVALUATION OF PUBLIC ACTIVITIES

Many public activities result in loss of taxes through the removal
of property from tax rolls or by other means, as, for example, the
exemption from sales taxes.

In a nation where free enterprise is a fundamental philosophy, the
basis for comparison of the cost of carrying on activities is the cost
for which they can be carried on by well-managed private enterprises. Therefore, it seems logical to take taxes into consideration
in economy analysis, particularly where the activities are competitive
with private enterprise.

14.9. PAYMENTS FOR AND BENEFITS RECEIVED FROM PUBLIC ACTIVITIES

Because of the two basic tenets of taxation on the basis of ability
to pay and expenditure of tax funds on the basis of equalization of
opportunity, there often is little relationship between the benefits
that an individual receives and the amount he pays for public activities. This is in large measure true of such major activities as government itself, military and police protection, the highway system, and
most educational activities.

There are, however, some public services that are paid for at the
point of exchange in much the same way as occurs with services
provided by private interests. This is common practice in the sale
of city water, irrigation water, and electric current by public agencies.
In such cases, the benefits received by an individual may be expected
to be related quite closely to the payments he makes for them.

Illustration of distribution of paving costs on the basis of benefit to users. Let it be assumed that a certain state is contemplating a highway development embracing the construction of 8,000,000 square yards of pavement. Vehicle registration in the state is as follows:

Passenger cars	500,000
Light trucks	100,000
Medium trucks	20,000
Heavy trucks	5,000

The characteristics and pavements necessary to carry the vehicles are taken as follows:

Class of Vehicle	Pavement Thickness	Cost Per Sq. Yard	Incremental Cost
Passenger cars	5.5 inches	$1.80	$14,400,000
Light trucks	6.0 inches	2.10	2,400,000
Medium trucks	6.5 inches	2.30	1,600,000
Heavy trucks	7.0 inches	2.50	1,600,000

On the assumption that paving costs should be distributed on the basis of the number of vehicles in each class and the incremental costs of paving required for each class of vehicle, the following analysis applies:

Allocation of Increment Per Vehicle	Passenger Cars	Light Trucks	Medium Trucks	Heavy Trucks
$14,400,000 ÷ 500,000	$28.80	$28.80	$28.80	$ 28.80
2,400,000 ÷ 100,000		24.00	24.00	24.00
1,600,000 ÷ 20,000			80.00	80.00
1,600,000 ÷ 5,000				320.00
Total	$28.80	$52.80	$132.80	$452.80

If it is desired to collect taxes on the basis of the cost of service, a suitable tax plan must be devised. This may be done by assessing a fuel tax and a vehicle license tax of proper amounts.

14.10. ECONOMIC COST OF PERSONAL INJURIES OR DEATH

The National Safety Council makes extensive and continual analyses of accidents involving motor vehicles. The calculable costs of such accidents embrace loss of wages, medical expense, overhead costs of insurance companies and property damage. On the average there are 35 non-fatal accidents and 240 property-damage accidents for each fatal accident. The average cost of these three classes of accidents is calculated to be as follows:

Fatality per person.....................................	$25,800
Non-fatal, injury accidents...............................	1,250
Property damage accidents................................	220

From the data above the aggregate cost of motor-vehicle accidents per death may be calculated as follows:

Fatality per person..	$ 25,800
Non-fatal, injury accident $1,250 × 35....................	43,750
Property damage accident $220 × 240.....................	52,800
Total...	$122,350

The National Safety Council rounds this total to $120,000. The total cost of motor-vechicle accidents results in about 36,000 deaths per year in the United States and also results in a total loss of about $4,000,000,000 per year. Some progress is being made in coping with motor-vehicle hazards and it is interesting to note that the death rate per 10,000 motor vehicles has dropped from 13.2 in 1933 to 6.2 in 1954. The deaths per 100,000,000 motor-vehicle miles decreased from 15.6 in 1933 to 6.4 in 1954. These and similar statistics are useful in justifying expenditures to reduce the hazards of public and private structures, machines and practices.

Consider the following example. The death rate on a certain highway has been eight per 100,000,000 vehicle miles. How much expenditure per mile is justified for improvements that will result in a decrease in the death rate to four deaths per 100,000,000 if the traffic density on the highway is 6,000 vehicles per day, if annual maintenance is 4 per cent of the cost of improvements, if the improvement will be used for thirty years and if money is worth 3 per cent? Let P equal the cost of the improvement. Then

$$\text{RP 3-30}$$
$$P(0.05102) + P \times 0.04 = (8 - 4)\frac{6,000 \times 365}{100,000,000} \times \$120,000$$
$$P = \$115,490.$$

14.11. COMPETITIVE BIDDING, A CHECK ON COSTS OF PUBLIC ACTIVITIES

The point has been made that one basis for the evaluation of public activities is the cost for which they can be carried on by private enterprise. One common method for determining the cost of constructing and operating a public activity is to call for competitive bids from private organizations. The lowest bid received, after allowances for the bidder's ability to discharge the terms of his contract, is then a measure of cost. Except in unusual circumstances, there seems no justification for a governmental agency to undertake the construction and operation of a project unless it can do so for less than would be charged by private enterprise although there are times when governmental agencies carry on activities as a means of determining if costs of private enterprise are fair.

It should be borne in mind that many of the activities of governmental units are of such a nature or size or of such uncertainty that they are beyond the scope of private enterprise. Such activities are not measurable through competitive bidding.

PROBLEMS

1. Contrast the criteria for evaluation of private and public activities.

2. Outline the function of government and the nature of public activities.

3. Explain how engineering is an important factor in nearly all public activities.

4. Describe the meaning of the general welfare objective as it relates to engineering economy analysis applied to public activities.

5. Describe the impediments to efficiency in governmental activities.

6. Name the elements that should be considered in deciding on an interest rate to be used in the evaluation of public activities.

7. An integrated water supply system for a municipality of 30,000 people is proposed. The estimated first cost of the required dam, treatment plant, and pipelines is $120,000. The system will have a service life of 20 years and an annual operating expense of $37,500. The project can be financed by floating 3 per cent bonds at par to be sold to the citizens or by arranging for a 4.75 per cent loan from an insurance company. Calculate the cost of 1,000 gallons of water under each plan if the average consumption of water per day is 80 gallons per person.

8. A turnpike has been opened between Cities A and B, a distance of 180 miles via the toll road and 208 miles via the shortest alternate free highway. From the following data, determine the economic advantage, if any, of using the toll road for the following conditions applicable to the operation of a light truck: toll cost, $1.80; driver cost, $2.10 per hour; average driving rate between entrances via toll road and free road, respectively, 55 m.p.h. and 40 m.p.h.; estimated average cost of operating truck per mile via toll road, $0.09, via free road, $0.095.

9. Analysis of accidents in one state indicates that increasing the width of highways from 18 feet to 22 feet may decrease the accident rate from 260 per 100,000,000 to 180 per 100,000,000 vehicle miles. Calculate the average daily number of vehicles that should use a highway to justify widening on the basis of the following estimates: Average loss per accident, $440; per mile cost of widening pavement 4 feet, $7,100; useful life of improvement, 25 years; annual maintenance, 3 per cent of first cost; interest rate, 5 per cent compounded continuously.

10. It is estimated that increasing the width of highway shoulders from 2 feet to 7 feet on each side of the pavement will reduce highway accidents from 280 to 190 per 100,000,000 vehicle miles. What will be the equivalent annual net benefit of widening shoulders for the following conditions: Average traffic, 3,600 vehicles per day; average accident loss, $1,260; cost of extending shoulders from 2 feet to 7 feet, $4,200; additional maintenance cost, 4 per cent; estimated useful life, 20 years; interest rate, 4 per cent compounded continuously.

11. A suburban area has been annexed by a city which henceforth is to supply water service to the area. The prospective growth of the suburb has been estimated and on the basis of this the requirements for pipelines needed to meet the demand for water are as follows:

Years from Now	Pipe Diameter	First Cost	Pumping Cost Per Year
0	10″	$200,000	$11,000
10	14″	$260,000	$12,000
25	18″	$300,000	$13,000

From the standpoint of water-carrying capacity, a 14-inch pipe is equivalent to two 10-inch pipes and an 18-inch pipe is equivalent to three 10-inch pipes. On the basis of a minimum equivalent expenditure over the next 40 years, compare the following plans if the interest rate is 4 per cent and if used pipeline can be sold for 20 per cent of its original cost.

Years from Now	Plan A	Plan B	Plan C	Plan D	Plan E
0	Install 10″	Install 10″	Install 14″	Install 14″	Install 18″
14	Sell 10″ Install 14″	Install 10″	....	....	....
25	Sell 14″ Install 18″	Install 10″	Install 10″	Sell 14″ Install 18″	....

12. It is proposed to eliminate the grade crossing between a railway and a busy highway. An underpass will cost $368,000 and involve an annual maintenance cost of $3,500 over and above the normal maintenance of the highway. The traffic on the highway has been analyzed as follows:

Type of Vehicle	Vehicles Per Day	Operating Cost/ Mile	Equivalent Length of the Grade Crossing at Average Speed	Cost of Stopping and Delay
Passenger	2,900	$0.08	0.08 miles	$0.006
Light comm.	300	$0.14	0.06 miles	$0.040
Heavy comm.	100	$0.20	0.05 miles	$0.050

At present, the railroad employs one watchman on the crossing at a salary of $3,000 per year, who will not be needed on the underpass. The project can be financed by floating 3 per cent bonds at par. What would be the annual economic benefit of accepting the proposal?

13. A city operates a trolley line through a downtown section with an annual operating loss of $275,000. A proposal to abandon the trolley line contains the following information: passenger miles absorbed by the trolley line, 11.2 million per year; number of private automobiles in the city, 12,750; passenger miles by private automobile, 29.6 million per year; number of parking spaces in the city, 7,500.

(a) What would be the per cent increase in the vehicular traffic density in the city as a result of the abandonment of the trolley line?

(b) What would be the per cent increase in the cost of accidents in the city if the cost of an accident is proportional to the vehicular traffic density to the 1.3 power?

(c) How many more public parking spaces will be needed?

14. At present, the fire insurance rate in a small community is $0.28 per $100 of property valuation. The rate would be reduced to $0.18 per $100 if the community had an adequate fire department.

The community has 1,800 dwelling units with an average valuation of $5,580 each. The estimated expenses for establishing a suitable fire department are as follows:

Item	Cost	Service Life
Water line	$23,000	40 years
Pumping equipment	$ 4,600	20 years
Supply tank	$32,000	40 years
Fire truck	$ 3,700	20 years
Fire chief	$ 5,400 per year	
Assistant	$ 4,200 per year	

Should the community establish a fire department if the required capital can be secured at an interest rate of 3 per cent? What other considerations would be involved?

15. Two sections of a city are separated by a marsh area. It is proposed to correct the sections by a four lane highway. Plan A consists of a 2.4 mile highway directly over the marsh by the use of earth fill. The initial cost will be $250,000 and the required annual maintenance will be $11,000. Plan B consists of a 5.2 mile road skirting the swamp. The initial cost will be $480,000 with an annual maintenance cost of $5,600. A traffic survey estimates the traffic density to be as follows:

Years after Construction	Traffic Density in Vehicles Per Lane Per Hour
0	150
10	800
20	2200

The estimated average speed under these densities would be 45 m.p.h., 40 m.p.h., and 28 m.p.h., respectively. The traffic consists of 75 per cent noncommercial vehicles with an operating cost of $0.072 per mile and 25 per cent commercial vechicles with an operating cost of $0.16 per mile and $2.40 per hour. If Plan B is accepted the development of the property adjacent to the highway will result in an increase in tax revenue of $4,800 per year.

(a) Compare the alternatives on the basis of a 20-year period.

(b) At what traffic density are the plans equivalent for an interest rate of 6 per cent?

16. An inland state is presently connected to a seaport by means of a railroad system. The annual goods transported is 360 million ton miles. The average transport charge is 5 mills per ton mile. Within the next 20 years, the transport is likely to increase by 60 per cent.

It is proposed that a river flowing from the state to the seaport be improved at a cost of $700,000,000. This will make the river navigable to barges and will reduce the transport cost to 2 mills per ton mile.

The project will be financed by 70 per cent federal funds at no interest, and 30 per cent raised by 3 per cent bonds at par. There would be some side effects of the change over as follows:

(1) The railroad would be bankrupt and be sold for no salvage value. The right of way, worth about $6.5 millions, will revert to the state.

(2) 3,600 employees will be out of employment. The state will have to pay them welfare checks of $120 per month.

(3) The reduction in the income from the taxes on the railroad will be compensated by the taxes on the barges.

(a) Would it be economical to undertake the project based on the next 20 years operation?

(b) At what average rate of transport per year will the two alternatives be equal?

PART V

ACCOUNTING, COST ACCOUNTING, AND INCOME TAXES

CHAPTER 15

ACCOUNTING, COST ACCOUNTING, AND ECONOMY ANALYSIS

The accounting system of an enterprise provides a media for recording historical data arising from the essential activities employed in the production of goods and services. Engineering economy analysis provides a means for quantifying the expected future differences in the worth and cost of alternative engineering proposals. As compared with this function, accounting has the objective of providing summaries of the status of an enterprise in terms of assets and liabilities so that the condition of the enterprise may be judged at any point in time. Therefore, it is essential that both the function of accounting and engineering economy be understood and accepted.

Accounting records are one of the most important sources of data for engineering economy studies. In them the analyst will find detailed quantitative data useful in estimating the future outcome of activities similar to those completed. In addition, the outcome of decisions based on economy studies will eventually be revealed in these records. For these reasons, it is desirable that the data provided by accounting systems be examined in relation to the requirements of engineering economy studies.

15.1. GENERAL ACCOUNTING

Two classifications of accounting are recognized; general accounting and cost accounting. Cost accounting is a branch of general accounting and is usually of greater importance in engineering economy studies than is general accounting. Cost accounting will be considered in the next section.

The primary purpose of the general accounting system is to make possible the periodic preparation of:

1. A *balance sheet* setting out the assets, liabilities, and net worth of the enterprise at a stated date.
2. A *profit and loss statement* showing the revenues and expenses of the enterprise for a stated period.

The accounts of an enterprise fall into five general classifications — assets, liabilities, net worth, revenue, and expense. Three of these — assets, liabilities, and net worth — serve to give the position of the enterprise at a certain date. The other two accounts — revenue and expense — accumulate profit and loss information for a stated period, which act to change the position of the enterprise at different points in time. Each of these five accounts is a summary of other accounts utilized as part of the total accounting system.

The balance sheet is prepared for the purpose of exhibiting the financial position of an enterprise at a specific point in time. It lists the assets, liabilities, and net worth of the enterprise as of a certain date. For example, the balance sheet for Company A shows these major accounts as of December 31, 19xx.

Assets		Liabilities	
Cash.................	$161,000	Notes payable........	$ 22,000
Accounts receivable...	7,000	Accounts payable.....	4,700
Raw materials........	9,000	Accrued taxes........	3,200
Work in process......	17,000	Declared dividends....	40,000
Finished goods........	3,700		
Land................	11,000		$ 69,900
Factory building......	82,000	*Net Worth*	
Equipment...........	34,000	Capital stock........	$200,000
Prepaid services......	1,300	Profit for December...	56,100
			256,100
	$326,000		$326,000

Balance sheets are normally drawn up annually, quarterly, monthly, or at other regular intervals. The change of a company's condition during the interval between balance sheets may be determined by comparing successive balance sheets.

Information relative to the change of conditions that have taken place during the interval between successive balance sheets is provided by a profit and loss statement. This statement is a summary of the income and expense for a stated period of time. For example, the profit and loss statement for Company A shows the income, expense, and net profit for the month of December, 19xx.

Gross income from sales.................................		$251,200
Cost of goods sold......................................		$142,800
Net income from sales...................................		$108,400
Operating expense:		
Rent......................................	$11,700	
Salaries..................................	$28,200	
Depreciation..............................	$ 4,800	
Advertising...............................	$ 6,500	
Insurance.................................	$ 1,100	$ 52,300
Net profit from operations..............................		$ 56,100

The balance sheet and the profit and loss statement are summaries in more or less detail, depending on the purpose they are to serve. They are related to each other; the net profit developed on the profit and loss statement is entered under net worth on the balance sheet.

Together, the balance sheet and the profit and loss statement summarize the five major accounts of an enterprise. The major accounts are summaries of other accounts falling within these general classifications as, for example, cash, notes payable, capital stock, cost of goods sold, and rent. Each of these accounts is a summary in itself. For example, the asset item of raw material is a summary of the value of all items of raw material as revealed by detailed inventory records. In the search for data upon which to base economy studies, it will be necessary to trace each account back through the accounting system until the required information is found.

15.2. COST ACCOUNTING

Cost accounting is a branch of general accounting adapted to registering the costs for labor, material, and overhead on an item-by-item basis as a means of determining the cost of production. The final summary of this information is presented in the form of a cost of goods made and sold statement. It lists the costs of labor, material, and overhead applicable to all goods made and sold during a certain period. For example, the cost of goods made and sold statement for Company A during the month of December, 19xx is as follows:

Direct Material

In process Dec. 1, 19xx	$ 3,400	
Applied during the month	$39,500	
Total	$42,900	
In process Dec. 31, 19xx	$ 4,200	$ 38,700

Direct Labor

In process Dec. 1, 19xx	$ 4,300	
Applied during the month	$51,900	
Total	$56,200	
In process Dec. 31, 19xx	$ 5,700	$ 50,500

Factory Overhead

In process Dec. 1, 19xx	$ 5,800	
Applied during the month	$60,100	
Total	$65,900	
In process Dec. 31, 19xx	$ 7,100	$ 58,800

Cost of Goods Made	$148,000
Finished goods Dec. 1, 19xx	$ 16,200
Total	$164,200
Finished goods Dec. 31, 19xx	$ 21,400
Cost of goods sold	$142,800

The cost of goods made and sold statement reflects summary data derived from the four accounts of materials in process, labor in process, overhead in process, and finished goods. The statement is subsidiary to the profit and loss statement since the "cost of goods sold" amount it develops is transferred to the profit statement. Similarly, the profit and loss statement was shown to be subsidiary to the balance sheet since the profit or loss amount developed thereon is transferred to the net worth section of the balance sheet.

The costs that are incurred to produce and sell an item of product are commonly classified as direct material, direct labor, factory overhead, factory cost, administrative cost, and selling cost. The first three are exhibited on the cost of goods made and sold statement, and give rise to the cost of goods sold entry on the profit and loss statement. Administrative and selling costs appear on the profit and loss statement under operating expense, and are subtracted from net income to arrive at the net profit amount. Each of these cost classifications will be considered in the paragraphs that follow.

Direct material. The material whose cost is directly charged to a product is termed *direct material.* Ordinarily, the costs of principal items of material required to make a product are charged to it as direct material costs. Charges for direct material are made to the product at the time the material is issued, through the use of forms and procedures designed for that purpose. The sum of charges for materials that accumulate against the product during its passage through the factory constitutes the total direct material cost.

In the manufacture of many products, small amounts of a number of items of material may be consumed which are not directly charged to the product. These items are charged to factory overhead, as will be explained later. They are not directly charged to the product on the premise that the advantage to be gained will not be enough to offset the increased cost of record keeping.

Although perhaps less subject to gross error than records of other elements of cost, records of direct material costs should not be used in engineering economy studies without being questioned. Their accuracy in regard to quantity and price of material should be ascertained. Also, their applicability to the situation being considered should be established before they are used.

Direct labor. *Direct labor* is labor whose cost is charged directly to the product. The source of this charge is time tickets or similar forms used to record the time and wages of workmen whose efforts are applied to a product during its journey through the factory. Unless the allocation of labor costs to products is very closely controlled, records of labor costs charged to specific products are likely to be in error.

As a result of either carelessness or a desire to conceal an undue amount of time spent on a job, some of the time applied to one job may be reported as being applied to another. Thus, direct-labor cost records should be carefully examined for accuracy and applicability to the situations under investigation before being used as data for engineering economy studies.

Various small amounts of labor may not be considered to warrant the record-keeping that is required to charge them as direct labor. Such items of labor became part of the factory overhead. The labor of personnel engaged in such activities as inspection, testing, or moving the product from machine to machine or in pickling, painting, or washing the product is often charged in this way.

Such items as social security, pension and insurance costs that are nearly proportional to direct wages are sometimes included in arriving at direct labor costs.

Factory overhead. *Factory overhead* is also designated by such terms as factory expense, shop expense, burden, indirect costs, and on-cost. Factory overhead costs embrace all expenses incurred in factory production which are not directly charged to products as direct material or direct labor.

The practice of applying overhead charges arises because prohibitive costly accounting procedures would be required to charge all items of cost directly to the product.

Factory overhead costs embrace costs of material and labor not charged directly to product and fixed costs. Fixed costs embrace charges for such things as taxes, insurance, interest, rental, depreciation and maintenance of buildings, furniture and equipment, and salaries of factory supervision, which are considered to be independent of volume of production.

Indirect material and labor costs embrace costs of all items of material and labor consumed in manufacture which are not charged to the product as direct material or direct labor.

Factory cost. The *factory cost* of a product is the sum of direct material, direct labor, and factory overhead. It is these items that are summarized on the cost of goods made and sold statement. This cost classification separates the manufacturing cost from administrative and selling costs thus giving an indication of production costs over time.

Administrative costs. *Administrative costs* arise from expenditures for such items as salaries of executive, clerical, and technical personnel, office space, office supplies, depreciation of office equipment, travel, and fees for legal, technical, and auditing services that are necessary to direct the enterprise as a whole as distinct from its production and selling activities. Expenses so incurred are often recorded on the basis of the cost of carrying on subdivisions of administrative activities deemed necessary to take appropriate action to improve the effectiveness of administration.

In most cases, it is not practical to relate administrative costs directly to specific products. The usual practice is to allocate administrative costs to the product as a percentage of the product's factory cost. For example, if the annual administrative costs and factory costs of a concern are estimated at $10,000 and $100,000, respectively, for a given year, 10 per cent will be added to the factory cost of products manufactured to absorb the administrative costs.

Selling cost. The *selling cost* of a product arises from expenditures incurred in disposing of the products and services produced. This class of expense includes such items as salaries, commissions, office space, office supplies, rental and depreciation, operation of office equipment and automobiles, travel, market surveys, entertainment of customers, displays, and sales space.

Selling expenses may be allocated to various classes of products, sales territories, sales of individual salesmen, and so forth, as a means of improving the effectiveness of selling activities. In many cases it is considered adequate to allocate selling expense to products as a percentage of their production cost. For example, if the annual selling expense is estimated at $22,000 and the annual production cost is estimated at $110,000, 20 per cent will be added to the production cost of products to obtain the cost of sales.

15.3. BASES FOR ALLOCATION OF FACTORY OVERHEAD

There are four common methods of allocating factory overhead charges to the product being produced. These are the direct-labor-cost method, the direct-labor-hour method, the direct-material-cost method, and the machine-rate method. Each of these bases for allocation will be illustrated by reference to a hypothetical manufacturing concern which will serve to exhibit some aspects of cost accounting pertinent in engineering economy studies.

The Acme Company is a small manufacturing concern with plant facilities as is shown in Figure 15.1. Land for the plant cost $3,000 and the plant itself, constructed four years ago, cost $12,000. Two-

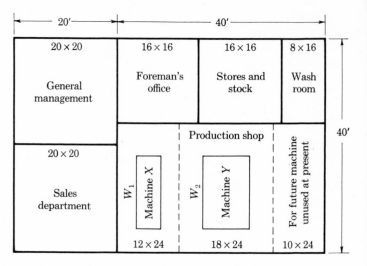

Figure 15.1. Plan of Acme company plant facilities.

thirds of each of these items, or $2,000 and $8,000, is attributed to the production department. Other data pertinent to the determination of rates for the allocation of overhead charges for the fifth year of operation are given in the following paragraphs.

The production facilities of the Acme Company consist of the following items.

Description	Cost	Age	Depreciation Rate	Depreciation 5th Year	Present Value
Land.....................	$ 2,000	...	0	$ 0	$ 2,000
Building and equipment..	8,000	4	4%	320	6,720
Factory furniture........	400	4	10%	40	240
Small tools (pres. value).	400	...	40%	160	400
Machine X.............	2,000	4	10%	200	1,200
Machine Y.............	8,000	4	10%	800	4,800
Stores and stock inventory	5,000	...	0	0	5,000
	$25,800			$1,520	$20,360

The factory salaries and wages during the fifth year are estimated to be as follows:

Foreman F supervises factory operation.....................	$3,000
Handyman H moves material, takes care of stock and stores, and does janitor work.......................................	1,600
Total indirect labor.....................................	$4,600
Workman W_1 operates Machine X, $1.80/hr. × 1,600 hr........	$2,880
Workman W_2 operates Machine Y, $1.20/hr. × 1,600 hr........	1,920
Total direct labor......................................	$4,800

The supplies to be used in the factory during the fifth year are estimated as follows:

Office and general supplies................................	$ 200
Water (est. as ¾ of bill for entire building).................	60
Lighting current (est. as ⅔ of bill for entire building).........	150
Heating fuel (est. as ⅔ of bill for entire building).............	210
Electric power ($160 for Machine X and $300 for Machine Y)...	460
Cutting oil, expendable tools, abrasive paper, etc. ($100 for Machine X and $280 for Machine Y)........................	380
	$1,460

The estimated activity of the Acme Company Factory during the fifth year is summarized in Table 15.1.

Annual taxes are estimated at 2 per cent of the cost of facilities. Insurance is estimated at 0.5 per cent of the cost of facilities. Annual maintenance of building and factory furniture is estimated at 3 per cent of original cost. The annual maintenance of Machine X and Machine Y is estimated at 8 per cent of original cost. Payroll taxes and compensation insurance are estimated to be 9 per cent of the factory payroll. Interest on invested funds will be taken at 6 per cent.

The calculation of the Acme Company overhead rates during the fifth year may be summarized as follows:

A. *Overhead Items Equivalent to Rent*

Depreciation, insurance, maintenance on building, $8,000 × (0.04 + 0.005 + 0.03)..............	$ 600
Taxes on cost of building and land, $10,000 × 0.02.	200
Interest on present value of building and land, $8,720 × 0.06.............................	523
Water, light, and fuel for factory, $60 + $150 + $210	420
Total...	$ 1,743

Table 15.1. ESTIMATED ACTIVITY DURING THE FIFTH YEAR

Product	Estimated output	Material cost		Direct-labor hours				Machine hours			
				Workman W_1		Workman W_2		Machine X		Machine Y	
		Each	Total	Each	Total	Each	Total	Each	Total	Each	Total
L	1,000	$4.00	$ 4,000	1	1,000	—	—	1	1,000	—	—
M	1,400	4.00	5,600	—	—	1	1,400	—	—	1	1,400
N	800	4.00	3,200	0.75	600	0.25	200	0.75	600	0.25	200
			$12,800		1,600		1,600		1,600		1,600

B. *Miscellaneous Items of Overhead*

Depreciation, taxes, insurance, and maintenance on factory furniture, $400 × (0.10 + 0.02 + 0.005 + 0.03)..............................	$ 62	
Interest on present value of factory furniture, $240 × 0.06..............................	14	
Depreciation, taxes, insurance, and interest on present value of small tools, $400 × (0.40 + 0.02 + 0.005 + 0.06)..............................	194	
Taxes, insurance, and interest on stores and stock inventory, $5,000 × (0.02 + 0.005 + 0.06)......	425	
Office and general supplies......................	200	
Total...		$ 895

C. *Indirect Labor and Labor Overhead*

Salaries of indirect labor of F and H, $3,000 + 1,600.	$4,600	
Payroll taxes, ($3,000 + $1,600 + $2,880 + $1,920) × 0.09.............................	846	
Total...		$ 5,446

D. *Machine X Overhead Items*

Depreciation, taxes, insurance, and maintenance on Machine X, $2,000 × (0.10 + 0.02 + 0.005 + 0.08)..............................	$ 410	
Interest on present value of Machine X, $1,200 × 0.06.............................	72	
Supplies for Machine X.........................	100	
Power for Machine X...........................	160	
Total...		$ 742

E. *Machine Y Overhead Items*

Depreciation, taxes, insurance, and maintenance on Machine Y, $8,000 × (0.10 + 0.02 + 0.005 + 0.08)..............................	$1,640	
Interest on present value of Machine Y, $4,800 × 0.06.............................	288	
Supplies for Machine Y.........................	280	
Power for Machine Y...........................	300	
Total...		$ 2,508
Grand total, all factory overhead items................		$11,334

On the basis of the information given, overhead allocation rates may be calculated as follows:

$$\text{direct-labor-cost rate} = \frac{\text{total factory overhead}}{\text{total direct labor wages}}$$

$$= \frac{\$11,334}{\$4,800} = 2.36$$

$$\text{direct-labor-hour rate} = \frac{\text{total factory overhead}}{\text{total hours of direct labor}}$$

$$= \frac{\$11,334}{3,200 \text{ hours}} = \$3.54 \text{ per hour}$$

$$\text{direct-material-cost rate} = \frac{\text{total factory overhead}}{\text{total direct material cost}}$$

$$= \frac{\$11,334}{\$12,800} = 0.89.$$

Further analysis must be made before machine rates can be established for Machine X and Machine Y. In establishing machine rates, as many items of overhead as possible are directly allocated to each machine before their identity is lost by being charged to an overhead account.

Consider Item A above. This item is equal to $1,743 and is equivalent to rent of the factory building, which has a floor area of 1,600 square feet.

Annual cost per sq. ft. of floor area, $1,743 ÷ 1,600.........	$1.09
Area directly occupied by Machine X, 12 × 24.............	288 sq. ft.
Area directly occupied by Machine Y, 18 × 24.............	432 sq. ft.
Space charge, Machine X, 288 × $1.09....................	$314
Space charge, Machine Y, 432 × $1.09....................	$471
Total space charged to Machines X and Y...............	$785
Balance of space cost to be allocated, $1,743 − $785........	$958

This balance of Item A, together with Items B and C must be distributed to Machine X and Machine Y on some basis that is estimated to reflect actual conditions. In this example the sums of these items will be allocated equally to the two machines. One-half of the unallocated sum is equal to ½ ($958 + $895 + $5,446) = $3,649.

Machine X Overhead Charges and Machine Rate

Item D...	$ 742
Space charge as calculated above............................	314
One-half of unallocated balance of Item A, Item B, and Item C,	
½ ($958 + $895 + $5,446)...............................	3,649
Total..	$4,705

$$\text{machine rate (Machine X)} = \frac{\text{overhead allocated to Machine X}}{\text{estimated annual hours of operation}}$$

$$= \frac{\$4,705}{1,600 \text{ hr.}} = \$2.94 \text{ per hour.}$$

Machine Y Overhead Charges and Machine Rate

Item E..	$2,508
Space charge as calculated above............................	471
One-half of unallocated balance of Item A, Item B, and Item C,	
½ ($958 + $895 + $5,446)...............................	3,649
Total..	$6,628

$$\text{machine rate (Machine Y)} = \frac{\$6,628}{1,600 \text{ hr.}} = \$4.14 \text{ per hour.}$$

The cost of Products L, M, and N may now be determined by each of the four methods of allocating factory overhead.

The Factory Cost of Product L

Direct-labor-cost method:	
Direct material...	$ 4.00
Direct labor, 1 hr. × $1.80/hr............................	1.80
Overhead, $1.80 × 2.36.................................	4.25
	$10.05
Direct-labor-hour method:	
Direct material...	$ 4.00
Direct labor, 1 hr. × $1.80/hr............................	1.80
Overhead, 1 hr. × $3.54/hr..............................	3.54
	$ 9.34
Direct-material-cost method:	
Direct material...	$ 4.00
Direct labor, 1 hr. × $1.80/hr............................	1.80
Overhead, $4 × 0.89...................................	3.56
	$ 9.36

Machine-rate method:

Direct material...	$ 4.00
Direct labor, 1 hr. × $1.80/hr..........................	1.80
Overhead, 1 hr. × $2.94/hr.............................	2.94
	$ 8.74

The Factory Cost of Product M

Direct-labor-cost method:

Direct material...	$ 4.00
Direct labor, 1 hr. × $1.20/hr..........................	1.20
Overhead, $1.20 × 2.36................................	2.83
	$ 8.03

Direct-labor-hour method:

Direct material...	$ 4.00
Direct labor, 1 hr. × $1.20/hr..........................	1.20
Overhead, 1 hr. × $3.54/hr.............................	3.54
	$ 8.74

Direct-material-cost method:

Direct material...	$ 4.00
Direct labor, 1 hr. × $1.20/hr..........................	1.20
Overhead, $4 × 0.89..................................	3.56
	$ 8.76

Machine-rate method:

Direct material...	$ 4.00
Direct labor, 1 hr. × $1.20/hr..........................	1.20
Overhead, 1 hr. × $4.14...............................	4.14
	$ 9.34

The Factory Cost of Product N

Direct-labor-cost method:

Direct material...	$ 4.00
Direct labor, 0.75 hr. × $1.80/hr. + 0.25 hr. × $1.20/hr......	1.65
Overhead, $1.65 × 2.36................................	3.89
	$ 9.54

Direct-labor-hour method:

Direct material...	$ 4.00
Direct labor (calculated as above).......................	1.65
Overhead, (0.75 hr. + 0.25 hr.) × $3.54/hr................	3.54
	$ 9.19

Direct-material-cost method:

Direct material..	$ 4.00
Direct labor..	1.65
Overhead, $4 × 0.89...................................	3.56
	$ 9.21

Machine-rate method:

Direct material..	$ 4.00
Direct labor..	1.65
Overhead, 0.75 hr. × $2.94 hr. + 0.25 hr. × $4.14/hr........	3.24
	$ 8.89

The cost of sales for the Acme Company is obtained by adding administrative and selling costs to the factory cost. Continuing with the example of the Acme Company, suppose that after careful analysis of expenditures, annual administrative costs have been estimated at $4,600 and annual selling costs at $9,300.

Annual direct material costs, direct labor costs, and factory overhead costs for the Acme Company have been estimated previously as $12,800, $4,800, and $11,334, respectively. Therefore, the annual estimated cost of sales of the Acme Company for the fifth year may be summarized as follows:

Estimated annual direct material cost......	$12,800	
Estimated annual direct labor cost........	4,800	
Estimated annual factory overhead cost....	11,334	
Estimated annual factory cost....................	$28,934	
Estimated annual administrative cost..............	4,600	
Estimated annual production cost.........................		$33,534
Estimated annual selling cost............................		9,300
Estimated annual cost of sales...........................		$42,834

15.4. EVALUATION OF COST ACCOUNTING DATA

An examination of the factory costs obtained for Product L in the Acme Company example with the four methods of factory overhead employed shows considerable variation.

Each of the three costs that make up the total is subject to error. Direct material costs may be incorrect because of such errors as pricing, charging a product with more material than is actually used, and the use of approximate methods generally. Similarly, and for much the same reasons, direct labor costs as charged will usually be in error to some extent. However, with reasonably good control and accounting procedures, direct material costs and direct labor costs are generally fairly reliable.

If attention is directed to factory overhead costs allocated to Product L, it will be observed that amounts allocated by the several methods range from $4.25 to $2.94. The ratio of these amounts is equal to approximately 1.5. The fact that the amounts shown for the several methods differ is proof that at least three of the methods of allocations are in error. It is probable that all are in error.

In actual practice the item of factory overhead is a summation of a great number and variety of costs. It is therefore not surprising that the use of a single, simple method will not allocate factory overhead costs to specific products with precision. Although a particular method may be generally quite satisfactory, gross errors may result in some specific situations.

For example, consider the direct-labor-hour method as it applies to Product L and Product M. The assumption is that $3.54 will be incurred for each hour of direct labor, regardless of equipment used. Thus, the amount of overhead allocated to Product L and Product M is identical, even though it is apparent that the cost of operating the respective machines on which they are processed is quite different. Note that the machine rates of Machine X and Machine Y are $2.94 and $4.14, respectively.

If the direct-material-cost method is used, it is clear that overhead allocations to products will be dependent upon the unit price as well as upon the quantity of materials used. Suppose, for example, that in the manufacture of tables a certain model may be made from either pine or mahogany. Processing might be identical but the amount charged for overhead might be several times as much for mahogany as for pine because of the difference in the unit price of the materials used.

Effect of changes in extent of activity. In the determination of rates for the allocation of overhead, the activity of the Acme Company for the fifth year was estimated in terms of Products L, M, and N. This estimate served as a basis for determining annual material cost, annual direct labor cost, annual direct labor hours, and machine hours. These items then became the denominator of the several allocation rates.

The numerator of the allocation rates was the estimated factory overhead, totaling $11,334. This numerator quantity will remain relatively constant for changes in activity, as an examination of the items of which it is composed will reveal.

For this reason the several rates for allocating factory overhead will vary in some generally inverse proportion with activity. Thus, if the actual activity is less than the estimated activity, the overhead rate charged will be less than the amount necessary to absorb the estimated total overhead. The reverse is also true. When the under or overabsorbed balance of overhead becomes known at the end of the year, it is usually charged to profit and loss, or surplus.

In engineering economy analyses, the effect of activity on overhead charges and overhead rates is an important consideration. The total overhead charges of the Acme Company would remain relatively constant over a range of activity represented, for example, by 800 to 2,000 hours of activity for each of the two machines. Thus, after the total overhead has been allocated, the incremental cost of producing additional units of product will consist of direct material and direct labor costs.

Cost data must be pertinent. The need for exercising care to see that cost accounting data are pertinent to situations under consideration will be illustrated by two examples.

It is a common error to infer that a reduction in labor costs will result in a proportionate decrease in overhead costs, particularly if overhead is allocated on a labor cost basis. In one instance a company was manufacturing an oil field specialty. An analysis revealed costs as follows:

Direct labor..	$2.18
Direct material...	0.84
Factory overhead, $2.18 × 2.56......................................	5.58
	$8.60

The factory cost of $8.60 was slightly less than was being received for the item in question. The first suggestion was to cease making the article. But after further analysis it became clear that the overhead of $5.58 would not be saved if the item was discontinued. The burden rate used was based on heavy equipment required for most of the work in the department and on hourly earnings of workmen who averaged $1.56 per hour. For the job in question only a light drill press and hand tools were used. Little actual reduction in cost would have resulted from not using them in the manufacture of the article.

It has previously been calculated that items of overhead of the Acme Company that are equivalent to rent are equal to $1.09 per square foot of factory floor space. Figure 15.1 reveals a currently unused 10 ft. × 24 ft. space for future machines. The annual rental cost equivalent of this space is 10 ft. × 24 ft. × $1.09/ft.² = $262.

The item need not be included as an item of cost attributable to a machine that may be purchased to occupy the space in question, since no actual additional cost will arise should the space be occupied. The $262 item has been entered as an overhead charge to be allocated to products made on the basis of one of several overhead rates. The addition of a new machine will probably result in changes in the overhead allocation rate used, but it will not result in a change in the overhead item equivalent to rent.

Average costs are inadequate for specific analysis. An important function of cost accounting, if not the primary one, is to provide data for decisions relative to the reduction of production costs and the increase of profit from sales. Errors in cost data that are believed to be accurate may lead to costly errors in decisions. Cost data that give true average values and are adequate for over-all analyses may be inadequate for specific detailed analyses. Thus, cost data must be carefully scrutinized and their accuracy established before they can be used with confidence in engineering economy studies.

In Table 15.2 actual and erroneous cost data relative to the cost of three products have been tabulated.

Table 15.2. ACTUAL AND ERRONEOUS COST DATA

Product	Direct labor and material costs	Overhead costs, actual	Overhead costs, believed to be	Production cost, actual	Production cost, believed to be
A	$6.50	$2.50	$3.50	$ 9.00	$10.00
B	7.00	3.00	3.00	10.00	10.00
C	7.50	3.50	2.50	11.00	10.00
Average	7.00	3.00	3.00	10.00	10.00

The actual production cost of Products A, B, and C are $9, $10, and $11, respectively, but owing to unknown errors in overhead costs, the production costs of Products A, B, and C are believed to be equal to $10 for each.

It should be noted that even though the average of a number of items of cost may be correct, there is no assurance that individual items are not in error. For this reason the accuracy of each item of cost should be ascertained before the item is used in an economic analysis.

If, for example, the selling price of the products is based upon their believed production cost, Product A will be overpriced and Product C will be underpriced. Buyers may be expected to shun Product A and to buy large quantities of Product C. This may lead to a serious unexplained loss of profit. Average values of cost data are of little value in making decisions relative to specific products.

QUESTIONS AND PROBLEMS

1. Describe the function of general accounting; of cost accounting.

2. What is the difference with respect to time between a balance sheet and an economy study?

3. What is the difference between cost accounting and engineering economy?

4. Describe the relationship between the balance sheet and the profit and loss statement; the profit and loss statement and the cost of goods manufactured statement.

5. Name and describe the basic classifications of cost incurred in the production of an item.

6. What precautions should be exercised in using accounting data in economy analysis?

7. The manufacturing costs of Products A and B are believed to be $10 per unit. On the basis of this estimate and a desired profit of 10 per cent, the selling price is set at $11 per unit.

   (a) What is the profit if 500 units of Product A and 1,500 units of Product B are sold?

   (b) If the actual manufacturing costs of Products A and B are $9 and $11, respectively, what is the actual profit?

8. An automobile parts manufacturer produces batteries and distributor assemblies in his electrical products department. It is believed that the cost of manufacturing the batteries and the distributor assemblies is $8.20 and $10.70 per unit, respectively. These costs were derived on the basis of an equal distribution of overhead charges.

A study of the firm's cost structure reveals that overhead would be more equitably distributed if overhead charges against the distributor assembly were 50 per cent more than those against the battery. This conclusion was reached after careful consideration of the nature and source of an $72,000 annual overhead expenditure for these products.

(a) Calculate the unit production cost applicable to the battery and to the distributor assembly if the annual production is made up of 24,000 batteries and 16,000 distributor assemblies.

(b) What is the annual profit if the selling price is $9.85 and $13.80 for the battery and the distributor assembly, respectively?

9. A small factory is divided into four departments for accounting purposes. The direct labor and direct material expenditures for a given year are as follows:

Department	Direct Labor Hours	Direct Labor Cost	Direct Material Cost
A	750	$4,300	$20,650
B	890	4,900	6,800
C	1100	5,050	11,200
D	670	3,900	15,000

Distribute an annual overhead charge of $24,000 to Departments A, B, C, and D on the basis of direct labor hours, direct labor cost, and direct material cost.

10. A factory producing lawn mowers works at 60 per cent of its capacity and produces 18,000 mowers per year. The unit manufacturing cost is computed as follows:

Direct labor cost.	$17.50
Direct material cost.	12.50
Overhead cost.	8.00
	$38.00

The mowers are marketed through a factory distributor for $42.50 each. It is anticipated that the volume of production can be increased to 28,000 units per year if the price is lowered to $40 per unit. This action would not increase the present total overhead cost. Compute the present profit per year and the profit per year if the volume of production is increased.

CHAPTER 16

INCOME TAXES IN
ECONOMY ANALYSIS

Income tax laws are the result of legislation over a period of time. Since they are man made, they incorporate many diverse ideas, some of which appear to be in conflict. These laws are expressed through a number of provisions and rules intended to meet current conditions. The provisions and rules are not absolute in application, but rather are subject to interpretation when applied.

Income taxes are levied by the federal government as well as by many individual states. State income tax laws will not be considered here because the principles involved are similar to those for federal tax laws, state income tax rates are relatively small, and there is a great diversity of state income tax law provisions.

Discussion of income taxes has been deferred until this chapter because it has simplified the development of the economy techniques presented and because income taxes are a result of a decision to pursue a course of action that leads to a profit. Thus, income taxes are usually the last element to be considered in economy analysis.

16.1. RELATION OF INCOME TAXES TO PROFIT

In most cases, the desirability of a venture is measured in terms of differences between income and cost, receipts and disbursements, or some other measure of profit. It is the specific function of economy analysis to determine future profit potential that may be expected from prospective engineering proposals being examined. But income taxes are levies on profit that result in a reduction of its magnitude.

Regardless of how public-spirited a person may be or how clearly he may understand the government's need for income taxes, and even if he should place a high value upon the services he may receive in return for his income tax payments, income taxes are disbursements that differ from other disbursements associated with undertakings only in the manner in which their magnitudes are determined. Thus, in relation to engineering economy studies, income taxes are merely another class of expenditure, which require special treatment. Such taxes must be taken into account along with other classes of costs in arriving at the fruits accruing to sponsors of an undertaking.

Of the aggregate profit earned in the United States from such productive activities as manufacturing, construction, mining, lumbering and others in which engineering analysis is important, the aggregate disbursement for income taxes will be approximately 30 to 40 per cent of net income. Their importance becomes clear when it is realized that in some cases income taxes may result in disbursements of as much as 91 per cent of the profit to be expected from a venture.

16.2. INDIVIDUAL FEDERAL INCOME TAX

With few exceptions, every individual with a gross income of $600 or more during the year must file a tax return. Individuals whose adjusted gross income is more than $5,000 during the year are required to file a tax return on Form 1040. This form must also be used by a husband and wife whose combined adjusted gross income exceeds $5,000 and who wish to file a joint return. The tax provisions applicable to individuals whose adjusted gross incomes are greater than $5,000 will be considered for illustrative purposes.

An individual's income tax obligation is determined by applying a graduated tax rate to his net income from salaries, fees, commissions, and business activities less certain exemptions and deductions. For example, consider Mr. Doe who is unmarried, qualifies as the head of a household, and has four dependents. An outline of the steps necessary to compute Mr. Doe's tax obligation is given below.

Individual Federal Income Tax Outline[1]

1. Salary, wages, commission or other compensation received $12,000

---

[1]Applicable to tax year 1962.

2. Net income from business activities:
   This item consists of income received from the conduct of trade or business activities less the expense of carrying on such activities. These expenses include such items as rents, wages, fees, raw material, supplies, services, depreciation of facilities and losses incurred from the sale and exchange of other than capital assets. Business income less business expense.........................   8,000

3. Income from capital gains:
   This item consists of 50 per cent of the amount that net long-term (assets held more than six months) capital gains exceed net short-term (assets not held more than six months) capital losses. ($900 long-term gain less $300 short-term loss) × 0.5.........................   300

4. Total adjusted gross income......................... $20,300

5. Less deductions as follows:
   a. Contributions not in excess of 20 per cent of adjusted gross income (plus 10 per cent of adjusted gross income contributed directly to religious, educational organizations and organizations providing medical care and hospitalization)....................... $1,000
   b. Interest paid...........................   200
   c. Taxes paid.............................   1,600
   d. Medical expenses in excess of 3 per cent of adjusted gross income.................   00
   e. Loss from fire, storms, or other casualty not compensated by insurance, etc...........   00
   f. Exemptions. The taxpayer is permitted an exemption of $600 ($1,200 if 65 years old or older) (Blindness entitles a taxpayer an additional exemption of $600) for himself and $600 for each dependent. ($1,200 for a dependent wife 65 years old or older and $600 additional if she is blind.) A dependent is a person, 50 per cent or more of whose support is paid for by the taxpayer, and whose annual earnings are less than $600 per year. The $600 limitation on income does not apply to any child who is under 19 years of age or who is a student (Doe, and his four dependents, five at $600)................................   3,000

   Total deductions and exemptions........ $5,800   5,800

6. Taxable income................................... $14,500

The amount of income tax due on the taxable income may be calculated from tabulated values such as those given in Tables 16.1 and 16.2. Table 16.2 is applicable to Mr. Doe's situation, therefore, his tax obligation will be $3,780 + 0.39 × $500, or $3,975.

For a second illustration, suppose that Mr. Blue has a wife and three children, and he had items of income identical with those of Mr. Doe. The number of exemptions in both cases is five. Mr. and Mrs. Blue elect to file a joint return. The taxable income will remain at $14,500, and Mr. and Mrs. Blue may file a joint return. If this is done, rates in Table 16.2 apply and the tax to be paid is $2,720 + 0.30 × $2,500, or $3,470.

If Mr. and Mrs. Blue had divided the $14,500 income equally between them and filed separate returns in accordance with Table

Table 16.1. TAX RATES FOR MARRIED TAXPAYERS FILING JOINT RETURNS AND CERTAIN WIDOWS AND WIDOWERS (1962)

If the taxable income is:	*The income tax is:*
Not over $4,000..................	20% of taxable income
Over $4,000 but not over $8,000......	$800 plus 22% of excess over $4,000
Over $8,000 but not over $12,000.....	$1,680 plus 26% of excess over $8,000
Over $12,000 but not over $16,000....	$2,720 plus 30% of excess over $12,000
Over $16,000 but not over $20,000....	$3,920 plus 34% of excess over $16,000
Over $20,000 but not over $24,000....	$5,280 plus 38% of excess over $20,000
Over $24,000 but not over $28,000....	$6,800 plus 43% of excess over $24,000
Over $28,000 but not over $32,000....	$8,520 plus 47% of excess over $28,000
Over $32,000 but not over $36,000....	$10,400 plus 50% of excess over $32,000
Over $36,000 but not over $40,000....	$12,400 plus 53% of excess over $36,000
Over $40,000 but not over $44,000....	$14,520 plus 56% of excess over $40,000
Over $44,000 but not over $52,000....	$16,760 plus 59% of excess over $44,000
Over $52,000 but not over $64,000....	$21,480 plus 62% of excess over $52,000
Over $64,000 but not over $76,000....	$28,920 plus 65% of excess over $64,000
Over $76,000 but not over $88,000....	$36,720 plus 69% of excess over $76,000
Over $88,000 but not over $100,000...	$45,000 plus 72% of excess over $88,000
Over $100,000 but not over $120,000..	$53,640 plus 75% of excess over $100,000
Over $120,000 but not over $140,000..	$68,640 plus 78% of excess over $120,000
Over $140,000 but not over $160,000..	$84,240 plus 81% of excess over $140,000
Over $160,000 but not over $180,000..	$100,440 plus 84% of excess over $160,000
Over $180,000 but not over $200,000..	$117,240 plus 87% of excess over $180,000
Over $200,000 but not over $300,000..	$134,640 plus 89% of excess over $200,000
Over $300,000 but not over $400,000..	$223,640 plus 90% of excess over $300,000
Over $400,000....................	$313,640 plus 91% of excess over $400,000

Table 16.2. TAX RATES FOR UNMARRIED OR LEGALLY SEPARATED TAXPAYERS WHO QUALIFY AS HEAD OF HOUSEHOLD (1962)

If the taxable income is:	The income tax is:
Not over $2,000	20% of taxable income
Over $2,000 but not over $4,000	$400 plus 21% of excess over $2,000
Over $4,000 but not over $6,000	$820 plus 24% of excess over $4,000
Over $6,000 but not over $8,000	$1,300 plus 26% of excess over $6,000
Over $8,000 but not over $10,000	$1,820 plus 30% of excess over $8,000
Over $10,000 but not over $12,000	$2,420 plus 32% of excess over $10,000
Over $12,000 but not over $14,000	$3,060 plus 36% of excess over $12,000
Over $14,000 but not over $16,000	$3,780 plus 39% of excess over $14,000
Over $16,000 but not over $18,000	$4,560 plus 42% of excess over $16,000
Over $18,000 but not over $20,000	$5,400 plus 43% of excess over $18,000
Over $20,000 but not over $22,000	$6,260 plus 47% of excess over $20,000
Over $22,000 but not over $24,000	$7,200 plus 49% of excess over $22,000
Over $24,000 but not over $28,000	$8,180 plus 52% of excess over $24,000
Over $28,000 but not over $32,000	$10,260 plus 54% of excess over $28,000
Over $32,000 but not over $38,000	$12,420 plus 58% of excess over $32,000
Over $38,000 but not over $44,000	$15,900 plus 62% of excess over $38,000
Over $44,000 but not over $50,000	$19,620 plus 66% of excess over $44,000
Over $50,000 but not over $60,000	$23,580 plus 68% of excess over $50,000
Over $60,000 but not over $70,000	$30,380 plus 71% of excess over $60,000
Over $70,000 but not over $80,000	$37,480 plus 74% of excess over $70,000
Over $80,000 but not over $90,000	$44,880 plus 76% of excess over $80,000
Over $90,000 but not over $100,000	$52,480 plus 80% of excess over $90,000
Over $100,000 but not over $150,000	$60,480 plus 83% of excess over $100,000
Over $150,000 but not over $200,000	$101,980 plus 87% of excess over $150,000
Over $200,000 but not over $300,000	$145,480 plus 90% of excess over $200,000
Over $300,000	$235,480 plus 91% of excess over $300,000

16.1, their total tax would have been $3,470, or the same as resulted from a joint return. However, if they had divided $14,500 income between them unequally, the tax to be paid would have been greater.

Item 2 in the outline above, *Net income from business activities*, consists essentially of business income less business expenses. Some items such as depreciation and allowed amortization must be determined by calculation. Such items are treated in subsequent sections as is the matter of capital gains appearing in Item 3 of the outline.

Adjusted gross income. The term adjusted gross income means net earnings as determined in accordance with the provisions of federal income tax law. The starting point is the taxpayer's total income. Certain items of income are excluded in whole or in part from the total income to determine gross income. Examples of excluded income are interest on certain federal, state or municipal obligations, health and accident insurance benefits, and annuities. From the gross income certain deductions are made to arrive at the adjusted gross income. These deductions consist essentially of expenses incurred in carrying on a trade, profession, or business, reimbursement for expenses incurred in employment and certain long-term capital gains explained elsewhere.

Taxable income. The individual's taxable income is his adjusted income less deductions he is permitted to take. Deductions up to 20 per cent of adjusted gross income (30 per cent under certain conditions) may be made for contributions to qualified individuals, fraternal organizations, governmental units of the United States, religious and educational organizations, and organizations providing medical care and hospitalization.

Interest paid by a taxpayer in carrying on business activities is taken into account in arriving at adjusted gross income. But interest paid on borrowed funds made for personal purposes is deductible under Item 5b in the above outline.

Practically all taxes, except federal income taxes, incurred and necessary to carry on business activity are taken into account in arriving at the adjusted gross income of an individual. In addition, individuals are permitted to make deductions for payment of most state and local taxes except estate, inheritance, and gift taxes, and for a few federal taxes with the exception of federal income, estate, and gift taxes.

Medical expenses in excess of 3 per cent of adjusted gross income, incurred by a taxpayer for himself or his dependents, are deductible under Item 5d, if these expenses are not compensated for by insurance or other means. Cost of medicines and drugs in excess of one per cent of adjusted gross income is included as a part of medical expense.

Losses sustained from fire, storm, theft or other casualties are deductible to the extent they are not compensated by insurance or similar means as shown under Item 5c.

The exemptions listed in Item 5f of the outline cover most of the provisions relative to this classification.

In lieu of itemized deductions 5a to 5c, the taxpayer may elect to take a standard deduction. The standard deductions on the separate return of an individual or the joint return of a husband and wife on an adjusted income of $5,000 or over is $1,000 or 10 per cent of the adjusted income, whichever is the least. The standard deduction on a separate return of a married person is $500 on an adjusted income of $5,000 or more.

16.3. CORPORATION FEDERAL INCOME TAX

The term *corporation*, as used in income tax law, is not limited to the artificial entity usually known as a corporation but may include joint stock associations or companies, some types of trusts, and some limited partnerships. In general, all business entities whose activities or purposes are the same as those of corporations organized for profit are taxed as such. This discussion will be based upon the tax requirements that apply to the usual business corporation.

The business corporation is subject to two taxes — the normal tax and the surtax. The normal tax is equal to 30 per cent of taxable income and the surtax is equal to 22 per cent of taxable income in excess of $25,000.[2] In addition, a corporation may be liable for an accumulated earnings tax.

As a general rule, the taxable income of a corporation is computed in the same manner as that of an individual. There are, however, several provisions peculiar to corporations. Although corporations are in general entitled to the same deductions as individuals, deductions of a personal nature such as medical expenses, child care, alimony, or exemptions for the taxpayer and his dependents are excluded. Corporations are entitled to deductions for partially exempt interest received as income on certain government obligations, for dividends received, and for certain organizational expenses to which individuals are not entitled.

In general, a corporation's income tax is a levy on its net earnings, the difference between the income derived from and the expense incurred in business activity, with some exceptions. Because of the continuing nature of business activity and the fact of annual tax periods, net income must usually be a calculated amount.

The following is an outline of steps to be taken in computing the normal income tax and the surtax of a corporation, illustrated by entering amounts applicable to a particular corporation:

---

[2]Applicable for fiscal years beginning in 1956.

1. Gross Income: This item embraces gross sales less cost of sales, dividends received on stocks, interest received on loans and bonds, rents, royalties, gains and losses from capital or other property............................ $700,000

2. Deductions: This item embraces expense not deducted elsewhere as, for example, in cost of sales. Includes compensation of officers, wages, and salaries, rent, repairs, bad debts, interest, taxes, contributions (not in excess of 5 per cent of taxable income), losses by fire, storms, and theft, depreciation, depletion, advertising, contributions to employee benefit plans, and special deductions for partially exempt bond interest and partially exempt dividends..... 600,000

3. Taxable Income..................................... $100,000

4. Taxable income multiplied by normal tax rate, $100,000 × 0.30... $ 30,000

5. Taxable income..................................... $100,000
   Plus partially exempt interest and partially exempt dividends not subject to normal tax and not included in gross income... 000

6. Total.. $100,000
   Less: $25,000 exemptions.......................... 25,000

7. Balance subject to surtax........................... $ 75,000

8. Balance multiplied by surtax rate $75,000 × 0.22........ $ 16,500

9. Total normal tax plus surtax (Items 4 and 8)........... $ 46,500

Corporate taxable income with some exceptions may be expressed as an equation applicable for taxable incomes from zero and up. This equation is

$$T = E_b \times \text{normal tax rate} + (E_b - \$25,000) \times \text{surtax rate}$$

where

T = total income tax;

E_b = taxable income.

The tax rate on any increment of taxable corporate income between $0 and $25,000 is of course 30 per cent, and the tax rate for any increment between $25,000 and up is 52 per cent. The previous statement does not hold to the extent that there are capital gains, exempt interest and dividends to which special rates apply.

The average tax rate, t_a, of any increment of income embracing taxable income less than \$25,000 and greater than \$25,000 may be calculated as follows:

Find the difference of the tax payable on incomes corresponding to the upper and lower limits of the increments and divide this difference by the amount of the increment. For example, suppose a corporation wishes to find the average tax rate on the increment of income between \$24,000 and \$27,000.

The tax payable on \$27,000 is equal to \$27,000 $\times$ 0.52 $-$ \$5,500 = \$8,540, and the tax payable on \$24,000 is equal to \$24,000 $\times$ 0.30 = \$7,200. The difference is \$8,540 $-$ \$7,200 = \$1,340. The average tax rate over the increment

$$t_a = \frac{\$1,340}{\$27,000 - \$24,000} = \frac{\$1,340}{\$3,000} = 0.447, \quad \text{or} \quad 44.7 \text{ per cent.}$$

The effect of interest on income taxes. Interest paid for funds borrowed by an individual or a corporation to carry on a profession, trade, or business is deductible from income as expense of carrying on such activity. In addition, interest paid on funds borrowed for purposes not connected with a profession, trade, or business is deductible from the adjusted income in computing an individual's income tax.

Because interest paid is deductible as an expense the amount of borrowed funds may have a marked effect upon the amount of income tax that must be paid. For example, consider two corporations designated as Case A and Case B that are essentially identical except that in Case A no borrowed funds are used and in Case B an average of \$100,000 is borrowed at the rate of 5 per cent during a year. Assume that taxable income before interest payments in both cases is \$40,000. Then the taxable income in Case A will be \$40,000 and taxable income in Case B will be \$40,000 $-$ \$100,000 $\times$ 0.05 = \$35,000.

On the basis of a normal tax of 30 per cent and a surtax of 22 per cent the income tax in Case A will be \$40,000 $\times$ 0.30 + (\$40,000 $-$ \$25,000) $\times$ 0.22 = \$15,300. And the income tax in Case B will be \$35,000 $\times$ 0.30 + (\$35,000 $-$ \$25,000) $\times$ 0.22 = \$12,700. This is a difference of \$2,600. Thus the net cost of borrowing the \$100,000 for one year is \$5,000 $-$ \$2,600 = \$2,400. This is equivalent to an interest rate of 2.4 per cent.

Capital gains and losses. Capital gains and losses are recognized as being short term if they apply to assets held not more than six months. Long-term gains and losses apply to assets held more than six months.

If the aggregate of short-term and long-term activities results in a net loss for a year, a corporation may not deduct such loss from current income. But such loss may be carried forward for five subsequent years, being considered as a short-term capital loss, and offset against capital gains during that period.

If the aggregate of short-term and long-term activities results in a net gain, it is added in full as an item of income. It will then be subject to the normal tax rate and the surtax rate.

But, as in the case of an individual taxpayer, the maximum tax that a corporation need pay on the excess of long-term capital gain over short-term capital loss is such excess multiplied by a tax rate of 25 per cent.

Research and experimental expenditures. Research and experimental activities result in new knowledge which has little value in itself, but is valuable only in application. If knowledge is used it may be presumed to result in increased taxable income of the activity in which it is used, and, therefore, in increased income taxes from this source. This viewpoint seems to be borne out by a provision which became effective for tax years beginning after December 31, 1953, and permits expenditures for research and experimentation to be deducted in the year in which they were incurred. The taxpayer also has the option of treating such expenditures as deferred expenses chargeable to capital account and deducting it rateably over a period of 60 or more months. In the latter case, the activity is treated essentially the same as an asset that depreciates.

The provision permitting expenditures for research and experimental activities to be deducted in the year in which they are incurred is indeed an encouragement to carry on such activities when the income tax rate is high. For example, suppose that the effective tax rate of a taxpayer applicable to the consideration of research expenditures is 0.45 and that such expenditures amount to $100,000 during a year. If the research results in no increase in income, its cost to the taxpayer will be $100,000 (1 − 0.45), or $55,000. Thus, in a sense, research expenditures are in part underwritten by the government until they result in increased income, if ever.

Effective income tax rates. Engineering economy studies involving income taxes can be simplified by the determination of applicable *effective income tax rates.* An effective income tax rate, as the term is used here, is a single rate which when multiplied by the taxable income of a venture under consideration will result in the income tax attributable to the venture. Effective income tax rates are essentially average rates that are applicable over increments of income.

Where there are capital gains, losses to be carried back or over, actual depreciation and depletion rates different from those allowed by tax schedules and other conditions, many factors may be involved in the determination of effective income tax rates. These determinations require careful study by individuals proficient in tax matters.

Once they are determined for a particular purpose, effective rates serve as a means for transmitting the thought and analyses that went into the determination in a single figure. By the use of effective rates the consideration of income taxes in economy studies is reduced to two distinct factors, namely, (1) the determination of effective tax rates applicable to particular activities or particular classes of activities and (2) the application of the effective tax rates in economy studies.

16.4. DEPRECIATION AND INCOME TAXES

Since the amount of taxes to be paid during any one year is dependent upon deductions made for depreciation, the latter is a matter of consideration for the Bureau of Internal Revenue of the United States Treasury Department and state taxing agencies. Directives are issued by governmental agencies as guides to the taxpayers in properly handling depreciation for tax purposes. In this connection the following statement from Bulletin F of the Bureau of Internal Revenue, a publication giving the probable service life and the depreciation rate of several thousand kinds of property, is of interest:

ESTIMATED AVERAGE USEFUL LIVES AND DEPRECIATION RATES[3]

A reasonable rate for depreciation is dependent not only on the prospec-

---

[3]"Income Tax Depreciation and Obsolescence, Estimated Useful Lives and Depreciation Rates" (Bureau of Internal Revenue; Revised, January 1942).

tive useful life of the property when acquired, but also on the particular conditions under which the property is used as reflected in the taxpayer's operating policy and the accounting policy followed with respect to repairs, maintenance replacements, charges to the capital asset account and to the depreciation reserve. If the useful life of the various assets shown hereafter could be determined precisely, which can not be done, there still could not be established standard rates of depreciation unless there existed standard methods of operation and of accounting from which there could be no deviation.

Being based on the usual experience of property owners, the probable useful lives shown herein for each kind or class of assets are predicated on a reasonable expense policy as to the cost of repairs and maintenance. Therefore, in the determination of the depreciation allowance in each case, due consideration should be given the maintenance and replacement policy of the taxpayer and the accounting practice regarding the same.

The estimates of useful life set forth herein are for new properties only. In applying them, consideration should be given to salvage values, to that portion of the service life already expired, and to that portion of the cost previously recovered or recoverable through prior depreciation deductions or other allowances.

It has been found that normal obsolescence is a very important factor in determining the useful life of property. The estimated useful lives shown herein include an allowance for normal obsolescence, but do not contain any provision for extraordinary obsolescence, such as is occasioned by revolutionary inventions, abnormal growth or development, radical economic changes, or other unpredictable factors which may force the retirement or other disposition of property prior to the termination of its normal useful life.

In general, an asset must be used for the purpose of producing an income, whether or not an income actually results from its use, in order that a deduction may be made for its depreciation. In cases where an asset such as an automobile is used both as a means for earning income that is taxable and for personal use, a proportional deduction is allowable for depreciation. Intangible property such as patents, designs, drawings, models, copyrights, licenses, and franchises may be depreciated.

There are restrictions which limit the percentage of the first cost of an asset that may be depreciated during the initial years of life. Depreciation models that yield depreciation amounts in early years which are in excess of that permitted by the Bureau of Internal Revenue may not be used for tax purposes. For example, where the fixed percentage model is used the rate of depreciation must not exceed twice the allowable straight-line rate. If a five year life is considered reasonable for an asset whose installed cost is $1,000 and there is no salvage value, its straight-line depreciation rate would be 20 per cent and its annual depreciation would be $200 per year. The corresponding maximum allowable declining balance rate would be 40 per cent. This would result in a deduction for depreciation of $1,000 × 0.40 = $400 the first year, ($1,000 − $400) × 0.40 = $240 the second year, etc.

Effect of method of depreciation on income taxes. A taxpayer has considerable choice in the method of depreciation he may use for tax computation. If the effective tax rate remains constant and the operating expense is constant over the life of the equipment, the depreciation method used will not alter the total of the taxes payable over the life of the equipment. But, methods providing for high depreciation and consequent low taxes in the first years of life will be of advantage to the taxpayer because of the time value of money.

For illustration of the comparative effect of the straight line and the fixed percentage on a diminishing balance method, consider the following example. Assume that a taxpayer has just installed a machine whose first cost is $1,000, whose estimated life is 10 years, and whose salvage value is nil. The machine is estimated to have a constant operating income before depreciation and income taxes of $200 per year. The taxpayer estimates the applicable effective income tax rate for the life of the machine to be 40 per cent. He considers money to be worth 6 per cent and wishes to compare the effect of the straight-line method and the fixed percentage on a diminishing balance method. Let the first method be represented by Alternative A and the second method be represented by Alternative B. These alternatives are summarized in the following tabulations.

The total income tax paid during the life of the equipment is equal to $400 with either alternative, but the present worths of the taxes paid differ. For Alternative A, the present worth of taxes paid as of the beginning of year No. 1 is equal to $294.40. The corresponding figure for Alternative B is $275.60. The difference in favor of the fixed percentage on a diminishing balance method is $18.80, or 6.4 per cent of the Alternative A tax.

ALTERNATIVE A

Income Taxes for Straight-Line Method of Depreciation and 10 Year Life

Year end no.	First cost	Income before depr. and income tax	Annual book depr.	Total book depr. to date, ΣD	Income less depr. (taxable income), C − D	Income tax rate	Income tax F × G
A	B	C	D	E	F	G	H
0	$1,000						
1		$ 200	$100	$ 100	$100	0.4	$ 40
2		200	100	200	100	0.4	40
3		200	100	300	100	0.4	40
4		200	100	400	100	0.4	40
5		200	100	500	100	0.4	40
6		200	100	600	100	0.4	40
7		200	100	700	100	0.4	40
8		200	100	800	100	0.4	40
9		200	100	900	100	0.4	40
10		200	100	1,000	100	0.4	40
		$2,000					$400

PR 6-10

Present worth of income taxes = $40(7.360) = $294.40

ALTERNATIVE B

Income Taxes for Percentage on Diminishing Balance
Method of Depreciation (20 per cent) and 10 Year Life

Year end no.	First cost	Income before depr. and income tax	Annual book depr.	Total book depr. to date, ΣD	Income less depr. (taxable income), C − D	Income tax rate	Income tax F × G
A	B	C	D	E	F	G	H
0	$1,000						
1		$ 200	$200	$ 200	$ 0	0.4	$ 0
2		200	160	360	40	0.4	16
3		200	128	488	72	0.4	29
4		200	102	590	98	0.4	39
5		200	82	672	118	0.4	47
6		200	66	738	134	0.4	54
7		200	52	790	148	0.4	59
8		200	42	832	158	0.4	63
9		200	34	866	166	0.4	66
10		200	134	1,000	66	0.4	27
		$2,000					$400

PS 6-n

Present worth of income taxes = Col. *H* × (   ) = $275.60

Effect of estimated life on income taxes. There is often little connection between the life of an asset that will be realized and that which a taxpayer may use for tax purposes. If the applicable effective tax rate remains constant through the realized life of an asset, the use of a shorter life for tax purposes will usually be favorable to a taxpayer. The reason is that use of short estimated lives for tax purposes results in relatively high annual depreciation, low annual taxable income and consequently, low annual income taxes during the early years of an asset's life. Even though early low annual income taxes will result in correspondingly higher annual income taxes during the later years of an asset's life, the present worth of all income taxes during the asset's life will be less.

If the conditions in Alternative A in the previous section had permitted the use of an estimated life of five years for tax purposes, the annual income tax for the first five years would have been nil, and during the second five years of life, $80 per year. The present worth of these payments at 6 per cent as of the beginning of the first year would be equal to

$$\text{PR 6-5}\quad\text{PS 6-5}$$
$$\$80(4.212)(0.7473) = \$251.78.$$

The difference in favor of the shorter life is $42.62.

The matter of useful life may be settled by entering into an agreement with the Treasury Department as to useful lives of assets. Such agreements are binding on both parties and will not be changed unless facts not previously contemplated arise.

If challenged in regard to the estimated life selected for assets, the burden of proof rests upon the taxpayer. Changes of rate during the life of an asset must be based upon facts related to the use of the asset. For example, markedly increased use of a machine over that on which a depreciation rate was initially established would generally be considered an acceptable reason for using an increased rate of depreciation.

The lessening in value due to extraordinary obsolescence ordinarily cannot be anticipated; consequently, it will usually be taken into account by an adjustment in the remaining life of an asset. When it becomes apparent that the value of an asset is being adversely affected by revolutionary inventions, radical economic changes, and abnormal needs that will result in retirement of the asset at a shorter life than originally estimated, the estimated life may be decreased to reflect the new conditions.

Special provisions are made for the rapid amortization of facilities that have been certified by proper authority as necessary in the national defense. Deductions for tax purposes may be made for such assets on the basis of amortization over a 60-month period regardless of their estimated useful life. This provision has essentially the same effect as permission to use an estimated life of five years for the assets involved.

16.5. DEPLETION AND INCOME TAXES

Natural resources such as minerals, oil, gas, timber, and certain others are found in deposits or stands of definite quantities. They are exploited by removal. As quantities are removed to produce income, the amount remaining in a deposit or stand is reduced.

In arriving at taxable income, depletion is deducted from gross income. The basis for determining the amount of depletion for a given year is the total cost of the property, the total number of units in the property, and the number of units sold during the year in question. This may be expressed by the equation:

$$\text{depletion for year} = \frac{\text{cost of property}}{\text{total units in property}} \times \text{units sold during year.}$$

Oil, gas, and mineral properties are also depleted for tax purposes on the basis of a percentage of gross income, provided that the amount allowed for depletion is not greater than 50 per cent of the taxable income of the property before depletion allowances. In general, percentage depletion will be elected if it results in less tax than does depletion based on cost.

Typical of percentage depletion allowances for mineral and similar resources are the following:

Oil and gas wells	$27\frac{1}{2}\%$
Sulphur, uranium, asbestos, bauxite, graphite, mica, antimony, bismuth, cadmium, cobalt, lead, manganese, nickel, tin, tungsten, vanadium, zinc	23%
Various clays, diatomaceous earth, dolomite, feldspar, and metal mines if not in 23 per cent group	15%
Coal, lignite, sodium chloride	10%
Brick and tile clay, gravel, mollusk shells, peat, pumice, and sand	5%

Suppose that a property estimated to have 1,000,000 barrels of oil was purchased for $400,000 or at a cost of $0.40 per barrel. During the tax year 50,000 barrels were pumped and sold from the property for a gross income of $100,000. Total operating expenses during the year, deductible from gross income to obtain taxable income, amounted to $40,000.

If the taxpayer did not use the $27\frac{1}{2}$ per cent depletion allowance, his taxable income would be calculated as follows:

Gross income, 50,000 barrels sold at $2		$100,000
Deductible operating expense	$40,000	
Depletion, 50,000 barrels at $0.40	20,000	
	60,000	60,000
Taxable income		$ 40,000

If the taxpayer uses the $27\frac{1}{2}$ per cent depletion allowance, his taxable income would be calculated as follows:

Gross income, 50,000 barrels sold at $2		$100,000
Deductible operating expense	$40,000	40,000
Taxable income before depletion		$ 60,000
Depletion allowance, $100,000 × 0.275 (since this is less than 50 per cent of the taxable income before depletion, this method of depletion may be used)	$27,500	27,500
Taxable income		$ 32,500

Timber may not be depleted on a percentage basis. In general, timber is depleted for tax purposes on the basis of its cost at a specific date, the total number of units of timber on the property and the units of timber removed during the tax year. Special rules are applicable for determining cost and for revising the number of units on the property from time to time.

Effect of depletion method on income taxes. Most resources subject to depletion may be depleted on either a cost basis or a percentage basis in computing income taxes. Consider an example of a mineral deposit estimated to contain 60,000 units of ore and purchased at a cost of $24,000 including equipment. The depletion rate is $24,000 ÷ 60,000, or $0.40 per unit of ore.

This property is also subject to percentage depletion at rate of 23 per cent per year, but not in excess of 50 per cent of the net taxable income of the property before depletion. An analysis of this situation is presented in Table 16.3.

Table 16.3. APPLICATION OF COST AND PERCENTAGE DEPLETION TO A MINERAL DEPOSIT

Year	Units produced	Gross income (B × $2)	Operating cost	Net income before depletion and income tax	50% of net income (E × 0.5)	Allowable cost depletion at $0.40 per unit	Allowable percentage depletion at 23% (C × 0.23)	Taxable income (E less F, H, or I)	Income tax (tax rate of 0.3) (J × 0.3)
A	B	C	D	E	F	H	I	J	K
1	20,000	$40,000	$20,000	$20,000	$10,000	$8,000	$9,200‡	$10,800	$3,240
2	16,000	32,000	16,000	16,000	8,000	6,400	7,360‡	8,640	2,592
3	12,000	24,000	13,000	11,000	5,500*	4,800	5,520	5,500	1,650
4	8,000	16,000	8,000	8,000	4,000	3,200	3,680‡	4,320	1,296
5	4,000	8,000	6,000	2,000	1,000	1,600†	1,840	400	120
									$8,898

*Deduct this amount for depletion as full percentage depletion will not be allowed and because it is greater than cost depletion.
†Deduct this amount for depletion because it is greater than the allowable percentage depletion that may be used.
‡Deduct this amount for depletion because it is full percentage depletion allowances and it is greater than allowable cost depletion.

By taking advantage of the two methods of depletion, the income taxes on the property above total $8,898. If only cost depletion had been used, income taxes in successive years would have been $3,600, $2,880, $1,860, $1,440 and $120 for a total of $9,900.

16.6. ECONOMY CALCULATIONS INVOLVING INCOME TAXES

The introduction of income taxes into economy studies requires special consideration because of three factors in the nature of income taxes. One factor is that income taxes are dependent upon net income. What interests a taxpayer is the net return of a venture after income taxes. Net earning before income taxes, which determines the amount of income taxes, is a difference of income and cost which makes net earning subject to the joint effect of errors in estimates of the latter two quantities. A second factor is that in computing income taxes only interest on borrowed money may be considered a cost. A third factor is that the method of depreciation used in computing income taxes must be considered in analyses.

A basic tax equation. The following symbolism will be used and will apply to annual quantities:

E_b = net profit before income taxes;

E_a = net profit after income taxes;

G = estimated gross income from the activity under consideration;

C = estimated annual costs, all not included elsewhere;

D = estimated annual depreciation;

D_t = estimated annual depreciation allowed for tax purposes;

I = interest paid on borrowed funds;

t = effective applicable income tax rate;

T = income tax payable.

A general equation for annual profit before income taxes is derived as follows:

$$E_b = G - (C + D + I) \quad \text{and} \quad E_a = E_b - T$$

and
$$T = [G - (C + D_t + I)]t.$$

Then

$$E_a = [G - (C + D + I)] - [G - (C + D_t + I)]t.$$

This equation may be simplified by assuming that $D_t = D$, and substituting D for D_t. This may be justified by the fact that although actual and allowed annual depreciations may differ, the total actual depreciation should equal the total allowed depreciations over the life of an asset. If this substitution is made

$$E_a = E_b(1 - t) = [G - (C + D + I)](1 - t).$$

Notice should be taken of the fact demonstrated in this equation that income after income taxes of a venture is equal to its gross income times $(1 - t)$ less its costs times $(1 - t)$.

Comparison of alternatives with equal income. When two alternatives have equal income, their comparison may be based only upon costs. In many cases, gross incomes of alternatives can be assumed to be identical even though their amount may not be known. For example, when either of two machines can satisfactorily handle an equal flow of production, their contribution to the total income of the enterprise may be assumed to be equal even though the amount of the contribution of each to income may not be known. Assume that Machine A and Machine B result in gross incomes of G and G', respectively. Then income taxes of the alternatives can be taken into account as follows:

Machine A: $E_a = G'(1 - t) - (C + D + I)(1 - t)$

Machine B: $E'_a = G'(1 - t) - (C' + D' + I')(1 - t)$.

But by the conditions given, $G = G'$
and,

$$E_a - E'_a = [-(C + D + I) + (C' + D' + I')](1 - t).$$

If the costs of Machine A are less than the costs of Machine B, the annual "saving" in operating costs before income taxes will amount to $(C' + D' + I') - (C + D + I)$. Thus the advantage of Machine A over Machine B after income taxes will be equal to this "saving" multiplied by $(1 - t)$.

16.7. RATE OF RETURN AFTER INCOME TAXES

Annual income, E_a, of an activity after depreciation and after income taxes is given by

$$E_a = [G - (C + D + I)] - [G - (C + D_t + I)]t.$$

If D is added to both sides of the equation, the result will be net profit after income taxes plus depreciation. The result is the amount available for capital recovery with a return for the year under consideration. The resulting expression is

$$E_a + D = [G - (C + I)] - [G - (C + D_t + I)]t.$$

If the annual quantities in the expression are representative of quantities estimated for each year of life of an asset, the following equation can be applicable.

$$E_a + D = (P - L)(\overset{\text{RP } i\text{-}n}{}) + Li$$

or

$$[G - (C + I)] - [G - (C + D_t + I)]t = (P - L)(\overset{\text{RP }i\text{-}n}{\quad}) + Li$$

or, if $D = D_t$

$$[G - (C + I)](1 - t) + Dt = (P - L)(\overset{\text{RP }i\text{-}n}{\quad}) + Li.$$

From these expressions a rate of return can be obtained by trial and error. This method is applicable in many situations in which the several quantities are uniform throughout the life of the asset or where averages can be used. Where averages and other modifications are used, errors will be introduced. Nevertheless, this method of calculating a rate of return where income taxes are involved may be quite useful in experienced hands, especially for preliminary studies.

Tabular method for rate of return after income taxes. When the methods for calculating rate of return after income taxes previously presented are inadequate, a tabular method may be used. Tabular methods have the advantage that they can be made to reflect even complex situations with simple mathematics. They are also easy for laymen to understand. This method will be illustrated first with a simple situation where the asset has no salvage value, and net income after taxes is constant. Consider the situation represented in Table 16.4, designated Case A.

Table 16.4. TABULAR METHOD FOR CASE A

Year A	Total investment during year, $800 - \Sigma D$ B	Operating costs C	Depreciation D	Gross income E	Net income before income tax, $E - (C + D)$ F	Income tax rate G	Income tax, $F \times G$ H	Net income after income tax, $F - H$ I
1	$800	$400	$200	$675	$75	0.40	$30	$45
2	600	400	200	675	75	0.40	30	45
3	400	400	200	675	75	0.40	30	45
4	200	400	200	675	75	0.40	30	45

The sum of $800 was put into the enterprise at the beginning of year No. 1. The fact that there has been a net income after income tax in the amount of $45 means that $800 plus $45 or $845 would be recovered if the enterprise were liquidated at investment value at the end of year No. 1. Remember that the end of year No. 1 coincides with the beginning of year No. 2, etc. Determine the disbursements and receipts that would occur if the activity were liquidated at the end of each year of its life. The result would be as is given in the tabulation that follows:

Beginning of Year Number	*Disbursements*	*Receipts*
1	$800	. . .
2	600	$845
3	400	645
4	200	445
5	. . .	245

By subtractions this tabulation may be altered as follows:

Beginning of Year Number	*Disbursements*	*Receipts*
1	$800	. . .
2	. . .	$245
3	. . .	245
4	. . .	245
5	. . .	245

At some rate of return these two series of payment are equivalent. In this particular tabulation the present worth of disbursements is $800 and the present worth of receipts is $245 ($\overset{\text{PR } i\text{-}4}{\qquad}$) and

$$\$800 = \$245(\overset{\text{PR } i\text{-}4}{\qquad}) \quad \text{and} \quad (\overset{\text{PR } i\text{-}4}{\qquad}) = \frac{\$800}{\$245} = 3.265.$$

By interpolation $i = 8 + (2)\dfrac{3.312 - 3.265}{3.312 - 3.170} = 8.66$ per cent.

The interest rate at which the series of disbursements and receipts are equivalent can also be found from the equation

$$\$800 = \$245(\overset{\text{PS } i\text{-}1}{\qquad}) + \$245(\overset{\text{PS } i\text{-}2}{\qquad}) + \$245(\overset{\text{PS } i\text{-}3}{\qquad}) + \$245(\overset{\text{PS } i\text{-}4}{\qquad}).$$

This equation is usable when receipts vary in amount from year to year. It is solved by trial and interpolation.

The method above can be extended to cover yearly variations in gross income, operating expenses, depreciation, income tax rates, and the amount of borrowed funds. Consider the situation represented in Table 16.5, designated Case B.

Table 16.5. TABULAR METHOD FOR CASE B

Year	Total investment during year, $1,000 - \Sigma G$	Borrowed funds used during year	Ownership fund used during year, $B - C$	Operating costs	Interest paid on borrowed funds, $C + 0.05$	Depreciation	Gross income	Net income before income taxes, $H - (E + F + G)$	Income tax rate	Income tax, $I \times J$	Net income after income tax, $I - K$	Net receipt at end of year if liquidated, $D + L$
A	B	C	D	E	F	G	H	I	J	K	L	M
1	$1000	$200	$800	$600	$10	$200	$910	$100	$0.40	$40	$60	$860
2	800	100	700	650	5	200	925	70	0.40	28	42	742
3	600	. . .	600	700	. . .	200	990	90	0.30	27	63	663
4	400	. . .	400	600	. . .	200	880	80	0.30	24	56	456
5	200	. . .	. . .	. . .	. . .	. . .	. . .	. . .	. . .	. . .	. . .	. . .

The disbursements and receipts of the tabulations above are given below:

Beginning of Year Number	Disbursements	Receipts
1	$800	. . .
2	700	$860
3	600	742
4	400	663
5	. . .	456

This is reduced to the following tabulation by subtraction:

Beginning of Year Number	Disbursements	Receipts
1	$800	. . .
2	. . .	$160
3	. . .	142
4	. . .	263
5	. . .	456

Since the present worth of disbursements is equal to the present worth of the receipts at some rate of return, the rate of return may be obtained from the following equation:

$$\$800 = \$160(\overset{\text{PS }i\text{-}1}{\qquad}) + \$142(\overset{\text{PS }i\text{-}2}{\qquad}) + \$263(\overset{\text{PS }i\text{-}3}{\qquad}) + \$456(\overset{\text{PS }i\text{-}4}{\qquad}).$$

The rate of return on ownership funds may be found by interpolation. For this case it will be 8.7 per cent.

PROBLEMS

1. A consulting mechanical engineer who is married and has two children received \$12,600 in professional fees during the year. Office and traveling expenses applicable to his consulting activity amounted to \$2,800. The engineer also manages a small instrument repair shop from which he grossed \$9,200. Operating expenses applicable to the shop amounted to \$5,800. In addition, he sold a building lot for \$2,400 that cost him \$1,900 eight months ago.

   During the year, the engineer paid \$820 in interest on his home mortgage and \$120 interest on a personal note. Other deductible expenditures include \$180 in state taxes, \$90 in local taxes, \$320 in church contributions, \$280 in contributions to charitable organizations, \$620 in medical and dental expenses, a \$220 loss due to a leaky water pipe not covered by insurance, and \$85 for annual dues in professional societies.

   (a) Determine the engineer's adjusted gross income.

   (b) Determine the engineer's taxable income.

   (c) Determine the engineer's tax liability if he files a joint return.

2. The consulting engineer of Prob. 1 has been considering the desirability of closing his instrument repair shop and devoting his entire energy to consulting activity. He estimates that his professional fees would have been increased by one-third, with a corresponding increase in office and traveling expenses, had the shop been closed during the tax year. What would have been the change in the engineer's net income after income taxes if all other conditions outlined in Prob. 1 remain the same.

3. A self-employed manufacturer's representative, who is single and does not qualify as the head of a household, has a taxable income of \$9,400 of which \$2,200 results from interest on an investment in corporate bonds. He is considering the establishment of a small training institute which will require an investment of \$28,000. The required capital can be raised by the sale of a portion of the corporate bonds, which will

reduce the interest income to $300, or by a bank loan at 6 per cent interest. It is anticipated that the institute will yield a return of $4,600 per year from which interest on the bank loan must be deducted if bank financing is used. An estimated one-fourth reduction in commission will result if the manufacturer's representative diverts some of his time to the establishment of the institute.

(a) Determine the net income after income taxes if the institute is not established.

(b) Compare this with the net income after income taxes if the institute is financed by the sale of bonds; by a bank loan.

4. A corporation has a taxable income of $500,000 per year. A venture that will result in an additional $60,000 taxable income per year is under consideration.

(a) Calculate the income after taxes if the venture is undertaken; if the venture is not undertaken.

(b) Calculate the income after taxes from the venture alone.

5. The same conditions exist as in Prob. 4, except that here the new venture results in a decrease in taxable income of $18,000 instead of the anticipated $60,000 increase. Calculate the net income after income taxes under the loss condition and the loss in income from the anticipated income of Prob. 4.

6. A corporation is considering a $350,000 investment in a research and development effort to evolve a new product. The anticipated increase in taxable income from the marketing of the product in the coming year is $12,000,000. The current taxable income of the firm is $28,000,000 per year.

(a) What will be the increase in the net income after taxes if the research and marketing program is successful?

(b) What will be the decrease in the net income after taxes if the research and marketing program is unsuccessful?

7. A corporation is considering a study to develop a new process to replace a present method of fabricating a metal part which, if successful, is estimated to result in a saving of $20,000 in fulfilling a contract that will be completed during the current tax year. The study is estimated to cost $8,000 during the same tax year. If the new process is not successful, the corporation taxable income will be $500,000.

(a) If the study is successful, what will be the increase in income after taxes?

(b) If the study is unsuccessful, what will be the decrease in income after taxes?

8. A corporation purchases machinery for $48,000 with an estimated life of 6 years and a salvage value of zero. The gross income per year will be $20,000 before depreciation and taxes. If the tax rate applicable to this activity is 50 per cent and if the interest rate is 6 per cent, calculate the present worth of the income taxes if the straight-line method of depreciation is used; if the sinking-fund method of depreciation is used.

9. A prospector acquired a mine containing 300,000 tons of tungsten ore for $540,000. Annual operating costs of the mine are $132,000, and 40,000 tons of ore are being sold at the rate of $7.20 per ton. The prospector wishes to compare the results of using cost depletion and percentage depletion (23 per cent). Determine the income tax for each method assuming that the applicable income tax rate is 0.35.

10. A producer of minerals may exchange minerals for needed equipment. If he does this he may reduce his net income before income taxes by the amount of the value of the minerals exchanged for the equipment. The effect of this exchange is equivalent to depreciating the equipment to zero value in the year it is purchased. Assume that the applicable tax rate covering this situation is 0.42, that as of the beginning of the tax year, the needed equipment can be purchased for $10,000 cash or by exchange of minerals valued at $10,300. If the life of the equipment is four years and it depreciates to zero, what will be the present-worth cost of the equipment after allowing for tax deductions for depreciation for an interest rate of 6 per cent for each method of purchase?

11. A contractor purchased $300,000 worth of equipment to built a dam. For tax purposes, he was permitted to depreciate the equipment by the straight-line method on the basis of no salvage value and a five year life. After two years and the completion of the dam, the contractor sold the equipment for $200,000. The contractor attributed sale of the equipment at an amount higher than the "book value" to the excellence of maintenance. He estimated that he spent $16,000 per year more for maintenance than necessary "just to keep the equipment running," and by so doing reduced his operating costs exclusive of maintenance on the contract by $12,000 per year. The contractor's income tax rate is 32 per cent and the long-term capital gain tax rate is 25 per cent. The contractor averaged $48,000 taxable income for the two years required to complete the contract. There were no short-term capital losses.

(a) How much capital gains tax would the contractor pay as a result of selling his equipment?

(b) What was his total income tax including capital gains tax for the two-year period, and what was his total income after income taxes?

(c) What would have been his total income tax for the two-year period if he had spent $12,000 per year less maintenance and as a result his operating cost had been increased by $16,000 per year and his equipment had been sold for its book value. What was his total income after income taxes for the two-year period?

(d) How much was his total income after income taxes for the two-year period increased by his maintenance policy if his estimates were correct?

12. The income tax rate of a corporation is 32 per cent. Four months ago it purchased a warehouse for $22,000. It has just received an offer to sell the warehouse for $28,000 for a short-term gain of $6,000. What selling price two to eight months later will be equivalent to the present $28,000 offer in terms of income after taxes if the corporation has no other short-term gains in prospect?

13. The equivalent annual operating costs of Machine A and Machine B are, respectively, $1,460 and $1,584. What must be the annual value of irreducibles in favor of Machine B for the two machines to be equally economically desirable, if the applicable income tax rate is 42 per cent of income?

14. The net income of a corporation is $2.70 per share. If the tax obligation is $1.80 per share, what is the effective income tax rate applicable to the corporation?

15. A machinist earns $10,000 per year in wages from which $3,700 is deducted during the tax year. He is considering an additional part-time activity which will yield $2,000 per year and will increase his tax deduction by $300.

(a) What is the effective income tax rate if the additional activity is not undertaken?

(b) What is the effective income tax rate if the additional activity is undertaken?

(c) What is the effective income tax rate on the additional income alone?

16. A new activity is under consideration relative to which the following average annual estimates have been made covering a period of six years: gross income, $1,800; operating costs, $600; depreciation for tax purposes and realizable, $700; interest paid, $80. The cost of equipment is $4,200 and it depreciates to zero in six years. If the applicable effective income tax rate is 36 per cent, what will be the rate of return on this machine?

PART VI

OPERATIONS ECONOMY

CHAPTER 17

EVALUATION OF EXISTING OPERATIONS

Many activities of an enterprise may be classified under the heading of operations. Included here are the routine activities associated with engineering, finance, manufacturing, marketing, industrial relations, and so forth. Such operations are the result of organized activity directed to the satisfaction of human wants through the production of goods and services. The purpose of evaluating operations is for the attainment of objectives through the selection of operational alternatives that are most favorable from an economic standpoint.

In this chapter, existing operations will be considered without giving much attention to the desirability of the activity in question. The emphasis here will be on the economy of performance as it relates to operations that are assumed to be desirable by previous analysis. Several illustrations representative of the analysis required for existing operations will be presented in the following sections. The evaluation of proposals for new operations will be considered in the next chapter.

17.1. MANUFACTURING TO A VARIABLE DEMAND

The demand for many manufactured goods is seasonal. Such variation in demand reflects changes in human wants caused by seasonal changes such as temperature, rainfall, and hours of sunshine. Some items may vary in demand because of social customs as is the case with the sale of fireworks.

The seasonal-goods manufacturer may make his product at a relatively low rate throughout the year and store it until it is needed. Or he may acquire sufficient facilities to manufacture the product at a rate equal to the demand during the period in which it is sold.

The disadvantage of the first plan is that storage cost is relatively high, and the disadvantage of the second method is that a rather large equipment investment will be required. The most desirable plan may be a compromise of the two plans above.

The method of solution of this and similar situations may be illustrated by an example. Let it be assumed that 36,000 units of a product are sold during a four-month period each year as follows:

Month of Year	Number Sold
9th	2,000
10th	10,000
11th	15,000
12th	9,000

One machine can make 36,000 units of this product during a year. The fixed charges on the required machine for such items as interest, taxes, insurance, space to house machine, and depreciation due to causes exclusive of usage amounts to $2,000 per year. The cost for depreciation due exclusively to usage, power, supplies, maintenance, and so forth amounts to $0.25 per hour or $40 per month of operation on the basis of a 160-hour month.

Although one machine can meet the demand for the product, the accumulation of finished products throughout the year will result in considerable expense for storage. The expense for storage can be reduced by using more machines to shorten the period required to make the year's needs.

The costs associated with plans of production based on using one, two, and three machines will be determined. For an output of 36,000 units per machine, 12, 6, and 4 months respectively will be required to manufacture the annual output of 36,000 units with one, two, and three machines. The number sold each month and the number in storage at the end of each month during the year are given in Table 17.1 and are shown graphically in Figure 17.1.

The average number in storage for one, two and three machines is 13,083, 4,083, and 1,083, respectively. These results are obtained by adding the average of the number of units of product in storage at the beginning and end of each month in the year for each plan and divid-

Table 17.1. STORAGE REQUIREMENTS FOR MANUFACTURING TO A SEASONAL DEMAND

Month	Sales during month	Number in storage at end of month for		
		1 Machine	2 Machines	3 Machines
1		3,000		
2		6,000		
3		9,000		
4		12,000		
5		15,000		
6		18,000		
7		21,000	6,000	
8		24,000	12,000	
9	2,000	25,000	16,000	7,000
10	10,000	18,000	12,000	6,000
11	15,000	6,000	3,000	0
12	9,000	0	0	0

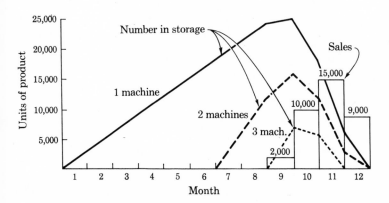

Figure 17.1. Graphical presentation of storage requirements.

ing the resulting sum by 12. The product is valued at $3 per unit. The sum of interest, taxes, and insurance is taken as 10 per cent of the unit cost and storage costs as $0.20 per unit per year of storage.

On the basis of the above data the cost with one, two, and three machines will be as follows.

One Machine

Fixed charges on machine, $1 \times \$2,000$................	$2,000
Variable charge on machine, $12 \times \$40$................	480
Interest, taxes, and insurance, $13,083 \times \$3 \times 0.10$...........	3,925
Storage cost, $13,083 \times \$0.20$................	2,617
Total cost with one machine................	$9,022

Two Machines

Fixed charges on machines, $2 \times \$2,000$................	$4,000
Variable charge on machines, $6 \times 2 \times \$40$................	480
Interest, taxes, and insurance, $4,083 \times \$3 \times 0.10$...........	1,225
Storage cost, $4,083 \times \$0.20$................	817
Total cost with two machines................	$6,522

Three Machines

Fixed charges on machines, $3 \times \$2,000$................	$6,000
Variable charge on machines, $4 \times 3 \times \$40$................	480
Interest, taxes, and insurance, $1,083 \times \$3 \times 0.10$...........	325
Storage cost, $1,083 \times \$0.20$................	217
Total cost with three machines................	$7,022

On the basis of the analysis above, a saving of $500 per year would result from using two machines in place of three and a saving of $2,500 would result from using two machines in place of one. It should be realized that there may be considerable hazard in the use of any of the three plans. If only one machine is used, there is a possibility that the product may become outmoded before the sales period or that sales may not be up to expectations. If three machines are used, there is a large investment that may not be recovered before the machines are rendered obsolete or inadequate.

17.2. ECONOMIC LOADING OF EQUIPMENT

Most production facilities may be operated at rates below, equal to, or above their normal capacity. Facilities are usually inefficient and costly to operate when utilized at a rate of output below their normal capacity. For example, if a production department is allotted more space than is needed for its efficient operation, a number of losses may be expected to arise. The fixed costs such as maintenance, taxes, insurance, and interest will be higher than necessary. Heat, light, and janitor service will be wasted in the unused space, and the cost of supervision and material handling may be expected to be higher than necessary.

The load that is considered proper to impose on equipment is usually indicated by their makers. Such indicated normal loads are often not the optimum for economy. Operation of equipment above its normal capacity will result in increased production at the expense of increased power consumption and shortened life. But, in many cases, the over-all result is a reduced cost per unit produced. If such is the case, the equipment in question should be overloaded so that the resulting economy may be realized.

The economy of loading to normal capacity. A mining company that is expanding its operations is in need of direct current for an electrolytic process. During the next year, an average of 12 kilowatts of direct current energy will be needed. Planned expansion of the existing operations is expected to increase the rate at which direct current is needed by 2 kilowatts per year until 30 kilowatts are needed. At this point, the demand for current will remain constant. Energy will be needed 2,000 hours per year regardless of the rate at which it is used.

Investigation reveals that the need for direct current can best be provided by an a-c to d-c motor-generator set. These sets can be purchased in a variety of capacities. Plan A involves the purchase of a 20-kilowatt set now for five years of use at which time the demand will have reached 20 kilowatts. At this time, a 30-kilowatt set will be purchased.

Efficiency-load curves provided by the vendor show that the 20-kw set has efficiencies of 48, 69, 78, and 76 per cent at $\frac{1}{4}$, $\frac{1}{2}$, $\frac{3}{4}$, and full load respectively. The 30-kw set is slightly more efficient at its $\frac{1}{4}$, $\frac{1}{2}$, $\frac{3}{4}$ and full load. The purchase rate of a-c current is $0.02 per kilowatt-hour. Interest is taken at 10 per cent. Taxes, insurance maintenance, and operating costs will be neglected in the interest of simplicity. The 20-kw set will cost $1,230 installed. It is estimated that $800 will be allowed for the 20-kw set on the installed purchase price of $1,580 of the 30-kw set 5 years hence. An analysis of the present-worth cost of the power consumed for each of the 5 years is given in Table 17.2.

Table 17.2. PRESENT-WORTH COST OF CONSUMED POWER FOR PLAN A

Year	Output rate d-c current, in kw (A)	Efficiency at d-c output rate (B)	Input rate a-c current, A ÷ B (C)	Annual power bill C × $0.02 × 2,000 hr. (D)	Present worth of annual power bill PS 10-n D × ( ) (E)
1	12	74	16.2	$ 648	$589
2	14	77	18.2	728	602
3	16	78	20.5	820	616
4	18	78	23.1	924	631
5	20	76	26.3	1,052	653

The present-worth of providing 5 years of service under Plan A is calculated as follows:

Total present worth of power bill for 5 years (ΣE in table)...... $3,091

Present-worth cost of 20-kw set installed..................... $1,230

Present worth of 20-kw set trade-in receipt, $800(0.6209)....... -497

Present worth of 30-kw set, $1,580(0.6209).................... 981

$4,805

Plan B involves the purchase of the 30-kilowatt set now so that it will be available to meet the anticipated demand. The present-

Table 17.3. PRESENT-WORTH COST OF CONSUMED POWER FOR PLAN B

Year	Output rate d-c current, in kw (A)	Efficiency at d-c output rate (B)	Input rate a-c current, A ÷ B (C)	Annual power bill C × $0.02 × 2,000 hr. (D)	Present worth of annual power bill, PS 10-n D × ( ) (E)
1	12	65	18.5	$ 740	$673
2	14	70	20.0	800	661
3	16	74	21.6	864	649
4	18	77	23.4	936	639
5	20	79	25.3	1,012	628

worth cost of the power consumed for each of the first five years is given in Table 17.3.

The present-worth cost of providing five years of service under Plan B is calculated as follows:

Total present worth of power bill for 5 years (ΣE in table)...... $3,250
Present-worth cost of 30-kw set installed..................... $1,580

$4,830

Power costs beyond the first five years have not been taken into account in the analysis above because they will be equal in subsequent years since a 30-kilowatt set will be used regardless of whether Plan A or B is adopted. The assumption that a 30-kilowatt unit five years old is equivalent to a new set was made to simplify the analyses and because electrical equipment ordinarily has a long service life.

The example indicates how economy of operations will result if equipment is loaded close to its normal operating capacity.

The economy of loading above normal capacity. The life of a piece of equipment is usually inversely proportional to the load imposed upon it. But the output is directly proportional to the load imposed. Where such is the case there exists a least cost load that will determine the level of operation for maximum economy.

In some cases, particularly with short-lived assets, the economic load may be determined by experiment. If the effect of various loadings upon the life, maintenance, and other operating costs of a unit of equipment are known or can be estimated with reasonable accuracy, it is practical to determine the load that will result in the greatest economy.

Consider the following example. A concern has a bending machine that produces one piece for each revolution it makes. It is now being operated at the rate of 150 rpm and produces 18.6 pounds of product per hour. The machine costs $6,150 and is estimated to have an operating life of 10,000 hours. Direct wages plus labor overhead of the operation amount to $1.37 per hour. Average present maintenance and power are $0.072 and $0.064 per hour, respectively. Output of product and cost of power used per hour are estimated to be directly proportional to the rpm of the machine. Since centrifugal forces on machine parts increase with the square of the speed, it is estimated that maintenance costs will increase in proportion to the square of the speed, and that the useful life of the machine will be inversely proportional to the square of the speed. On the basis of these assumptions Table 17.4 is constructed.

Table 17.4. RELATIONSHIP OF COST TO OPERATING SPEED

Operating speed in r.p.m. A	Estimated life in hr., $10{,}000 \times (150)^2/A^2$ B	Average output in pounds per hr. $18.6 \times A/150$ C	Labor cost per hour D	Average maintenance cost per hr., $\$0.072 \times A^2/(150)^2$ E	Power cost per hr., $\$0.064 \times A/150$ F	Average depreciation cost per hr., $\$6{,}150 \div B$ G	Total cost of operation per hr., $D+E+F+G$ H	Cost per pound, $H \div C$ I
150	10,000	18.6	$1.37	$0.072	$0.064	$0.615	$2.121	$0.114
200	5,630	24.8	1.37	0.128	0.085	1.092	2.675	0.108
250	3,600	31.0	1.37	0.200	0.107	1.708	3.385	0.109

On the basis of the estimated use, it would be desirable to increase the speed of the machine to 200 rpm. The expected saving per pound of product would be

$$(\$0.114 - \$0.108) \div \$0.114 = 5.3 \text{ per cent.}$$

This is a worthwhile saving, particularly since it shortens the capital recovery period and so lessens the possibilities of losses from obsolescence and inadequacy.

17.3. ECONOMIC LOAD DISTRIBUTION BETWEEN MACHINES

In many cases two or more machines are available for the same kind of production. Thus two or more boilers may be available to produce steam or two or more turbine generators may be on hand to produce power. If the total load is less than the combined capacity of the machines that are available, the economy of operation will, in some measure, depend upon the portion of the total load that is carried by each machine.

As an example of a simple method of determining the load distribution between two machines suppose that two Diesel-engine-driven d-c generators, one of 1,000 kw capacity and the other of 500 kw capacity, are available. The efficiencies for different outputs and the corresponding inputs for each are given in Table 17.5.

Table 17.5. EFFICIENCIES FOR DIFFERENT OUTPUTS

Output, in kw	MACHINE A, 1,000 KW OUTPUT		MACHINE B, 500 KW OUTPUT	
	Efficiency in per cent	Input, in kw	Efficiency in per cent	Input, in kw
100	15.1	663	20.7	483
200	22.0	909	27.9	719
300	26.3	1,141	31.8	943
400	29.5	1,356	32.5	1,231
500	31.2	1,603	32.0	1,563
600	32.3	1,858		
700	32.5	2,154		
800	32.6	2,454		
900	32.4	2,778		
1,000	32.3	3,096		

Suppose that the total load to be met at a certain time is 1,200 kw. This load may be distributed in several ways as is shown in

Table 17.6. DISTRIBUTION OF LOAD BETWEEN MACHINES

OUTPUT IN KW			INPUT IN KW		
Machine A	Machine B	Total	Machine A	Machine B	Total
1,000	200	1,200	3,096	719	3,815
900	300	1,200	2,778	943	3,721
800	400	1,200	2,454	1,231	3,685
700	500	1,200	2,154	1,563	3,717

Table 17.6. It is observed that the desired output of 1,200 kw can be produced with a minimum input when the larger unit carries 800 kw and the smaller unit 400 kw.

In the example above input can readily be converted to units other than kw. Suppose that it is desired to express input in terms of dollars.

Let it be assumed that fuel oil having an energy content of 18,800 Btu weighs 7.48 pounds per gallon and costs $0.084 per gallon delivered. One kw-hr. is equivalent to 3,410 Btu. From these data the cost per kw-hr. is calculated to be

$$\frac{\$0.084 \times 3,410}{7.48 \times 18,800} = \$0.002037.$$

At this rate of cost for fuel, 1,200 kw-hr. output of energy can be produced for $3,685 \times \$0.002037 = \$7.51$ if the loads on the two machines are 800 kw and 400 kw, respectively. If the load distribution had been 1,000 kw and 200 kw on the machines, the cost would have been $7.78, an increase over the better method of operation of $0.27, or $0.27/$7.51 = 3.7 per cent. This is a rather high rate of saving considering the ease with which it is made. The saving is a result of a correct decision based on knowledge of load distribution.

This method for determining load distribution is applicable to all types of machines and to entire plants as well. Its greatest usefulness is perhaps in relation to the application of power machines and machines having similar efficiency characteristics. When more than three machines are involved, the process illustrated above becomes cumbersome and should be replaced by more refined methods based on incremental rates.

17.4. MACHINE INTERFERENCE AND ECONOMY[1]

Machine interference occurs when one or more machines are nonproductive because, having been shut down in need of attention, they stand idle while the operator or operators are attending to other machines. For example, when one operator attends to two or more semiautomatic machines that have irregular shutdown times, machine idleness caused by interference must be tolerated because the running cycles of these machines cannot be coordinated.

The effects of machine interference are particularly apparent in the textile industry, where each operator usually attends to several semiautomatic machines. For a given work assignment, there may be

[1]Adapted from W. D. Jones, "Mathematical and Experimental Calculations of Machine Interference Time," *The Research Engineer*, Georgia Institute of Technology, January 1949.

times when all machines are producing and the operator is merely waiting for something to happen. There are other occasions, however, when many of the machines will have chanced to shut down simultaneously. In most cases, there is little or nothing that the operator can do to control unpredictable chance shutdowns of the machines and the consequent interference idleness.

The problem of evaluating machine interference losses is important to the engineer in two respects. First, machine interference loss must be known quantitatively before the economic number of semiautomatic machines to assign to one operator can be known. Second, the operator's actual productive efficiency cannot be determined for wage incentive purposes until the loss of production occasioned by machine intererence has been properly evaluated.

Countless hours have been spent by time-study men in attempts to evaluate machine interference by use of stop watches. However, the unpredictable, variable shutdowns of the many machines involved in a given assignment make the job of recording interference time an almost impossible task. Moreover, the question always arises whether the period of timing was of sufficient length to be representative of the actual conditions of operation.

Since machine interference is unpredictable, spasmodic, and variable in magnitude, accurate predetermination of interference mathematically requires some means of measurement that will take into account these uncertain characteristics. It has been found that one of the laws of probability serves this purpose very well; this law states, in effect, that when an event is based on chance as pertaining to each of several participants acting together, the various possible combinations of occurrence of that event will be distributed according to the terms of a binomial expansion. For example, suppose it is desired to determine the probabilities of each of the possible combinations of occurrence of the ace when rolling three dice together — the chance of all three dice turning up aces, the chance of rolling two aces, one ace, and a non-ace, and so forth. Substituting in the equation

$$(d + r)^n = d^n + nd^{n-1}r + \frac{n(n - 1)d^{n-2}r^2}{1(2)} + \ldots + r^n$$

$(d + r)^n$ becomes $(\frac{1}{6} + \frac{5}{6})^3$, where d is the probability of occurrence of the ace for each participant for each roll, r is the probability of nonoccurrence of the ace, and n is the number of participants. Expanding $(\frac{1}{6} + \frac{5}{6})^3$, the following distribution of probabilities is obtained:

Number of Aces Showing	Coefficient Sums	(d)		(r)	Probability
3	1	$\times \ (1/6)^3$	$\times$		1/216
2	3	$\times \ (1/6)^2$	$\times$	$(5/6)^1$	15/216
1	3	$\times \ (1/6)^1$	$\times$	$(5/6)^2$	75/216
0	1		$\times$	$(5/6)^3$	125/216

Here it can be seen that on the average, during 216 rolls of three dice, three aces would turn up once, two aces and a non-ace would occur 15 times, one ace and two non-aces would show 75 times, and three non-aces would turn up 125 times.

The expansion of $(d + r)^n$ as employed in this dice problem is also valid for evaluating interference when one operator tends several semiautomatic machines having either the same or different degrees of servicing-time requirements. The problem of computing interference for a given number of machines is handled in the same manner as the dice problem, except that interference waiting time for each probability must be factored in. For example, assume that three machines chance to shut down during the same interval of time. While one machine is being attended to by the operator, the other two must wait. The interference idleness inherent in the probability of three machines being down at the same time would therefore by that probability be multiplied by the two consequent waits.

The total interference idleness for a given group of machines is secured by adding the products of the various shut-down probabilities and consequent number of waits. This total interference is then divided by the number of machines in the group to secure the average interference idleness per machine.

Example of interference calculations. As an example of the above reasoning, assume that one operator attends to six semiautomatic machines. A count of the production at the end of the day shows that the average down time (nonproducing time) per machine was 20 per cent of the time the machines were operated. What then, was the average percentage interference per machine for the period of operation? Also, what was the average percentage servicing time per machine? Substituting, $(d + r)^n$ becomes $(\frac{1}{5} + \frac{4}{5})^6$ when

d = probability of occurrence of down time = $\frac{1}{5}$;

r = probability of nonoccurrence of down time = $\frac{4}{5}$;

n = the number of machines = 6.

Number of Machines Down Together	Coefficient Sums	(d)		(r)		Waits	Interference
6	1	$\times$ $(1/5)^6$			$\times$	5	5/15,625
5	6	$\times$ $(1/5)^5$	$\times$	$(4/5)^1$	$\times$	4	96/15,625
4	15	$\times$ $(1/5)^4$	$\times$	$(4/5)^2$	$\times$	3	720/15,625
3	20	$\times$ $(1/5)^3$	$\times$	$(4/5)^3$	$\times$	2	2,650/15,625
2	15	$\times$ $(1/5)^2$	$\times$	$(4/5)^4$	$\times$	1	3,840/15,625
1	6	$\times$ $(1/5)^1$	$\times$	$(4/5)^5$	$\times$	0	
0	1			$(4/5)^6$	$\times$	0	

$$\text{Total Interference} = 7,221/15,625$$
$$= 0.462$$

Since there are six machines in the group, the average interference per machine would be 0.462 ÷ 6, or 7.7 per cent. Since down time D is equal to average servicing time plus average interference time, the average servicing time per machine would be 20.0 − 7.7 = 12.3 per cent.

It is interesting to note that, since total down time D is equal to regular servicing time plus average interference time, interference *causes* interference. Interference caused by regular servicing time would result when, for instance, three machines out of a group shut down at the same time. Two machines must wait while the other is being serviced. Later, moreover, while the operator services one of the remaining two idle machines, the other must continue to wait. This waiting time of the third machine would be attributed to the prior interference of the second machine, and it would therefore be a case of interference causing interference. Meanwhile, if any of the other machines in the group chances to shut down while the operator is engaged in servicing the three machines described above, there would be another case of interference causing interference.

Tables or charts can be compiled showing the relationships between interference, servicing time, and down time for a group of any number of machines. This can be done by assuming various percentages of down time, proceeding with calculations as illustrated above, and then recording or plotting the results.

In some cases the servicing time of a machine operated separately is the only known quantity. The interference that will take place in a bank of any number of similar machines can be determined from charts or tables compiled as mentioned above, even though total down time is the basis of the original calculations.

The economical number of machines per operator. Assume that a certain machine, typical of a bank of machines, when tended individually will have an average down time of 15 per cent of the over-all operating time. It is desired to calculate the number of these machines that should be tended by one operator for greatest economy when the hourly cost of power, depreciation, and so forth of each machine is \$1 and the operators hourly wage is \$1. Let

S = servicing time per machine in per cent of over-all operating time, assuming each machine is individually tended.

I = average interference time per machine in per cent of over-all operating time. The average interference time per machine for groups of 3, 4, 5, and 6 machines, each having an S of 15 per cent, as determined from tables described above, is 3, 5, 8, and 11 per cent, respectively.

D = average down time per machine in per cent of total operating time.

P = average productive time per machine (or the efficiency) in percentage of over-all operating time.

L = hourly pay for the operator's labor.

M = hourly machine rate (power, depreciation, etc.).

n = number of machines tended by one operator.

When one operator tends one machine, the average productive time P of the machine is $100\% - D$. When one operator tends several machines, however, interference I becomes a factor in the operating disposition of each machine and D therefore becomes $I + S(100\% - I)$. In multiple machine operation then,

$$P = 100\% - I - S(100\% - I).$$

It therefore follows that the "equivalent" number of 100 per cent productive machines (an imaginary term) when one operator tends n machines is nP. Now, through the use of the formulas just developed, the economical number of machines for the stated conditions will be determined.

n	S	I	P	nP	nM	L	$nM + L$	$(nM + L)/nP$
3	15%	3%	82.5%	2.48	$3	$1	$4	$1.61
4	15%	5%	80.7%	3.23	4	1	5	1.55
5	15%	8%	78.2%	3.91	5	1	6	1.53
6	15%	11%	75.7%	4.54	6	1	7	1.54

Here it can be seen that an assignment of 5 machines would result in the lowest cost per equivalent machine (the lowest unit cost) for the conditions of this problem.

17.5. ECONOMIC PURCHASE QUANTITY

When the decision has been made to purchase a certain item it becomes necessary to determine the purchase quantity that will result in minimum cost. The demand for the item may be met by purchasing a year's supply at the beginning of the year, or by purchasing a day's supply at the beginning of each day. But neither of these extremes may be the most economical in terms of the sum of all costs associated with the activities of purchasing and holding the item in inventory.

If the demand for the item is met by purchasing once per year, the cost incident to purchasing will occur once, but the large quantity received will result in a relatively high inventory holding cost for the year. Conversely, if orders are placed several times per year, the cost incident to purchasing will be incurred several times per year, but since small quantities will be received, the cost of holding the item in inventory will be relatively small. If the decision is to be based on economy of the total operation the purchase quantity that will result in a minimum annual cost must be determined. Let

TC = total yearly cost of providing the item;

D = yearly demand for the item;

N = number of purchases per year;

t = time between purchases;

Q = purchase quantity;

C_i = item cost per unit (purchase price);

C_p = purchase cost per purchase order;

C_h = holding cost per unit per year made up of such items as interest, insurance, taxes, storage space, and handling.

If it is assumed that the demand for the item is constant throughout the year, the purchase lead time is zero, and no shortages are allowed; the resulting inventory system may be represented graphically as shown in Figure 17.2.

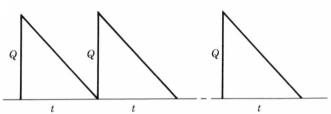

Figure 17.2. Graphical representation of an inventory process for purchasing.

The total yearly cost will be the sum of the item cost for the year, the purchase cost for the year, and the holding cost for the year. That is,

$$TC = IC + PC + HC.$$

The item cost for the year will be the item cost per unit times the yearly demand in units, or

$$IC = C_i(D).$$

The purchase cost for the year will be the cost per purchase times the number of purchases per year, or

$$PC = C_p(N).$$

But since N is the yearly demand divided by the purchase quantity

$$PC = \frac{C_p(D)}{Q}.$$

Since the interval, t, begins with Q units in stock and ends with none, the average inventory during the cycle will be $Q/2$. Therefore, the holding cost for the year will be the holding cost per unit times the average number of units in stock for the year, or

$$HC = \frac{C_h(Q)}{2}.$$

The total yearly cost of providing the required item is the sum of the item cost, purchase cost, and holding cost, or

$$TC = C_i(D) + \frac{C_p(D)}{Q} + \frac{C_h(Q)}{2}.$$

The purchase quantity resulting in a minimum yearly cost may be found by differentiating with respect to Q, setting the result equal to zero, and solving for Q as follows:

$$\frac{dTC}{dQ} = -\frac{C_p(D)}{Q^2} + \frac{C_h}{2} = 0$$

$$Q^2 = \frac{2C_p(D)}{C_h}$$

$$Q = \sqrt{\frac{2\,C_p(D)}{C_h}}$$

Example of economic purchase quantity. The annual demand for a certain item is 1,000 units. The cost per unit is $6 delivered. Purchasing cost per purchase order is $10 and the cost of holding one unit in inventory for one year is estimated to be 22 per cent of the cost of the item.

The economic purchase quantity may be found by substituting the appropriate values in the derived relationship as follows:

$$Q = \sqrt{\frac{2(\$10)(1,000)}{0.22(\$6)}}$$

$$= 123 \text{ units.}$$

Total cost may be expressed as a function of Q by substituting the costs and various values of Q into the total cost equation. The result is shown in Table 17.7. The tabulated total cost value for $Q = 123$ is the minimum cost purchase quantity for the conditions specified. Total cost as a function of Q is illustrated in Figure 17.3.

Table 17.7. TABULATED VALUES OF TOTAL COST AS A FUNCTION OF PURCHASE QUANTITY

Purchase quantity	Total cost
50	$6,233
100	$6,166
123	$6,162
150	$6,165
200	$6,182
300	$6,231
400	$6,289
600	$6,413

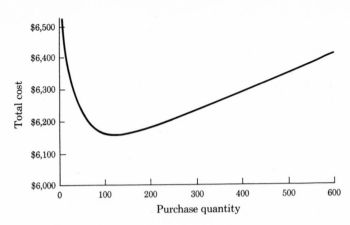

Figure 17.3. Total cost as a function of purchase quantity.

17.6. ECONOMIC PRODUCTION QUANTITY

When the decision has been made to produce a certain item, it becomes necessary to determine the production quantity that will result in minimum cost. Economic production quantities are determined in a manner similar to determining economic purchase quantities. The difference in analysis is brought about by the fact that a purchased lot is received at one time while a production lot accumulates as it is made. Let

TC = total yearly cost of providing the item;

D = yearly demand for the item;

N = number of production runs per year;

t = time between production runs;

Q = production quantity;

C_i = item cost per unit (production cost);

C_s = set-up cost per production run;

C_h = holding cost per unit per year made up of such items as interest, insurance, taxes, storage space, and handling;

R = production rate.

If it is assumed that the demand for the item is constant, the production rate is constant during the production period, the production lead time is zero, and no shortages are allowed; the resulting inventory system may be represented graphically as in Figure 17.4.

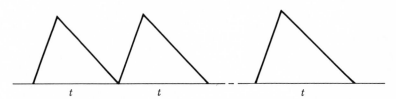

Figure 17.4. Graphical representation of an inventory process for production.

The total yearly cost will be the sum of the item cost for the year, the set-up cost for the year, and the holding cost for the year. That is,

$$TC = IC + SC + HC.$$

The item cost for the year will be the item cost per unit times the yearly demand in units, or

$$IC = C_i(D).$$

The set-up cost for the year will be the cost per set-up times the number of set-ups per year, or

$$SC = C_s(N).$$

But since N is the yearly demand divided by the production quantity

$$SC = \frac{C_s(D)}{Q}.$$

When items are added to inventory at the rate of R units per year and are taken from inventory at a rate D units per year, where R is greater than D, the net rate of accumulation is $(R - D)$ units per year. The time required to produce D units at the rate R units per year is D/R years. If D units are made in a single lot, the maximum accumulation in inventory will be $(R - D) D/R$. Since no units will be in storage at the end of the year, the average number in inventory will be

$$\frac{(R - D)\frac{D}{R} + 0}{2} = (R - D)\frac{D}{2R}.$$

If N lots are produced per year, the average number of units in storage will be

$$(R - D)\frac{D}{2RN}.$$

But, since $N = D/Q$, the average number of units in storage may be expressed as

$$(R - D)\frac{Q}{2R}.$$

The holding cost for the year will be the holding cost per unit times the average number of units in storage for the year, or

$$HC = C_h(R - D)\frac{Q}{2R}.$$

The total yearly cost of producing the required item is the sum of the item cost, set-up cost, and holding cost, or

$$TC = C_i(D) + \frac{C_s(D)}{Q} + C_h(R - D)\frac{Q}{2R}.$$

The production quantity resulting in a minimum yearly cost may be found by differentiating with respect to Q, setting the result equal to zero, and solving for Q as follows:

$$\frac{dTC}{dQ} = -\frac{C_s(D)}{Q^2} + \frac{C_h(R - D)}{2R}$$

$$Q^2 = \frac{C_s(D)2R}{C_h(R - D)} = \frac{C_s(D)2}{C_h\left(1 - \dfrac{D}{R}\right)}$$

$$Q = \sqrt{\frac{2C_s(D)}{C_h\left(1 - \dfrac{D}{R}\right)}}.$$

Example of economic production quantity. The annual demand for a certain item is 1,000 units. The cost of production is $5.90 per unit and includes the usual cost elements of direct labor, direct material, and factory overhead. The set-up cost per lot is $50 and the item can be produced at the rate of 6,000 units per year. The cost of holding one unit in inventory for one year is estimated to be 22 per cent of the cost of the item.

The economic production quantity may be found from the derived relationship by substituting the appropriate values as follows:

$$Q = \sqrt{\frac{2(\$50)(1,000)}{0.22(\$5.90)\left(1 - \dfrac{1,000}{6,000}\right)}}$$

$$= 302 \text{ units.}$$

Total cost may be expressed as a function of Q by substituting costs and various values of Q into the total cost equation. The result is shown in Table 17.8. The tabulated total cost value for $Q = 302$ is the minimum cost production quantity for the condition specified. Total cost as a function of Q is illustrated in Figure 17.5.

Table 17.8. TABULATED VALUES OF TOTAL COST AS A FUNCTION OF PRODUCTION QUANTITY

Production quantity	Total cost
100	$6,454
150	$6,314
200	$6,258
300	$6,229
302	$6,228
400	$6,241
500	$6,270
600	$6,307

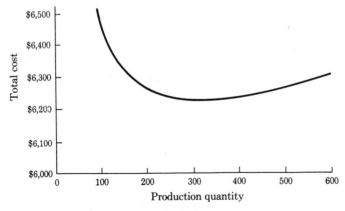

Figure 17.5. Total cost as a function of production quantity.

17.7. WHEN TO PRODUCE AND WHEN TO PURCHASE

The question of whether to "make or buy" a needed item may be resolved by the application of minimum cost analysis for multiple alternatives. The alternative of producing may be compared with the alternative of purchasing if the minimum cost lot size for each is computed and used to find the respective total cost values. Choice of the total cost value that is a minimum identifies the best of the two alternatives.

For example, suppose that an item will have a yearly demand of 1,000 units and that the costs associated with purchasing and producing are the same costs which were assumed in the previous two sections, that is,

	Purchase	*Produce*
Item cost.	$ 6.00	$ 5.90
Purchase cost.	$10.00	–
Set-up cost.	–	$50.00
Holding cost.	$ 1.32	$ 1.30

For the conditions assumed, total cost as a function of the purchase quantity was given in Table 17.7 and total cost as a function of production quantity was given in Table 17.8. Total cost as a function

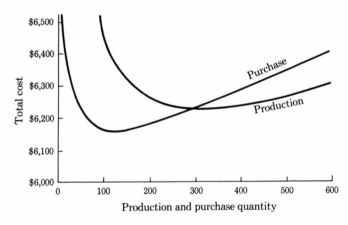

Figure 17.6. Total cost as a function of production and purchase quantities.

of purchase quantity was graphed in Figure 17.3 and total cost as a function of production quantity was graphed in Figure 17.5. If Figure 17.3 and 17.5 are superimposed, the result is as shown in Figure 17.6.

The decision of whether to produce or purchase may be made by examining and comparing the minimum cost for each alternative. In this case, the decision to purchase will be the least cost alternative and will result in a saving of $6,232 less $6,163, or $69 per year. If the decision were made on the basis of item cost alone, the needed item would have been supplied by producing with a resultant loss of $69 per year.

The optimal procurement policy may be formally stated by specifying that the item will be procured when the available stock falls to zero units on hand, for a procurement quantity of 123 units, from the purchasing source. In essence the policy states when, how much, and from what source. The policy, if the decision has been made to purchase, states when and how much, the source being fixed by restriction. Therefore, the decision of "make or buy" is essentially a release of the restriction that the source is fixed. This analysis may be extended to any number of sources; for example, it may be used to compare re-manufacturing with purchasing, to compare alternate manufacturing facilities, or to evaluate alternate vendors.

17.8. ECONOMICAL SIZE OF REPAIR CREWS

When nonrepetitive work that precludes pre-planning is performed, the number of men in a crew is an important consideration from the standpoint of the crew's effectiveness. Loss in effectiveness may arise from one or more characteristics inherent in the size of the crew. For example, as the size of the crew increases, loss of effectiveness will result from the time of going to and from the job.

As an absurd illustration, assume that a maintenance job involving 60 man-minutes of work is to be performed at such a distance that it will require 10 minutes to go to the job and 10 minutes to return from the job. Assume further that the work to be performed can be done effectively by either a one-man or a 60-man crew. Labor cost is taken at $1.80 per man-hour, or $0.03 per man-minute. A comparison of ths over-all effectiveness of each crew is revealed by the following analyses:

ONE-MAN CREW

Activity	Minutes Required in Performance	Man-Minutes
Walk to job	10	10
Perform job	60	60
Walk from job	10	10
		—
Total man-minutes...............................		80

Total cost, 80 man-min. @ \$0.03 = \$2.40

SIXTY-MAN CREW

Activity	Minutes Required in Performance	Man-Minutes
Walk to job	10	600
Perform job	1	60
Walk from job	10	600
		—
Total man-minutes................................		1260

Total cost, 1260 man-min. @ \$0.03 = \$37.80

The difference between \$37.80 and \$2.40, or \$35.40, is a measure of the loss of effectiveness in travel time because of an excessive crew size.

There are many situations in which economy depends upon a balance between losses associated with machine down time and the cost associated with maintaining a crew to undertake preventative maintenance and repair to minimize such losses.

Suppose that the failure of a machine will result in a loss of \$2 per hour during the period that it is inoperative or "down" for repairs. Past experience shows that a typical repair for this machine can be made by one man in 9 hours, by two men in 5 hours, by three men in 4 hours, by four men in 3.75 hours, and by five men in 4 hours. The wage rate of repair men is taken to be \$1 per hour. The costs incident to the failure of the machine are given in Table 17.9.

Table 17.9. COSTS INCIDENT TO REPAIR AND DOWN TIME

Number of men in repair crew	1	2	3	4	5
Hours required to make repair...............	9	5	4	3¾	4
Man-hours required to make repair...........	9	10	12	15	20
Labor cost of making repair at \$1 per hour.....	\$ 9	\$10	\$12	\$15	\$20
Down-time cost at \$2 per hour for machine.....	\$18	\$10	\$ 8	\$ 7.5	\$ 8
Resultant of labor cost of making repair and down-time loss of machine.................	\$27	\$20	\$20	\$22.5	\$28

The economy associated with the loss of use of the machine suggests that the repair crew should be the size that will result in minimum down time. A person concerned only with the down-time loss of a machine would select a four-man crew, which would hold the down-time loss to $7.50 per repair.

The economy of the repair activity points to a crew of one man so that the repair may be made most efficiently and at least cost. A person primarily interested in the efficient utilization of repair men and low repair costs would have his men work singly.

Usually it is the over-all economy that is desired. In this case the greatest over-all economy occurs when crews of two or three men are used; the use of either would result in a total cost of $20.

This example brings out the fact that there are two aspects to be considered in a repair program. One of these is to make the needed repairs at least cost; the other is to minimize losses associated with the down time of machinery.

17.9. ECONOMICAL NUMBER OF REPAIR CREWS

Failures of equipment do not occur with regularity. In addition, the amount of repair work needed for any given failure may be expected to vary above and below the average amount needed over a long period of time. Each of these events, the occurrence of a failure and the amount of repair needed, are a function of many unpredictable chance causes.

If the number of repair crews provided is just sufficient to take care of the average amount of repair work needed, there will be a considerable backlog of work waiting to be done and the cost of equipment down time will be high. Where down time is costly, it may be wise to maintain repair crew capacity in excess of that needed for the average repair load even though this will result in some idleness on the part of the repair crews.

As an example of the analysis required in finding the economical number of repair crews, consider an illustration from the petroleum industry. In petroleum production, heavy equipment is used to pump oil to the surface. When this equipment fails, it is necessary to remove it from the well for repairs. The required repairs are made by crews of three to five men who are equipped with heavy, portable machinery to pull the pumping equipment from the well.

Between the time the pumping equipment fails and the time it is repaired, the well is idle. This results in a loss, known as *lost production*, equal to the amount of oil that world have been produced if there had been no failure of equipment. In some cases lost production may be only production that is deferred to a later date. In other cases lost production is partially lost because of drainage to competitors' wells. This loss may be quite large. Two days' down time of a well producing 200 barrels of oil per day at $2.20 per barrel, for instance, when drainage to a competitor's well is judged to be half of lost production, results in a loss of $440.

The down time of a well is made up of the time that the well is idle before the repair crew gets to it and the time it is idle while repair is in process. Since the rate at which repairs can be made is substantially controlled by the repair equipment, reduction in loss is brought about by reducing the time a well is idle awaiting repair crews. This is done at the expense of having excess repair crews. Thus the problem is to balance the number of repair crews with the lost production associated with delays of repairs to wells. Consider the following data adapted from an actual situation in which the wells are operated 24 hours a day, 7 days per week:

N, number of oil wells in field = 30;

T, average interval at which individual wells fail = 15 days;

R, average actual time for company crew to repair well failure = 12 hours;

U, hourly cost for company-operated repair unit and repair crew = $6.90 per hour;

r, average actual time for contract crew to repair well failure = 16 hours;

u, hourly cost for contract repair unit and repair crew = $9 per hour;

L, lost production per well when "down" = $84 per day.

Under the present situation, analysis has revealed that operation of the equivalent of one repair unit 24 hours per day, seven days per week can keep up with the repair of failures in the long run. However, serious losses are arising from delays in getting to wells after notification of their failure. Delay is due to the chance bunching of well failures. For instance, one period during which no wells fail may be followed by a period of an above-average number of failures. Since repairs cannot be made before failures occur, it is clear that crews sufficient to take care of the average number of failures will have a backlog of failures awaiting them most of the time.

The first step in an analysis to determine the most economical number of repair crews is to determine the number of wells that may be expected to fail during each and every day of a period in the future. The number of failures to expect in the future may be estimated on the basis of past records or by mathematical analysis. The former method is used in the example because it is more revealing.

In the solution of this example the pattern of well failures of a previous 30-day period selected at random will be considered to be representative of future periods. A 30-day period will be taken in the interest of simplicity, even though experience has shown that longer periods are advantageous.

Since the company's unit can repair two wells per day when operating three eight-hour shifts per day, unrepaired wells will be carried over one day each day that the number of failures plus the carry-over from the previous day exceeds two.

Line A of Figure 17.7 shows the number of wells that failed during the 30-day period selected at random. The number of wells failing during any one day ranged between 0 and 5, and their total was 57.

Line B gives the number of wells repaired each day with the company's unit and crews. During the 30-day period, 57 wells failed and 55 were repaired. Thus, in spite of the periodic backlogs, there was idle time of the unit and crews on the days numbered 3, 6, 7, and 8 — sufficient to repair 5 wells.

The carry-over of unrepaired wells is given in Line C. The total carry-over for the 30-day period is 52 well-days.

On the present basis of operation, employing the equivalent of one unit 24 hours per day, the total cost incident to well-failures and repair during the 30-day period is calculated as follows:

Value of lost production due to carry-over of unrepaired wells, 52
    well-days × \$84 .... \$4,368
Cost of company's unit and crews, \$6.90 per hour × 24 hours ×
    30 days 4,968
                                                          ———
                                                          \$9,336

Day of period

1 2 3 4 5 6 7 8 9 10 11 12 13 14 15 16 17 18 19 20 21 22 23 24 25 26 27 28 29 30

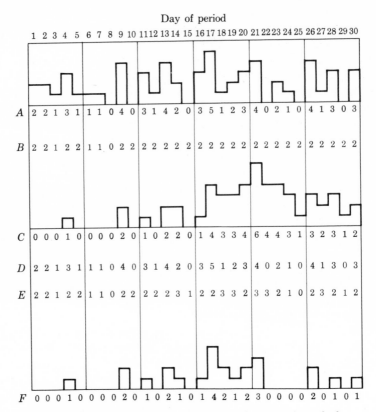

A | 2 2 1 3 1 | 1 1 0 4 0 | 3 1 4 2 0 | 3 5 1 2 3 | 4 0 2 1 0 | 4 1 3 0 3

B | 2 2 1 2 2 | 1 1 0 2 2 | 2 2 2 2 2 | 2 2 2 2 2 | 2 2 2 2 2 | 2 2 2 2 2

C | 0 0 0 1 0 | 0 0 0 2 0 | 1 0 2 2 0 | 1 4 3 3 4 | 6 4 4 3 1 | 3 2 3 1 2

D | 2 2 1 3 1 | 1 1 0 4 0 | 3 1 4 2 0 | 3 5 1 2 3 | 4 0 2 1 0 | 4 1 3 0 3

E | 2 2 1 2 2 | 1 1 0 2 2 | 2 2 2 3 1 | 2 2 3 3 2 | 3 3 2 1 0 | 2 3 2 1 2

F | 0 0 0 1 0 0 0 0 2 0 1 0 2 1 0 1 4 2 1 2 3 0 0 0 0 2 0 1 0 1

Figure 17.7. Pattern of oil-well failure and two repair methods.

Analysis of the pattern of occurrence of unrepaired wells carried over reveals that, once a backlog has accumulated, wells may remain unrepaired and unproductive for a long period. As a remedy the supervisor in charge considers the feasibility of hiring an additional unit and a crew whenever a backlog of unrepaired wells has accumulated. He finds that a repair unit and crew can be hired on short notice when needed for $9 per hour. Because of greater travel distance and other reasons, a hired unit and crew has been found to require an average of 16 hours to repair a well.

The supervisor wishes to determine the effect of a policy of hiring an additional unit and crew for a 16-hour period on days when there is a carry-over of two or more unrepaired wells from the previous day.

He assumes that the hired unit and crew will be paid for a minimum of 16 hours each time it is asked to report, whether or not it is used.

If this policy had been in effect during the 30-day period under consideration, the additional unit and repair crew would have been hired for 16 hours on the days numbered 10, 14, 18, 19, 21, 22, and 26; the total number of wells repaired during each day would have been as given in Line E of Figure 17.7.

Under this plan of operation, the total carry-over would have been 24 well-days as is shown in Line F.

Line E indicates that there was idle time of units and crew during the days numbered 3, 6, 7, 8, 10, 15, 24, 25, and 29 — sufficient for the repair of 11 wells.

On the basis of the analysis above, the total cost incident to well-failures and repair for the 30-day period is calculated as follows:

Value of lost production due to carry-over of unrepaired wells, 24
    well-days $\times$ \$84. . . . . $2,016
Cost of company's unit and crews, \$6.90 per hour $\times$ 24 hours $\times$
    30 days. 4,968
Cost of hired unit and crew, \$9 per hour $\times$ 16 hours $\times$ 7 days. . . . 1,008

                                                                             $7,992

Thus, the decision to hire an additional unit and crew on days when there is a carry-over of two or more unrepaired wells from a previous day will result in a reduction of the total cost of operations by \$9,336 less \$7,992, or \$1,344 per month.

17.10. ECONOMY OF TOOL MAINTENANCE

Through the ages man has developed many tools to increase his output and lighten his burden. Such tools as shovels, axes, saws, screw drivers, and chisels, although relatively inexpensive, increase the output of a person manyfold.

Many common tools are the results of centuries of use and experimentation and have reached a high state of perfection. Yet it appears that too little attention has been given to the consideration of the effectiveness of tools as an aid in reducing effort. In a famous study in 1898 at the Bethlehem Steel Works, Frederick W. Taylor investigated shoveling, an activity that composed much of the work of 600 men. Taylor found a great variety of shovels in use. Shovelers were lifting shovel loads ranging from 3.5 pounds (of rice coal) to 38 pounds (of ore). Taylor set out to determine what shovel load permitted a man to move the maximum amount of material per day. After an extended study, he found that a shovel designed to hold 21.5 pounds was most effective.

All too frequently tools actually found in the hands of workmen are in very poor condition. This is often the result of indifference or a false sense of economy on the part of workmen or supervisors. For example, consider the use of hand shovels by laborers on a construction job. As the shovel tips become blunt the shovel becomes more difficult to insert into the earth and, as a consequence, will be filled less frequently and with a reduced amount of soil.

In an experiment, workmen were given shovels in new condition and the amount of earth moved under uniform conditions as the shovel dulled was observed. The results are given in Table 17.10.

Table 17.10. POUNDS OF EARTH MOVED AS A FUNCTION OF SHARPENING INTERVAL

Eight-hour periods after sharpening between hours given A	Average load in pounds during period given B	Average number of shovelfulls moved for period given C	Total pounds moved in 8-hour period $B \times C \times 60 \times 8$
0 to 8	3.23	6.72	10,420
8 to 16	2.87	6.08	8,380
16 to 24	2.65	5.66	7,200
24 to 32	2.51	5.30	6,380
32 to 40	2.42	5.04	5,860

The cost of sharpening shovels was estimated to be $0.56. Each laborer receives $2 per hour. Therefore, the cost of moving 1,000 pounds of earth for different sharpening intervals is calculated as follows:

Interval of Sharpening		Cost Per 1,000 lbs.
8 hrs.	$(8 \times \$2 + \$0.56) \div 10.42$	$1.59
16 hrs.	$(16 \times \$2 + \$0.56) \div (10.42 + 8.38)$	1.73
24 hrs.	$(24 \times \$2 + \$0.56) \div (10.42 + 8.38 + 7.20)$	1.87
32 hrs.	$(32 \times \$2 + \$0.56) \div (10.42 + 8.38 + 7.20 + 6.38)$	2.00
40 hrs.	$(40 \times \$2 + \$0.56) \div (10.42 + 8.38 + 7.20 + 6.38 + 5.86)$	2.11

This analysis suggests that the cost of moving earth would be reduced by $2.11 less $1.59 ÷ $2.11, or 24.6 per cent by a policy of sharpening shovels at 8-hour intervals instead of at 40-hour intervals. In addition, it appears likely that adopting a policy of sharpening at intervals shorter than 8 hours will lead to a further reduction in the cost of the shoveling operation.

17.11. CONTROL AND ECONOMY

To control is to confine between limits, to make an action or a thing conform to a predetermined plan. An automobile being driven along a highway is in control as long as the driver can make it go where he has planned.

Absolute control is impossible since deviation must occur before lack of control can be ascertained. Practical control plans provide for deviation from perfection by setting up limits of acceptable variability. Action confined within these established limits is considered to be in control. When action goes beyond the established limits, corrective measures are initiated.

In general, the wider the control limits, the easier it is to maintain control. But, under these conditions, the worth of the action will be less than if the limits were set close. Therefore, the balance between the cost of maintaining control and its worth in terms of controlled action is an important consideration in the economy of operations.

Once the decision has been made to initiate a certain activity, it must be controlled if it is to be effective. Such control requires that the operation be analyzed from the standpoint of its various facets which, if controlled, will lead to economy. Among the most common areas subject to control are cost, material, production, and quality. For each, there is a least cost control limit that may be established by considering jointly the cost of control action and the cost of lack of control.

PROBLEMS

1. A manufacturer of a seasonal item finds that his sales are at the rate of 10,000 units per month, each month of the year except September and October when the rate of sales is 40,000 units per month. This product is made on single-purpose machines that have an initial cost of $12,000

each, an estimated life of 6 years, and no salvage value. Fixed charges other than interest and depreciation on each of these machines amount to $400 and the variable cost amounts to $0.42 per hour of operation. Machine operators are paid $2 per hour. Each machine normally produces 25 units of product per hour, and the plant operates 160 hours per month. The material entering the product is received as used and costs $2.80 per unit of product. Charges for interest, taxes, and insurance on the average inventory of finished goods are estimated to be 9 per cent of the variable cost of manufacture and materials. Charges for storage of inventory amount to $0.10 per unit per year of average inventory. How many machines should be employed in the production of the item for minimum cost if the interest rate is 8 per cent?

2. The expected demand for a certain item during the months of January through June is 10,000 per month. It is expected that the demand will be 30,000 per month during the months of July through September and 20,000 per month during the months of October through December. The item can be ordered for a January 1 delivery at $3.95 per unit, for an April 1 delivery at $4 per unit, and for an August 1 delivery at $4.05 per unit. The item cannot be delivered at other times during the year. The cost to initiate and complete a purchase is $150 and the storage cost is $0.10 per unit per year. Interest, insurance, taxes, and other storage costs are estimated to be 9 per cent of the investment in average inventory.

As an alternative, the item can be manufactured on single purpose machines with the following characteristics:

Machine cost..	$12,000
Service life in years................................	6
Salvage value.......................................	0
Annual fixed cost excluding depreciation.............	$400
Variable cost per hour of operation..................	$0.42
Hours available per month...........................	160
Production in units per hour........................	25
Interest rate......................................	8%

The direct labor cost for the operator is $2.80 per hour. The direct material cost per unit is $3. Calculate the number of machines for minimum cost if the manufacturing alternative is chosen and compare this with the least cost purchase policy.

3. Electric lamps rated at 200 watts and 110, 115, or 120 volts can be purchased for $0.46 each. When the lamps are placed in a 115-volt circuit, the following data apply:

	110 v Lamp	115 v Lamp	120 v Lamp
Average watts input	209.1	195.2	182.8
Average lumens output per watt of input	18.30	16.84	15.48
Average life of lamp in hours	420	750	1,340

Energy costs $0.042 per 1,000 watt-hours. Determine the cost per million lumen hours for each lamp under the three conditions.

4. The normal operating speed of wire weaving looms is 300 r.p.m. At this speed the looms have a life expectancy of 5 years, an annual maintenance cost of $200, and an annual power cost of $70. The machines cost $4,000 and have negligible salvage value. Annual space charges are estimated at $170 per machine. The operator's rate is $2.10 per hour and each operator runs three machines regardless of their speed.

Experimental work on the operation of these machines has resulted in the following data:

Speed r.p.m.	Life in Years	Annual Maintenance Cost	Annual Power Cost
250	7.2	$120	$ 60
300	5.0	$200	$ 70
350	3.7	$320	$ 90
400	2.8	$480	$120
450	2.2	$680	$160

Summarize the items of cost in a table and determine the most economical r.p.m. at which to run the machines. Assume that a loom operating at a normal operating speed of 300 r.p.m. will produce 300 units of product per year (each year consists of 40 hours a week for 50 weeks) and that production is directly proportional to the speed of the loom. Compute capital recovery on the basis of the straight-line depreciation and an interest rate of zero per cent.

5. An underground deposit has been estimated to contain 56,000 tons of recoverable sulphur, for which the market price at the mine is $15.50 per ton. The deposit will be recovered through wells by dissolution in hot water. Forty-five hundred tons per year can be recovered from each well. The time required to exhaust the deposit is inversely proportional to the number of wells. The company makes the following estimates of expenses for 1, 2, 3, and 4 wells:

Number of wells	1	2	3	4
Investment	$47,000	$85,000	$123,000	$161,000
Variable cost per ton	$2.72	$2.72	$2.72	$2.72
Years to mine	12	6	4	3
Tons per year	4,500	9,000	13,500	18,000

The property is valued at $400,000 and will have no value after the sulphur deposit is exhausted. Assume that all equipment must be paid for by this mining operation. What number of wells will result in the highest rate of return on the investment?

6. If tended individually, a certain machine would be nonproductive 12 per cent of the time for servicing. The average interference per machine if 4, 5, 6, 7, and 8 machines are assigned to one operator is 3, 5, 7, 10, and 13 per cent, respectively. Each machine assigned will require 12 per cent servicing time on an individual attention basis. Determine the number of these machines to be assigned to an operator whose wages are $2.60 per hour if each machine incurs an hourly expense of $1.80 for depreciation, power, and overhead.

7. The machine and handling time of Operation A on Machine X is 1.3 and 0.4 minutes, respectively. The machine and handling time of Operation B on Machine Y is 0.6 and 0.3 minutes, respectively. The hourly cost of operating Machines X and Y is $2.30 and $1.40, respectively. The operators of both machines receive $2.10 per hour. Determine the cost of Operations A and B.

The economy of letting one operator handle both machines is being considered even though it is realized that the handling times cannot overlap or be interrupted when started.

(a) Determine the percentage of idle time of Machine Y if Machine X is kept busy because of its higher rate.

(b) Determine the savings on each operation if the operator is paid $2.40 for operating both machines, of which $1.30 is charged to X and $1.10 to Y.

(c) Determine the percentage of the total time that the operator of two machines will be working.

8. In the operation of a certain type of equipment, repairs average $6 each and the cost of a shutdown for emergency repairs entails an additional loss of $14. In the past, there has been no routine periodic inspection of the equipment. It is believed that periodic inspections would result in a worthwhile saving.

In order to get data on which to determine the frequency of periodic inspections for greatest economy, five groups of an equal number of machines A, B, C, D, and E were inspected 0, 1, 2, 3, and 6 times per week, respectively. The cost per inspection was found to be $1.25. The plant operates 6 days per week, 50 weeks per year. The results of a year's run are shown below:

Machine Group	Inspections Per Week	Emergency Repairs	Non-emergency Repairs
A	0	31	27
B	1	20	36
C	2	13	41
D	3	9	43
E	6	3	47

What number of inspections should be made per week and what will be the total yearly cost for inspection, loss due to emergency repairs, and cost of repairs for this number of inspections per week?

9. A manufacturer purchases ball bearings in cases containing 1,000 bearings each. Some bearings from each case are inspected as part of the acceptance procedure. The cost of inspecting one bearing is $0.20 and the loss resulting from the acceptance of a defective bearing is $2. From past experience, the number of defective bearings that will be accepted if 100, 200, 300, and 400 bearings are inspected from each case is, respectively, 45, 30, 25, and 20. Determine the most economical number of bearings to inspect from each case.

10. A foundry uses 3,600 tons of pig iron per year at a constant rate. The cost per ton delivered to the foundry is $66. It is estimated that it costs $30 to place an order and $2.50 per ton per year for storage. Interest, taxes, insurance, and other warehousing costs are estimated to be 12 per cent of the average inventory investment. Calculate the economic purchase quantity.

11. A manufacturer requires one unit of a certain item per day for 360 days per year. The price quoted for the item is as follows:

Quantity Ordered	Price
1–12 units	$24 each
13–36 units	$23 each
37–72 units	$21 each
73 or more units	$18 each

It is estimated that it costs $56 to place an order and $70 per unit per year for storage. Interest, insurance, taxes, and other warehousing costs are estimated to be 16 per cent of the average inventory investment. Calculate the economic purchase quantity.

12. The demand for 1,000 units of a part to be used at a uniform rate throughout the year may be met by manufacturing. The part can be produced at the rate of 3 per hour in a department which works 1,880 hours per year. The set-up cost per lot is estimated to be $40 and the manufac-

turing cost has been established at $5.20 per unit. Interest, insurance, taxes, and other warehousing costs are estimated to be 12 per cent of the investment in average inventory. Warehouse space required for each unit is estimated to cost $0.80 per unit per year. Calculate the economic manufacturing quantity.

13. An aircraft manufacturer uses 1,000,000 special rivets per year at a uniform rate. The rivets are made on a single-spindle automatic screw machine at the rate of 3,000 per hour. The manufacturing cost is $0.0052 per rivet and the storage cost is estimated to be $0.0008 per rivet per year based on the average stock on hand. The set-up cost is $40 per set-up. Calculate the economic production quantity and the allowable variation in this quantity for a maximum deviation from the minimum cost of 5 per cent.

14. The annual demand for an item that can be either purchased or produced is 3,600 units. Costs associated with each alternative are as follows:

	Purchase	Produce
Item cost	$ 3.90	$ 3.75
Purchase cost per purchase	$15.00	–
Set-up cost per set-up	–	$175.00
Holding cost per item per year	$ 1.25	$ 1.25
Production rate per year	–	15,000

Should the item be manufactured or purchased? What is the economic lot size for the least cost alternative?

15. A company has 24 identical machines that are operated 24 hours per day, 360 days per year. On the average, each machine breaks down at intervals of 6 working days. The time required to repair each machine is 8 man-hours. Repairmen receive $2 per hour and work 8 hours per day. A loss of $32 is sustained for each day that a machine is "carried over" unrepaired.

(a) Determine the number of machines that may be expected by chance to go "down" during each day of a month by tossing a die 24 times to represent the 24 machines. Let the downs for each day be represented by the aces that come up.

(b) Assuming that all downs as found in part (a) occur at 12 midnight, determine the most economical number of regular repairmen to employ, if no extra repairmen or overtime wages are to be allowed and regular repairmen are not used except to repair the machines in question. Assume that the sequence for the 30-day month will be repeated 12 times during the year.

16. For a certain group of machines, a repair crew requires one day to repair a machine that breaks down. A loss of $180 is incurred for each day that a machine is "carried over" unrepaired. Each crew costs $75 per day to equip and maintain. The pattern of machine failures on succeeding days of a 30-day period is 7, 5, 8, 0, 3, 4, 5, 0, 2, 3, 8, 4, 5, 6, 1, 3, 4, 0, 2, 8, 6, 5, 5, 3, 4, 6, 7, 1, 3, 2. Assume that all breakdowns occur at the first of each day.

(a) Determine the idle time of crews when 4, 5, or 6 crews are employed.

(b) What is the optimum number of crews to employ?

17. A manufacturer of heavy earth-moving equipment estimates the rolling resistance of different qualities of roadbeds as follows:

Unstabilized, rutted, dirt roadway; soft under travel. . . 150 lb. per ton
Maintained, firm, smooth roadway; dirt surfacing flexing
  slightly under load............................... 65 lb. per ton
Maintained, hard-surfaced roadway; little penetration
  under load....................................... 40 lb. per ton

The outputs of earth haulers over a 5,000-foot roadway for various values of rolling resistance are as follows:

Rolling resistance of roadway, lbs. per ton.......... 150 65 40
Output, cubic yards per hour...................... 30 60 80

Twelve thousand cubic yards of earth are to be moved; the hauler and driver cost $9 per hour; and a roadway with a rolling resistance of 150 pounds per ton costs $260. What expenditure is justified for the construction of a roadway whose rolling resistance is (a) 65 and (b) 40 pounds per ton?

18. In a study involving the use of a pick it was found that the penetration of the pick into a certain soil decreased with time as follows:

Time after Sharpening in Hours	Average Penetration in Inches
0 to 4............................	3.99
4 to 8............................	3.76
8 to 12...........................	3.57
12 to 16..........................	3.41
16 to 20..........................	3.29

The labor rate is $2.20 per hour and it costs $1.08 to sharpen one pick. Assume that one hour of use at the average penetration for that hour is a measure of useful accomplishment.

(a) Calculate the ratio of the costs for equal accomplishment for resharpening a pick at 4-hour intervals and at 20-hour intervals.

(b) Calculate the most economical pick-sharpening interval.

CHAPTER **18**

EVALUATION OF PROPOSED OPERATIONS

Existing operations that are being pursued become outmoded and unprofitable through the initiation of new operations. The success of an enterprise depends upon the effectiveness of the new operations that are proposed as replacements for existing activities. Since engineers play a major role in the proposal formulation phase of new operations, they should be familiar with the methods useful in evaluating these proposals.

In this chapter a new activity will be considered as a proposed and new opportunity for profit, whose acceptance or rejection is substantially independent of previous commitments. The emphasis here will be on the economy of the choice, and only secondary attention will be given to the economy of performance after the new activity is initiated. Several selections representative of the evaluation of new operations will be presented in the sections that follow.

18.1. ADVANTAGES AND DISADVANTAGES OF A NEW ACTIVITY

Certain advantages favor a new activity. Since it is independent of previous commitments, it may be implemented in large measure on the basis of present and future considerations. Little consideration need be taken of the past except to profit by previous mistakes. Contrast this with the situation of railroads, whose future development is for all practical purposes limited by the present standard distance between rails. This gauge is not the best for either economy or comfort for higher-speed trains, but to change it is not feasible.

A new activity may enjoy a tremendous temporary advantage from being first in the field. Its launching is analogous to the surprise attack in war, where traditionally a small force overwhelms a much larger force. Where the new enterprise is based upon a patented device, initiative of discovery results in the advantage of monopoly to a greater or lesser extent. But even without patents the discovery and the vigorous prosecution of an economic opportunity often result in a tremendous initial gain before rivals can come into the field.

Embarking upon a new activity has an element of adventure associated with it and usually requires more creative thinking than the expansion of an old activity. New activities also result in employment of new personnel or in a change of activity of existing personnel. These factors often create enthusiasm and in turn superlative accomplishment of both individuals and groups.

A serious disadvantage faced in launching many new enterprises is that they often require an input of money and effort for long periods of time prior to realization of income from them. Many new ventures of ultimate promise fail because funds and enthusiasm are exhausted before adequate returns can be established. Unless strong financial backing without returns for long periods of time is available, many otherwise profitable undertakings are not feasible. Inadequate financing is recognized as one of the most important causes of failure of new enterprises.

In any pioneering activity lack of experience often results in the arising of unforeseen contingencies for which provision has not been made. Lack of experience or ability in regard to financing, organization, marketing, production, and other important activities is an important cause of failure in otherwise promising opportunities. Thus in launching a new enterprise competent personnel is of great importance. Incompetence of management ranks along with inadequate financing as a cause of failure of new enterprises.

Many new enterprises fail because the opportunities they are designed to exploit are inadequate for success. Although the opportunities for profit should be ascertained prior to deciding upon a proposal if possible, many opportunities cannot be evaluated even reasonably well except by trial. When this is the case, the uncertainty of the enterprise should be realized so that steps may be taken to meet the outcome, whatever it may be. If the outlook for the new activity seems promising, immediate steps should be taken to exploit the opportunity with vigor. If it seems unpromising, steps should be taken to withdraw from the venture with a minimum loss of money and effort.

18.2. UNFORESEEN RISKS CONFRONTING A NEW ACTIVITY

Experience leads to the conclusion that, despite the most careful planning, a new enterprise will be more subject to unforeseen hazards or contingencies than one that is well established. Furthermore, the new enterprise usually has very limited reserves to meet even temporary reversals.

Demands for new products are subject to both seasonal and long-time fluctuations. A new enterprise that begins on a long-time decline of demand for its product may fail from this cause. A new enterprise entering a seasonal market may lose much of its first year's income through any cause that may delay completion of its plant in time to take advantage of the active period for its product.

A new enterprise usually needs considerable credit during the period of rapid expansion before it has time to establish itself favorably with sources of credit. It is very vulnerable to any tightening of credit in this period. Even if its need for credit may arise from a more rapid expansion of sales than expected, it may fail from inability to secure funds to bridge the period between expenditures for the manufacture of its product and receipts from its sales.

Established firms do not ordinarily welcome a new competitor into the field with enthusiasm. Thus a new firm often finds active and concerted efforts directed toward discrediting it and its products. This can be very damaging and difficult to offset.

A most important factor in the success of a new venture is the enthusiasm and capabilities of its leaders. These men are subject to the hazards of sickness and accident. Impairment of health or death of a capable leader can easily cause a new enterprise to fail.

Steps to cope with risk. Certain recognizable hazards may be met by insurance coverage. Insurance consists essentially of spreading the financial burden of losses that may occur to individuals of a group to all members of the group with respect to certain hazards and in accordance with a certain plan.

For example, assume that the 1,000 houses in a community have an aggregate value of $8,000,000 and that the annual total loss due to fire in the future will average $20,000 per year. Loss due to fire would thus be equivalent to $2.50 per $1,000 of property per year. Individuals suffering loss could be compensated for their entire loss by assessing all house owners $2.50 per $1,000 of property each owned.

It should be noted that insurance as illustrated in the example above does not reduce losses; it merely spreads them. Thus insurance is "substitution of certain for uncertain loss." A person in the example above who owned a $12,000 house would substitute an annual certain loss of

$$\frac{\$12,000}{\$1,000} \times \$2.50 = \$30$$

in the form of an insurance premium for an uncertain loss that might be as great as $12,000.

The economy of insurance lies in the fact that the value of freedom from the necessity of being continually prepared to meet a loss that is unpredictable in respect to time and amount outweighs the cost of insurance.

In practice, the amount charged for insurance exceeds the aggregate of losses sustained by the insured, because of administrative expenses and profit to those engaged in insurance activities. These two items compose about 40 per cent of fire insurance premiums. The balance represents loss.

The effect of future risk may often be substantially reduced by precautionary measures that increase the initial cost of facilities. For example, the loss that might be sustained by the explosion of a boiler is minimized by making it capable of sustaining pressures several times the pressure it is expected to withstand and by adding such safety devices as pressure gauges, safety valves, and soft plugs. These precautions increase the initial costs but, unlike insurance, they may and often do serve to reduce the loss from hazards.

On the basis of economy, initial investments for precautionary measures may not exceed the present worth of the losses that they eliminate. Losses that may be sustained in the future and the amount that they may be reduced by specific precautionary measures are approached through consideration of probabilities. Probabilities, as they relate to loss that may result from specific causes, are determined by scientific analyses, past experience, estimates, or a combination of these. The aim is to establish the probability of a specific event's occurring during a given period of time.

For example, if the probability of temperatures below freezing can be established, steps that are economically feasible to prevent frost damage may be calculated. A truck gardener has a number of glass-covered but unheated propagating beds. If temperatures drop below 20 degrees F for a period of six hours during the propagating season, he estimates that he will sustain a loss of $7,200. An examination of weather records reveals that damaging conditions may be expected to occur at 12-year intervals. This is equivalent to stating that his annual probable loss will be equal to $7,200 ÷ 12, or $600. A precautionary measure such as the installation of electric heating elements that will eliminate prospective frost damage entirely may be expected to prove profitable if all annual costs associated with it are less than $600.

It is not always practical to entirely eliminate the chances of damage from a specific probable occurrence. Completely fireproof buildings, power lines that will withstand hurricanes, and practices that will prevent all theft of property are rarely feasible. Thus the usual problem is to find the extent of precautionary measures that it is practical to take. Precautionary measures may either reduce the probability of occurrence of loss or reduce the probable extent of loss. Overhead sprinkler fire protection systems are designed to do the latter. They do not prevent the incidence of fires, but they do limit their extent.

18.3. THE ECONOMIC LEVEL OF DEVELOPMENT

When a new activity has been proposed, a decision with respect to the level of development must be made. Since a new operation is not hampered by past commitments, the extent of its development is open for consideration. This permits an economic choice of the level of development after all factors concerning the activity are considered.

There are two basic considerations in the development of a new opportunity; the limitations of the opportunity itself, and the limitations of the means for exploiting it. Often only the limitations of the opportunity are considered. Such an incomplete analysis is a prime reason for the failure of many enterprises.

The effect of the level of development on the final outcome of a venture may be illustrated by an example from the chemical industry. A piping system to carry a corrosive liquid in a proposed chemical could be built either from steel or a more corrosive-resistant alloy. The steel pipe has an estimated life of four years and the alloy pipe has an estimated life of ten years. The equivalent annual cost comparison of the two systems is as follows:

Steel Piping

	RP 5-4	
Capital recovery and return on installed cost, $23,000 × (0.28201)		$6,486
Estimated average maintenance cost.....................		1,300
		$7,786

Alloy Piping

	RP 5-10	
Capital recovery and return on installed cost, $48,000 × (0.12950)		$6,216
Estimated average maintenance cost.....................		600
		$6,816

Net annual difference in favor of alloy piping............... $ 970

The rate of interest for which the equivalent annual costs for the two types of systems are equal is approximately 10.8 per cent. This is well above the rate of interest of 5 per cent which the new enterprise was paying on funds it was borrowing. The less expensive steel piping was selected because the officials of the new enterprise felt that the additional $25,000 required for alloy piping could not be justified in the face of the many opportunities to invest their limited funds to better advantage in other needed units of equipment. In fact, a policy had been adopted to limit purchases to equipment that would net a return of 25 per cent or more. For an interest rate of 25 per cent the equivalent annual cost of the two types of piping systems is:

Steel Piping

	RP 25-4	
Capital recovery and return on installed cost, $23,000 × (0.42344)		$ 9,739
Estimated average maintenance cost.....................		1,300
		$11,039

Alloy Piping

	RP 25-10	
Capital recovery and return on installed cost, $48,000 × (0.28007)		$13,443
Estimated average maintenance cost.....................		600
		$14,043

Net annual difference in favor of steel piping.............. $ 3,004

This difference of $3,004 can be considered to be the equivalent annual loss that would result if the more durable piping system were installed, assuming opportunities existed for investing all available funds in equipment that would net a return of 25 per cent.

As another example illustrating the choice of an economical level of development, consider what thickness of insulation to specify for a proposed, cold storage room. The purpose of insulation is to decrease the heat gain by the cold storage area. However, as the thickness of insulation increases so does the cost. However, the heat gain will be decreased as the insulation thickness increases. Thus, there is a level of insulation thickness for which the sum of the costs of heat gain and insulation will be a minimum. This is the desired level of development.

Suppose that the storage room will have a useful life of two years. Used cork board in place is estimated to cost $110 per thousand square feet for each inch of thickness and to have a salvage value of 30 per cent of the original cost at the end of two years.

The average difference in temperature outside and inside the storage room is estimated at 80 degrees Fahrenheit (F). The heat transfer through the cork board will be in accordance with the formula: heat transfer in Btu. per square foot of exposed surface per degree F temperature difference $= 0.26/t$, where t is the thickness of the cork board in inches. Thus the rate of heat inflow per thousand square feet of exposed surface for the conditions given above will be

$$\text{heat inflow, Btu. per hr.} = 1{,}000 \text{ sq. ft} \times 80 \text{ degrees F} \times \frac{0.26}{t}.$$

Accounts of the plant reveal that the energy and fixed costs are such that the cost of removing heat at the rate of 1 Btu. per hour over a period of one year amounts to $0.036. Interest is to be taken at 6 per cent. Insurance, taxes, and maintenance are considered negligible. On the basis of the conditions above, the desirability of various thicknesses of cork board may be calculated on the basis of a thousand square feet of wall surface. For insulation 2 inches thick:

Equivalent annual cost of cork board,
$$\overset{\text{RP 6-2}}{(\$220 - 0.3 \times \$220)} \ (0.54544) + \$220 \times 0.3 \times 0.06 \dots\dots\dots \quad \$ \ 88$$
Annual cost of refrigeration,
$$1{,}000 \text{ square feet} \times 80 \text{ deg. F} \times \frac{0.26}{2} \times \$0.036 \dots\dots\dots\dots \quad 374$$

Total equivalent annual cost. $462

In a similar manner costs are calculated for other thicknesses; a tabulation of the results appears in Table 18.1.

Table 18.1. COST SUMMARY FOR DIFFERENT INSULATION THICKNESSES

Thickness of cork board	Depreciation and interest	Cost of refrigeration	Total equivalent annual cost
2 in.	$ 88	$374	$462
3 in.	132	249	381
4 in.	176	187	363
5 in.	220	150	370
6 in.	264	125	389

On the basis of the conditions given, 4 inches of cork board will be most desirable. Note that the difference in annual cost between 2 and 3 is much larger than the difference between 3 and 4 inches of cork board. Cork board 4 inches thick was selected.

18.4. METHODS OF FINANCING NEW OPERATIONS

Many opportunities can be profitable only when prosecuted above certain levels. If funds cannot be obtained to reach the necessary level of development, the opportunity may have to be abandoned. In many cases a person or a firm controls an opportunity but has insufficient funds to exploit it to the best advantages. In such situations, sufficient funds for the optimum level of development from a profit standpoint can be acquired only by relinquishing control of the opportunity. Such a situation gives rise to three alternatives: to abandon the opportunity, to develop it at less than the optimum level, or to sell it to others more able to exploit it. The last-mentioned alternative is chosen, for example, by inventors who sell their patents.

Funds may be acquired in exchange for ownership. Ownership may be extended by taking in a partner who invests funds in the enterprise or by selling shares of a corporation's stock. A partner or stockholder is a part owner of an enterprise and as such may have a voice in management and be entitled to a share of the earnings. There is no obligation to pay him when profit has not been made.

Funds may also be acquired by borrowing. When funds are borrowed either directly or through the sale of bonds, the borrower agrees to pay interest at a given rate on the principal amount at stated intervals and to repay the principal amount on a stipulated date. The pledge to pay interest on borrowed funds and to repay the principal amount when it comes due must be honored whether or not the borrower's operations have been profitable. Thus loans represent fixed obligations. Failure to meet loan obligations may result in serious embarrassment, extending to loss of control and ownership under some circumstances.

Most enterprises use both ownership and borrowed funds. This leads to consideration of the proportion of each of these types of funds on which to operate. For example, consider an enterprise that can borrow funds at the rate of 5 per cent interest and that requires funds totaling $100,000.

The enterprise may elect to acquire the entire amount as ownership funds or it may elect to borrow varying amounts of the required total. The effect of several ratios of ownership funds to borrowed funds upon the rate of return on the ownership funds is shown for several assumed annual earnings before interest payments in Table 18.2.

Table 18.2. THE EFFECT OF THE RATIO OF OWNERSHIP TO BORROWED FUNDS AND ANNUAL EARNINGS BEFORE INTEREST UPON THE PER CENT RETURN ON OWNERSHIP FUNDS

	100%	80%	60%	40%
Per cent of ownership funds......	100%	80%	60%	40%
Per cent of borrowed funds......	0%	20%	40%	60%
Amount of ownership funds......	$100,000	$80,000	$60,000	$40,000
Amount of borrowed funds.......	0	$20,000	$40,000	$60,000
Interest on borrowed funds at				
5 per cent....................	0	$ 1,000	$ 2,000	$ 3,000
Return on ownership funds				
for annual earning				
before interest of.......$10,000	10.0%	11.2%	13.3%	17.5%
8,000	8.0	8.7	10.0	12.5
6,000	6.0	6.2	6.7	7.5
4,000	4.0	3.7	3.3	2.5
2,000	2.0	1.2	0.0	*
1,000	1.0	0.0	*	*
0	0.0	*	*	*

*Earnings insufficient to meet interest on borrowed funds.

It will be noticed that the return on ownership funds for earnings above $5,000, before interest, increases as the proportion of borrowed funds increases. Contrariwise, the return on ownership funds for earnings less than $5,000, before interest, decreases as the proportion of borrowed funds increases. The advantage of using a high proportion of borrowed funds is offset by the fact that if earnings are insufficient to pay the interest on the borrowed funds the owners may lose their control of and their equity in the enterprise.

18.5. PROVIDING FOR EXPANSION OF OPERATIONS

At its outset a new enterprise operates at a zero level of activity. From this level its activity expands if the enterprise is successful. Ordinarily the activity of a new enterprise may be expected to grow slowly but at an increasing rate in the early stages of its existence. Later growth may be expected to take place at a decreasing rate, which ultimately approaches zero as activities stabilize at an upper level.

The expansion of the activity of an enterprise poses many problems in economy. One of these is related to the capacity of facilities. Facilities for an expanding activity, like clothes for a growing boy, must be purchased too large in order that they may be large enough at a later date to take care of the growth that has taken place. Thus there will be a period when facilities are uneconomical because their capacity is too great for the volume of activity. Rarely is it feasible to add facilities in increments that closely parallel increments of growth. Thus equipment investments are an economic compromise between what is most desirable at present and what is necessary for the future.

The problem of planning for expansion involves determining how much now can be economically spent to reduce an expenditure for expansion in the future. In this connection, consider the following example. An engineer who is planning a home owns a car but expects to own two cars sometime in the future. He is confronted with a decision whether to build a single or a two-car garage now. Inquiry reveals that he can have a single garage built for $810 and a double garage built for $1,440. If he has a single garage constructed now, it can be rebuilt into a double garage any time in the future. To do so will require demolition of one wall and part of the roof of the original garage. It is estimated that the enlargement will cost $1,000 on the basis of present prices. On the basis that extra garage space has no value until the owner acquires a second car six years hence, that maintenance cost, insurance, and taxes will amount to 3 per cent of first cost per annum, that present building costs will prevail, and that the additional funds necessary can be had for 5 per cent, the situation can be analyzed as follows:

Plan A. Build Single Garage Now and Enlarge Later

Present-worth cost of building single garage....................	$ 810
Present worth of 6 years maintenance, insurance, and taxes, $\overset{\text{PR 5-6}}{\$810 \times 0.03 \, (5.076)}$.....................................	123
Present-worth cost of enlargement, $\overset{\text{PS 5-6}}{\$1,000 \times (0.7462)}$..........	746
	$1,679

Plan B. Build Double Garage Now

Present-worth cost of building double garage	$1,440
Present worth of 6 years maintenance, insurance, and taxes, $\overset{\text{PR 5-6}}{\$1,440 \times 0.03 \, (5.076)}$.....................................	219
	$1,659

On the basis of the data used, Plan B is slightly more advantageous. If a double garage were needed before a lapse of six years time, it would still be more advantageous. High interest rates and maintenance costs would tend to favor Plan A.

18.6. EQUIPMENT SELECTION FOR EXPANDING OPERATIONS

In the early stages of the enterprise, when production is low, it will usually prove to be economical to purchase equipment whose fixed costs are low. In the latter stages, when sales are approaching the ultimate level, high fixed cost equipment permitting low variable production costs may be most economical. In this connection consider the following example.

It is estimated that annual sales of a new product will begin at 1,000 units the first year and increase by increments of 1,000 units per year until 4,000 units are sold during the fourth and subsequent years. Two proposals for equipment to manufacture the product are under consideration.

Proposal A embraces equipment requiring an investment of approximately $10,000. Annual fixed cost with this equipment is calculated to be $2,000 and the variable cost per unit of product will be $0.90. The life of the equipment is estimated at four years.

Proposal B embraces equipment requiring an investment of approximately $20,000. Fixed cost of this equipment is estimated at $3,800 per year and variable cost per unit of product will be $0.30. The life of this equipment is also estimated at four years.

On the basis of the ultimate annual production of 4,000 units, cost per unit will be as follows:

Proposal A

Annual cost for 4,000 units of product,
$2,000 + ($4,000 × $0.90)............................... $5,600.00
Cost per unit, $5,600 ÷ 4,000........................... 1.40

Proposal B

Annual cost for 4,000 units of product,
$3,800 + (4,000 × $0.30)............................... $5,000.00
Cost per unit, $5,000 ÷ 4,000........................... 1.25

On the basis of the ultimate rate of production, Proposal B is superior to Proposal A. On the basis of the total production during the life of the equipment, the following analyses apply:

Proposal A

Year of Life	No. of Units Made	Fixed Cost	Variable Cost
1	1,000	$2,000	1,000 × $0.90 = $ 900
2	2,000	2,000	2,000 × $0.90 = 1,800
3	3,000	2,000	3,000 × $0.90 = 2,700
4	4,000	2,000	4,000 × $0.90 = 3,600
	10,000	$8,000	$9,000

Cost per unit = ($8,000 + $9,000) ÷ 10,000 = $1.70

Proposal B

Year of Life	No. of Units Made	Fixed Cost	Variable Cost
1	1,000	$ 3,800	1,000 × $0.30 = $ 300
2	2,000	3,800	2,000 × $0.30 = 600
3	3,000	3,800	3,000 × $0.30 = 900
4	4,000	3,800	4,000 × $0.30 = 1,200
	10,000	$15,200	$3,000

Cost per unit = ($15,200 + $3,000) ÷ 10,000 = $1.82

The calculated advantage of Proposal A over Proposal B would have been increased by considering the time value of money. But perhaps even more important than the difference in cost per unit, particularly for a new enterprise that must conserve its funds or where there is considerable doubt that production schedules will be reached, is the lesser investment required by Proposal A.

At rates of operation approaching capacity, single-purpose machines may be expected to produce more economically than general-purpose machines. Specialized facilities usually result in higher fixed costs and lower variable costs than general-purpose facilities. Consequently specialized equipment is generally advantageous for high volumes of work and general-purpose equipment is advantageous for low volumes of work.

Single-purpose machines particularly are subject to obsolescence owing to change in design or demand for the product on which they are specialized. Soundness of analyses involving specialized facilities rests heavily upon the accuracy of estimates of the volume of work to be performed by them.

18.7. ECONOMIC LOCATION FOR A NEW PLANT

The selection of a location for a plant is a long-time commitment. A new enterprise may be hampered throughout its life by an unfavorable location. Once a plant has been built, the expense and disruption of activities necessary to move it to a more favorable location is generally so great as to be impractical, even though failure may result from the unfavorable characteristics of the original location. Therefore, the search for and evaluation of plant sites justify very careful consideration.

When profit is the measure of success, the best location is the one in which production and marketing effort will result in the greatest profit. Location may affect the cost at which raw materials are gathered, the cost of production, the cost of marketing, and the volume of product that can be sold.

Evaluation of a location begins with research to determine the volume of sales and income promised by the given location. Then research is directed along the lines suggested by the factors listed above to gain data with which to calculate the cost of gathering raw material, processing it, and delivering finished products to the consumer in the volume that can be sold. Evaluation of plant locations consists essentially of operating the enterprise under consideration "on paper" at each location studied. The results of this approach in evaluating three locations for a small glassware plant requiring an investment of approximately $180,000 are given in Table 18.3.

Table 18.3. COMPARATIVE EVALUATION OF THREE PLANT LOCATIONS

	Location A	Location B	Location C
Market:			
Annual sales................(A)	$260,000	$260,000	$260,000
Selling expense.............(B)	44,000	43,000	46,000
Net income from sales..........	$216,000	$217,000	$214,000
Production costs:			
Supplies and raw materials........	$ 69,000	$ 71,000	$ 62,000
Transportation — in and out......	27,000	26,000	23,000
Fuel, power, and water...........	13,000	17,000	18,000
Wages and salaries.............	64,000	63,000	61,000
Miscellaneous items.............	8,000	8,000	10,000
Fixed costs other than interest....	11,000	11,000	11,000
Net production costs........(C)	$192,000	$196,000	$185,000
Selling plus production costs,			
B + C....................(D)	236,000	239,000	231,000
Annual profit, A − D...........(E)	24,000	21,000	29,000
Rate of return, E ÷ $180,000.......	13.3%	11.7%	16.1%

Consider the competitive advantage of a plant at Location C over one at Location B. A plant at Location C has an advantage in net income of over 4 per cent by virtue of its location to offset price reductions and operating and selling efficiency of a competing plant at Location B.

18.8. ECONOMY OF PRODUCTION AND DISTRIBUTION OPERATIONS

There are two aspects of an industrial enterprise. One consists of assembling labor, facilities, and material for the production of goods or services. The other consists of the distribution of the goods or services that have been produced. The success of an enterprise depends upon its ability to carry on these activities to the end that there may be a net difference between receipts for goods and services sold and the input necessary to produce and distribute them.

For simplicity, the cost of distribution will be considered to be a summation of an enterprise's expenditures to influence the sale of its products and services. Such items as advertising, sales administration, salesmen's salaries, and expenditures for packaging and decoration of products done primarily for sales appeal will be included in the cost of distribution.

Cost of production will be considered to be the summation of all costs of the enterprise not included in cost of distribution. Cost of production will embrace expenditures for labor, materials, power, equipment, insurance, taxes, interest, and the delivery of the product to the customer.

In Table 18.4 cost data are given relative to a hypothetical plant which has a maximum capacity of 10 units of product per year and rates of production ranging from 0 to 10 units per year. These data and those presented in Tables 18.5 and 18.6 will be used as a framework for an analysis of relationships between production costs, distribution cost, income, and profit.

Table 18.4. RELATIONSHIP OF PRODUCTION COST, NET INCOME FROM SALES, PROFIT, AND THE NUMBER OF UNITS MADE AND SOLD PER YEAR

(1) Annual output, number of units	(2) Annual total production cost, A, Fig. 18.1	(3) Annual fixed production cost, B, Fig. 18.1	(4) Annual variable production cost, C, Fig. 18.1	(5) Average production cost per unit, D, Fig. 18.1	(6) Average fixed cost per unit	(7) Average variable cost per unit, E, Fig. 18.1	(8) Incremental production cost per unit, F, Fig. 18.1
0	$200	$200	$ 0	$ ∝	$ ∝	$ 0	
1	300	200	100	300.00	200.00	100.00	$100
2	381	200	181	190.50	100.00	90.50	81
3	450	200	250	150.00	66.67	83.30	69
4	511	200	311	127.75	50.00	77.75	61
5	568	200	368	113.60	40.00	73.60	57
6	623	200	423	103.83	33.33	70.50	55
7	679	200	479	97.00	28.57	68.48	56
8	740	200	540	92.50	25.00	67.50	61
9	814	200	614	90.44	22.22	68.22	74
10	924	200	724	92.40	20.00	72.40	110

The annual total production cost of the hypothetical plant as its rate of production varies from 0 to 10 units per year is given in Column

(2) of Table 18.4. It should be specifically noted that no distribution costs are embraced in these data.

Annual fixed cost is given as $200 per year in Column (3). The annual fixed cost in this example should be considered to be the annual cost of maintaining the plant whose capacity is 10 units per year in operating condition at a production rate of zero units per year. The fixed cost of a plant is analogous to the standby costs of a steam boiler whose fire is banked but which is ready to furnish steam on short notice.

The difference between the annual total production cost in Column (2) and the fixed production cost in Column (3) constitutes the annual variable cost and appears in Column (4). Average unit production, fixed and variable costs appear in Columns (5), (6), and (7) respectively.

The increment production costs per unit given in Column (8) were obtained by dividing the differences between successive values of annual total production cost as given in Column (2) by the corresponding difference between successive values of annual output given in Column (1). In this case the divisor will be equal to unity but it should be understood that an increment of production of several units may be convenient in some analyses.

The values in all columns of Table 18.4 except those in Column (6) and the values of all columns of Tables 18.5 and 18.6 have been plotted with respect to the annual output in number of units in Figures 18.1, 18.2 and 18.3, and have been keyed for identification.

Consider Curve (A) in Figure 18.1. Total production cost curves of actual operations take a great variety of forms. Ordinarily, however, a producing unit will produce at minimum average cost at a rate of production between zero output and its maximum rate of output. Thus, the average unit cost of production will decrease with an increase in the rate of production from zero until a minimum average cost of production is reached and then the average cost per unit will rise.

The average total production cost is given by Curve (D) in Figure 18.1. It will be noted that it reaches a minimum at a rate of nine units per year. The average variable production cost is given in Curve (E); its minimum occurs at eight units per year. Curves (D) and (E) should be considered in relation to Column (6) of Table 18.4. It should be noted that fixed cost per unit is inversely proportional to

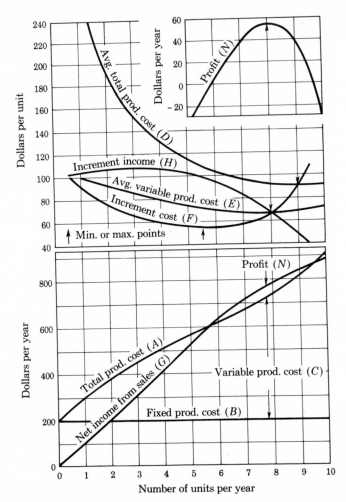

Figure 18.1. Graphical presentation of the data given in Table 18.4.

the number of units per year. Reduction of fixed cost per unit is an important factor tending toward lower average cost with increases in rates of production.

Incremental production costs are given in Curve (F); their minimum value is reached at six units per year. The form of this curve shows that the incremental cost of production per unit declines until 6 units per year are produced and then rises.

An interesting fact to observe is that the incremental cost Curve
(*F*) intersects the average total production cost Curve (*D*) and the
average variable production cost Curve (*E*) at their minimum points.

The incremental cost Curve (*F*) is a measure of the slope of curve
(*A*). It may be noted that the slope of Curve (*A*) decreases until six
units per year is reached and then increases. The same could have
been said of a variable production cost Curve (*C*) if one had been
plotted.

Further consideration will be given to the curves of Figure 18.1
after income from sales of product and the cost of distribution have
been explained.

Pattern of income and cost of distribution. Gross annual income from sales is the total income received from customers as payment for products. In Columns (2) and (3) of Table 18.5, gross annual
income from sales and the annual cost of distribution are given for
various rates of product sales of the firm for which cost-of-production
data were given in Table 18.4 and Figure 18.1.

Table 18.5. RELATIONSHIP OF GROSS INCOME FROM SALES, NET INCOME FROM
SALES, DISTRIBUTION COST, AND NUMBER OF UNITS SOLD PER YEAR

(1)	(2)	(3)	(4)	(5)	(6)
Annual output, number of units	Annual gross income from sales, J, Fig. 18.2	Annual distribution cost, K, Fig. 18.2	Annual net income from sales, G, Fig. 18.2	Incremental distribution cost per unit, L, Fig. 18.2	Incremental net annual income from sales per unit, H, Fig. 18.2
0	$ 0	$ 0	$ 0		
1	140	38	102	$ 38	$102
2	280	72	208	34	106
3	420	104	316	32	108
4	560	136	424	32	108
5	700	170	530	34	106
6	840	211	629	41	99
7	980	261	719	50	90
8	1,120	325	795	64	76
9	1,260	405	855	80	60
10	1,400	505	895	100	40

The difference between the gross annual income from sales and the annual cost of distribution is equal to the annual net income from sales given in Column (4). Incremental distribution costs per unit are given in Column (5) and incremental net income from sales per unit appears in Column (6). The values of each of these columns have

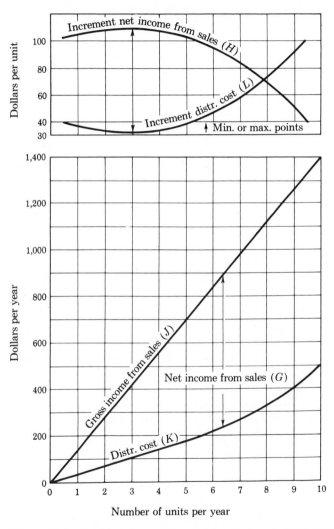

Figure 18.2. Graphical presentation of the data given in Table 18.5.

been plotted with respect to annual output in Figure 18.2. The gross annual income from sales, Curve (J) in Figure 18.2, is a straight line and is typical of situations in which products are sold at a fixed price. The annual incremental distribution cost, Curve (L), first falls slightly until a minimum is reached and then rises. This is typical of situations in which sales effort is relatively inefficient at low levels and where sales resistance increases with increased number of units sold.

A pattern of distribution cost, made up of fixed and variable costs similar to those of production, might have been taken. Ordinarily, fixed distribution costs are a minor consideration; they have been omitted from this analysis in the interest of simplicity.

A representation of the net income from sales is given as (G) in Figure 18.2. The positive difference between net income from sales and the total cost of production, Curve (A) in Figure 18.1, represents profit. Profit is shown as (N) in Figure 18.1; it should be noted that the maximum profit, or minimum loss if no profit is made, occurs at a rate of production at which the incremental income Curve (H) intersects the incremental cost Curve (F), or at eight units per year. From Column (8), Table 18.4, and Column (6), Table 18.5, it may be observed that the incremental production cost and incremental net income for a ninth unit are $74 and $60 respectively. Thus, a loss of $14 profit would be sustained if the activity were increased to nine units. When the profit motive governs, there is no point in producing beyond the point where the incremental cost of the next unit will exceed the incremental income from it.

If the sales effort in the example above is resulting in sales of nine or ten units per year, a number of steps might be taken. The sales effort could be reduced, causing sales to drop. The price could be increased, causing sales to decrease and the income per unit to increase. The plant could be expanded or other changes could be made to alter the pattern of production costs. Consideration of any of the steps above would require a new analysis embracing the altered factors.

Consolidation of production and distribution cost. It is common practice to consolidate production and distribution cost for analysis of operations. To illustrate this practice an analysis of the example above will be made in this manner. The method is illustrated

in Table 18.6, whose values have been plotted as several curves in
Figure 18.3.

Table 18.6. RELATIONSHIP OF GROSS INCOME, PRODUCTION COST, DISTRIBUTION
COST, PROFIT, AND NUMBER OF UNITS MADE AND SOLD PER YEAR

Annual output, number of units	Annual total production cost, A, Fig. 18.3	Annual distribution cost, K, Fig. 18.3	Annual total of production and distribution cost, M, Fig. 18.3	Annual gross income from sales, J, Fig. 18.3	Annual profit N, Figs. 18.1 and 18.3	Incremental total production and distribution costs, O, Fig. 18.3
0	$200	$ 0	$ 200	$ 0	−$200	
1	300	38	338	140	−198	$138
2	381	72	453	280	−173	115
3	450	104	554	420	−134	101
4	511	136	647	560	−87	93
5	568	170	738	700	−38	91
6	623	211	834	840	6	96
7	679	261	940	980	40	106
8	740	325	1,065	1,120	55	125
9	814	405	1,219	1,260	41	154
10	924	505	1,429	1,400	−29	210

Profit in this case will be equal to the difference between gross
income (J) and total production and distribution cost (M). The
point of maximum profit will occur when the incremental gross income
curve (P) is intersected by a rising incremental production and distribution cost Curve (O). This occurs at a rate of 8 units per year.
It should be noted that if production reaches 10 units, a loss of $29
will be sustained from the year's operation.

Relationship of production and distribution effort. Profits
are the combined result of effort to produce and distribute. The
results and the costs of production and distribution activities must
be considered in relation to their joint effect. Either one is meaningless
when considered independently of the other. One aspect of this
joint relationship will be illustrated by an example.

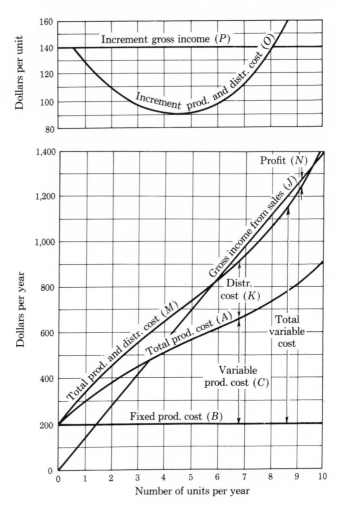

Figure 18.3. Graphical presentation of the data given in Table 18.6.

A firm had been marketing a specialized product for a number of years. On the basis of experience, sales research and estimate curves were drawn showing the relationship between price, cost of sales effort, and the number of units sold. Data taken and values calculated from these curves are given in Table 18.7. From this table

Table 18.7. RELATIONSHIP OF SELLING PRICE, SALES, SALES EFFORT, AND INCOME

| N, number of units sold | SELLING PRICE PER UNIT | | | | | | | | |
| | $P_1 = \$90$ | | | $P_2 = \$100$ | | | $P_3 = \$110$ | | |
	I, income $= N \times P_1$	S, sales effort cost	G, net income from sales, $S = I - S$	I, income $= N \times P_2$	S, sales effort cost	G, net income from sales, $S = I - S$	I, income $= N \times P_3$	S, sales effort cost	G, net income from sales, $S = (I - S)$
10	\$ 900	\$ 40	\$ 860	\$ 1,000	\$ 70	\$ 930	\$ 1,100	\$ 90	\$1,010
20	1,800	130	1,670	2,000	200	1,800	2,200	220	1,980
30	2,700	240	2,460	3,000	380	2,620	3,300	420	2,880
40	3,600	400	3,200	4,000	640	3,360	4,400	730	3,670
50	4,500	630	3,870	5,000	1,000	4,000	5,500	1,260	4,240
60	5,400	970	4,430	6,000	1,500	4,500	6,600	2,090	4,510
70	6,300	1,530	4,770	7,000	2,130	4,870	7,700	3,070	4,630
80	7,200	2,170	5,030	8,000	2,890	5,110	8,800	4,140	4,660
90	8,100	2,940	5,160	9,000	3,770	5,230	9,900	5,320	4,580
100	9,000	3,770	5,230	10,000	4,770	5,230	11,000	6,550	4,450
110	9,900	4,650	5,250	11,000	5,900	5,100	12,100	7,900	4,200
120	10,800	5,600	5,200	12,000	7,150	4,850	13,200	9,300	3,900

curves representing the relationship of net income from sales, I-S, and the number of units sold, N, were superimposed on a cost of production chart shown by Figure 18.4. The cost of production is composed of a fixed cost of \$3,000 and a variable cost of \$20 per unit. For the conditions given, the maximum profit will be approximately \$510 for sales of approximately 80 units at a price of \$100. Corresponding values for selling prices of \$90 and \$110 are \$430 and \$310 for sales of 80 and 60 units, respectively. These results illustrate the fact that sales effort, price, and cost of production must be considered jointly.

18.9. BREAK-EVEN CHART ANALYSIS FOR NEW OPERATIONS

The concepts and ideas of the previous section may be utilized to evaluate the economic desirability of new or changing activities by

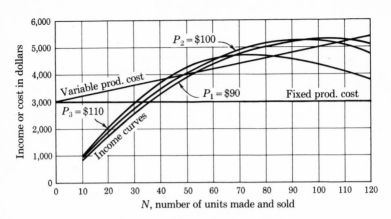

Figure 18.4. Relationship of net income from sales for different sale prices, cost of production and profit.

the application of break-even analysis. If income and variable cost are assumed to be linear functions of the quantity of products to be made and sold, analysis of their relationships to profit is greatly simplified. If this assumption is made, the patterns of income and costs

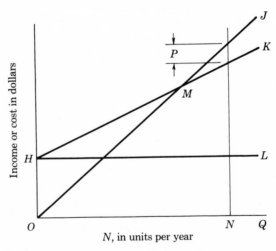

Figure 18.5. General graphical representation for income, cost, units of output, and profit.

of Figure 18.3, for example, can be replaced by a diagram shown in Figure 18.5.

In Figure 18.5 fixed production costs are represented by the Line *HL*. The sum of variable production costs and distribution costs is represented by the Line *HK*. Income from sales is represented by the Line *OJ*. It must be remembered that this representation is only an approximation of actual operating conditions.

Analysis of existing or proposed operations that are represented with a break-even chart can be made mathematically or graphically. For an illustration of the mathematical methods, let

N = number of units of product made and sold per year.

R = the amount received per unit of product in dollars. R is equal to the slope of *OJ*.

$I = RN$, the annual income from sales in dollars. $I = RN$ is the equation of Line *OJ*.

F = fixed cost in dollars per year, represented by *OH* and *HL*.

V = variable cost per unit of product. V is equal to the slope of *HK*.

C = the sum of fixed and variable cost of N units of product, $F + VN$. $C = F + VN$ is the equation of Line *HK*.

P = annual profit in dollars per year. $P = I - C$. Negative values of P represent loss.

M = break-even point. At this point $P = 0$.

Q = capacity of plant in units per year.

The break-even point occurs when income is equal to cost. In Figure 18.5 this occurs where Lines *OJ* and *HK* intersect. At this point $I = C$ and $RN = F + VN$. Solving for N,

$$N = \frac{F}{R - V}$$

which is the abscissa value of the break-even point.

If $F/(R - V)$ is substituted for N in $I = RN$ or $C = F + VN$, the ordinate of the break-even point may be found. The value of the ordinate in terms of dollars of income or cost will be

$$I = R\frac{F}{R - V} \quad \text{and} \quad C = F + \frac{VF}{R - V}.$$

As an example, suppose it is desired to find the break-even point when $R = \$11$, $F = \$4,000$, and $V = \$5$.

$$N = \frac{F}{R - V} = \frac{\$4,000}{\$11 - \$5} = 667 \text{ units per year}$$

and

$$I = C = RN = \$11 \times 667 = \$7,337.$$

Since P is the annual profit it is often desirable to have a relationship that expresses P as a function of the number of units made and sold, N. This relationship may be derived as follows:

$$\begin{aligned} P &= I - C \\ &= RN - (F + VN) \\ &= (R - V)N - F. \end{aligned}$$

For example, if the annual profit is required when $R = \$11$, $F = \$4,000$, $V = \$5$, and $N = 800$, the following calculations may be made:

$$\begin{aligned} P &= (R - V)N - F \\ &= (\$11 - \$5)800 - \$4,000 \\ &= \$6(800) - \$4,000 = \$800. \end{aligned}$$

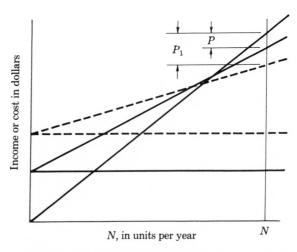

Figure 18.6. Effect on profit of an increase in fixed cost that results in reduced variable cost.

Certain graphical manipulations with the break-even chart are useful in evaluating proposals for new operations. For example, the effect of increasing fixed costs that result in reduced variable cost would give the new situation shown in Figure 18.6. The effect of a proposed change in price and/or change in volume may be evaluated as is shown in Figure 18.7.

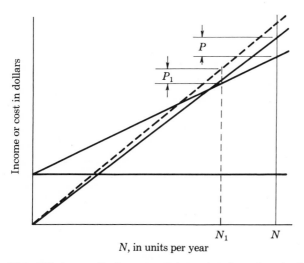

Figure 18.7. Effect on profit of a proposed change in price and production volume.

Even though the analysis presented was based upon the assumption that fixed cost, variable cost, and income are linear functions of the quantity made and sold, it is very useful in evaluating the effect on profit of proposals for altered operations. The linear assumption is the most logical in the case where the analysis is used to evaluate new operations not yet implemented and for which no data exists.

18.10. RATE-OF-RETURN EVALUATION OF NEW OPERATIONS

A proposed operation may be defined in terms of its future receipts and disbursements and the time of their occurrence. The economy of a proposed venture may be expressed in a number of ways, but the most useful is the rate of return on the amount of investment.

During its life a proposed operation may involve a number of assets of varying lives, borrowed funds of varying amounts, fluctuating income and may be otherwise complex. Such proposals can be evaluated with rather simple mathematics if data are presented in tabular form similar to that shown in Table 18.8.

Table 18.8. ESTIMATED COST AND INCOME DATA FOR A PROPOSED ACTIVITY

Year A	Total investment during year, $C + D$ B	Owner's equity C	Borrowed funds D	Depreciation E	Interest on borrowed funds, $D \times 0.05$ F	Operating costs G	Total dep., int. and oper. costs, $E + F + G$ H	Gross income I	Net earnings after depreciation, $I - (E + F + G)$ J	Owner's equity at end of year $C + J$ K
1	$ 8,000	$7,000	$1,000	$1,000	$ 50	$3,000	$4,050	$4,350	$300	$7,300
2	11,000	8,000	3,000	1,800	150	3,000	4,950	5,250	300	8,300
3	9,200	8,200	1,000	1,800	50	5,000	6,850	7,650	800	9,000
4	8,300	8,300	0	2,100	0	4,000	6,100	6,700	600	8,900
5	6,200	6,200	0	2,100	0	4,000	6,100	6,700	600	6,800
6	4,100	4,100	0	2,100	0	3,000	5,100	5,600	500	4,600

Table 18.8 illustrates estimates of a venture extending over 6 years and involving some borrowed funds. To carry on the activity in

Table 18.9. SUMMARY OF RECEIPTS AND DISBURSEMENTS FOR A PROPOSED ACTIVITY

Beginning of year	Disbursements	Receipts	Net Difference	
			Disbursements	Receipts
1	$7,000	. . .	$7,000	. . .
2	8,000	$7,300	700	. . .
3	8,200	8,300	. . .	$ 100
4	8,300	9,000	. . .	700
5	6,200	8,900	. . .	2,700
6	4,100	6,800	. . .	2,700
7	. . .	4,600	. . .	4,600

question, funds shown in Column B are invested in wages, services, supplies, and depreciable equipment. The owner's equity at the beginning of each year is shown in Column C, and his equity at the end of each year is shown in Column K. The quantities in Column C and K are summarized in Table 18.9.

This summary may be more easily understood if the activity being evaluated is considered to consist of subactivities of one year's duration, each requiring disbursements in the amount given in Column C and each resulting in net receipts in the amounts given in Column K. The present worth of the disbursements will be equal to the present worth of the receipts at some rate of return which, for this example may be found from the following equation:

$$\$7{,}000 + \$700(\overset{\text{PS } i\text{-}1}{\ \ \ }) = \$100(\overset{\text{PS } i\text{-}2}{\ \ \ }) + \$700(\overset{\text{PS } i\text{-}3}{\ \ \ }) + \$2{,}700$$

$$(\overset{\text{PS } i\text{-}4}{\ \ \ }) + \$2{,}700(\overset{\text{PS } i\text{-}5}{\ \ \ }) + \$4{,}600(\overset{\text{PS } i\text{-}6}{\ \ \ }).$$

By trial-and-error solution, the rate of return in this example is approximately 7.3 per cent.

This method of evaluation of new activities is very flexible in application. Data need not be abridged or distorted to conform to mathematical requirements. The extension of the method to include income taxes was presented in Chapter 16.

PROBLEMS

1. An architectural engineer has $60,000 invested in his firm with no outstanding indebtedness. He anticipates that increased capability in mechanical design will increase the net earnings of the firm. The required office expansion will necessitate an additional investment of $50,000 which can be borrowed from a local bank for 6 per cent interest. As an alternative, he can sell a one-fourth interest in his firm to a mechanical engineer for $20,000 and borrow the remaining $30,000 from him at 5 per cent interest. The new partner would take charge of a mechanical design section.

(a) What minimum earnings before interest are necessary to meet interest payments on borrowed funds for each method of financing?

(b) What will be the rate of return on the original $60,000 investment if the annual net earnings of the expanded office amount to $7,700 before interest for each method of financing?

2. A group of 25-horsepower 3-phase electric motors are required to power pumping equipment for a proposed chemical processing plant. Three bids exhibiting the following specifications are proposed.

Bid	Price	Full Load Efficiency	Estimated Life in Years
A	$960	90%	10
B	$700	87%	7
C	$650	85%	6

The motors are to be operated at full load for 1,800 hours per year. Power costs $0.024 per kilowatt-hour. Maintenance and other operation costs are assumed to be equal. Calculate the annual cost for each type of motor for an interest rate of 8 per cent and zero salvage value.

3. A firm is considering the expansion of its operations to include a plating department that will require 5,000,000 kilowatt-hours of electrical energy per year. The maximum rate of consumption is estimated to be 1,400 kilowatts. The power can be purchased from a power company for $0.013 per kilowatt-hour providing the firm will construct the required 25 miles of transmission line and furnish necessary transformers. The cost of the high tension line will be $9,500 per mile and the transformers required will cost $22,000. The life of these assets will be 30 years with a salvage value of $12,000.

As an alternative, the firm can construct and operate its own power plant. The plant can be located on a river which would furnish adequate cooling water for condensing purposes if a steam plant is selected or for cooling if a diesel plant is installed. A good location is also available for a hydrogenerating plant 36 miles from the firm's plant site. Costs involved in the construction and maintenance of the three types of power plants are as follows:

	Steam	Diesel	Hydro
Total investment per kw of capacity.	$210.00	$260.00	$310.00
Transmission equipment cost........	0	0	$364,000
Fuel required in pounds per kw-hr...	1.85	0.68	0
Cost of fuel per pound.............	$0.00375	$0.0092	0
Annual cost of maintenance........	$27,000	$19,000	$15,000
Taxes and ins. as a % of investment ..	2	2	2
Life of plant and equipment in years.	20	16	30
Salvage value as % of original cost...	10	12	5

Determine the cost of each of the four methods of supplying the required power if the interest rate is 6 per cent compounded continuously.

4. Two locations are under consideration for the location of a new brick plant. A cost analysis applicable to each location is given below.

	Location A	Location B
Capital cost per 1,000 bricks.............	$ 2.17	$ 1.56
Material cost per 1,000 bricks............	2.92	3.36
Labor cost per 1,000 bricks..............	6.73	5.28
Distribution cost per 1,000 bricks........	6.35	6.41
Total cost per 1,000 bricks...........	$18.17	$16.61

(a) Calculate the ratio of the profit per 1,000 bricks produced at Location A to the profit per 1,000 bricks produced at Location B for selling prices of $17.50, $18.50, $19.50, and $20.50 per 1,000 bricks.

(b) What is the minimum selling price per 1,000 bricks at each location if the profit is at least 10 per cent?

5. A market survey of Towns A, B, and C reveals that it will be possible to sell 2,000, 4,000 and 7,000 loaves of bread per day, 6 days per week, respectively. Two alternatives are under consideration. The first requires the construction of a plant of sufficient capacity in Town C to take care of the total requirement. The second calls for the construction of a plant in all three towns. Town C is between Towns A and B and is 20 miles from Town A and 30 miles from Town B. Base labor rates in Towns A, B, and C are, respectively, $1.80, $2, and $2.20 per hour. On the basis of labor at $1 per hour, the comparison of labor cost per loaf to capacity of plant is as follows:

Capacity in loaves per day...	1,000	2,000	5,000	10,000	15,000
Labor cost in cents per loaf..	3.4	2.8	2.4	2.0	1.8

Experience on overhead costs likely to be applicable in Towns A, B, and C indicate that the following relationship exists:

Capacity in loaves per day.....	1,000	2,000	5,000	10,000	15,000
Overhead cost per loaf in cents.	3.2	2.6	2.2	2.0	1.9

If the first alternative is accepted, trucking costs of $0.18 per truck mile will be incurred to ship bread to Towns A and B. In addition, terminal space costing $80 per month in Town A and $120 in Town B must be leased. Eleven hundred loaves constitute a load. Determine the average cost per loaf and the total annual cost for each alternative. Interpolation may be used for capacities between those given.

6. A firm has been organized to manufacture 1,200,000 units of a single product per year. The principal equipment needed to make the product is special machines costing $6,200 each and having a life of 12,000 hours with no salvage value. If the plant operates 40 hours per week 50 weeks per year, 12 machines will be required. The number of machines needed to meet the demand for the product will be in inverse proportion to the number of hours the plant operates per week. The variable cost of operating a machine, excluding labor, is $1.50 per hour. The material cost per unit of product is $0.03. Direct labor will be $0.04 per unit of product when the plant is operated 40 hours per week for 50 weeks per year.

Two plans are being considered: Plan A — purchase 12 machines and operate the plant 2,000 hours per year; Plan B — purchase 4 machines and operate the plant 6,000 hours per year with 3 shifts of workmen. With Plan A, it is estimated that supervision will cost $9,000 per year and that fixed costs, exclusive of supervision, interest, and depreciation for the 12 machines, will be $12,000 per year. With Plan B fixed costs, exclusive of supervision, interest, and depreciation on the 4 machines, will be only $8,000 because less building space will be required.

Plan B has been rejected because it is believed that operation in three shifts will result in increased cost of supervision and direct labor which will more than offset the advantages of a smaller investment in equipment and building space. In the analysis of these plans it can be assumed that supervision and direct labor costs will be increased by X per cent by the difficulties of three-shift operation. Calculate the value of X for Plans A and B to break even.

7. A manufacturing concern estimates that its expenses per year for different levels of operation would be as follows:

Output in units of product........	0	10	20	30	40	50
Administrative and sales...........	$4,900	$ 5,700	$ 6,200	$ 6,700	$ 7,100	$ 7,500
Direct labor and materials.......	0	2,500	4,600	6,400	8,100	9,800
Overhead expense.	4,120	4,190	4,270	4,350	4,440	4,550
Total.......	$9,020	$12,390	$15,070	$17,450	$19,640	$21,850

(a) What is the incremental cost of maintaining the plant ready to operate (the incremental cost of making zero units of product)?

(b) What is the average incremental cost per unit of manufacturing the first increment of 10 units of product per year?

(c) What is the average incremental cost per unit of manufacturing the increment of 31 to 40 units per year?

(d) What is the average total cost per unit when manufacturing at the rate of 20 units per year?

(e) At a time when the rate of manufacture is 20 units per year, a salesman reports that he can sell 10 additional units at $260 per unit without disturbing the market in which the company sells. Would it be profitable for the company to undertake the production of the 10 additional units?

8. An analysis of an enterprise and the market in which its product is sold results in the following data:

Level of Operation, Units of Product	Production Cost, Dollars	Net Income from Sales, Dollars	Level of Operation, Units of Product	Production Cost, Dollars	Net Income from Sales, Dollars
0	10,900	0	700	41,700	43,000
100	17,600	8,000	800	44,800	46,800
200	23,000	15,400	900	48,000	50,000
300	27,500	22,000	1,000	51,300	52,700
400	31,500	28,000	1,100	54,800	54,800
500	35,100	33,500	1,200	58,500	56,300
600	38,500	38,500			

(a) Determine the profit for each level of operation.

(b) Plot production cost, net income from sales, profit, average incremental production cost per unit, and average incremental net income from sales per unit for each level of operation.

9. The product of an enterprise has a fixed selling price of $62. An analysis of production and sales costs and the market in which the product is sold has produced the following results:

Level of Operation, Units of Product	Total Production and Selling Cost, Dollars	Level of Operation, Units of Product	Total Production and Selling Cost, Dollars
0	13,200	600	35,000
100	17,900	700	40,400
200	21,400	800	47,100
300	24,600	900	55,600
400	27,200	1,000	65,400
500	30,600		

(a) Determine the profit for each level of operation.

(b) Plot production and selling cost, income from sales, profit, average incremental production and selling cost per unit, and average incremental income per unit, for each level of operation.

10. An analysis of the current operations of a firm results in the conclusion that the production cost is $10,900 + 80x + 1500x^{1/2}$ where x is the number of units produced. The selling cost is $500y^{1/2}$ where y is the number of units sold during the year. The selling price is $180 per unit. Plot the production cost, the selling cost, the total production and selling cost, the gross income from sales, and profit for production levels ranging from 0 to 200 units per year. Determine the level of production for maximum profit.

11. The annual fixed production and selling cost of a company producing a certain product is estimated at $40,000. The variable cost is estimated at $65 per unit. Dissatisfied with the small margin of profit, the company is studying a plan to improve their product and increase selling effort. The plan of improvement requires an additional annual fixed expenditure of $10,000 on production and selling. Also, an additional $25 per unit will be spent to improve the product from the standpoints of quality and customer appeal. On the basis of a market survey, estimated sales, with and without the improvements, at various selling prices are given below:

Unit Selling Price	Sales Without Improvements	Sales With Improvements
$350	0	55
300	20	180
250	90	360
200	225	610
150	460	920
125	680	–
110	1,010	–

Plot the total production and selling cost of each plan, and plot the total income from each plan for the various selling prices against output as the abscissa. Determine whether or not the plan for improvements should be adopted and determine the production and selling price that will result in the maximum profit.

12. A manufacturer of radio receivers has an annual fixed cost of $300,000 and a variable cost of $6.60 per unit produced. An engineering proposal under consideration involves redesign of the present AM unit to include FM. The production engineering staff estimates that the redesigned product will increase the annual fixed cost by $200,000 and the variable cost by $2.60 per unit. A market survey produced the following information:

Unit Selling Price	Sales With AM Only	Sales With AM and FM
$35.00	0	6,200
30.00	3,000	21,000
25.00	11,000	39,500
20.00	25,500	64,000
15.00	48,000	100,000
12.50	74,000	–
11.00	98,000	–

(a) Determine the selling price for maximum annual profit if only AM receivers are manufactured; if AM and FM receivers are manufactured.

(b) Should the design change be adopted?

13. A company has priced its product at $1 per pound, and is operating at a loss. Sales at this price total 850,000 pounds per year. The company's fixed cost of manufacture and selling is $480,000 per year and the variable cost is $0.46 per pound. It appears, from information obtained by a market survey, that price reductions of $0.05, $0.10, $0.15, and $0.20 per pound from the present selling price will result in total annual sales of 1,030,000 pounds, 1,190,000 pounds, 1,360,000 pounds, and 1,480,000 pounds per year, respectively.

(a) Calculate the annual profit that will result from each of the selling prices given, assuming variable cost per unit will be the same for all production levels.

(b) Determine graphically the annual profit that will result from each of the selling prices by the use of a break-even type chart.

14. A certain firm has the capacity to produce 650,000 units of product per year. At present, it is operating at 64 per cent of capacity. The firm's annual income is $416,000. Annual fixed costs are $192,000 and the variable costs are equal to $0.356 per unit of product.

(a) What is the firm's annual profit or loss?

(b) At what volume of sales does the firm break even?

(c) What will be the profit or loss at 70, 80, and 90 per cent of capacity on the basis of constant income per unit and constant variable cost per unit?

15. A company is operating at capacity for one shift per day. Annual sales are 3,600 units per year and the income per unit is $200. Fixed costs are $280,000 and total variable costs are $440,000 per year at the present rate of operation.

If output can be increased, 400 additional units can be sold at $200 per unit during the coming year. These additional units can be produced through overtime operation at the expense of a 20 per cent increase in the unit variable cost of the additional units. The elasticity of demand for the product in question is believed to be such that an increase in selling price to $208 will result in curtailing demand to 3,600 units. For greatest profit in the coming year should output be increased or should selling price be increased?

16. A manufacturing company owns two Plants, A and B, that produce an identical product. The capacity of Plant A is 60,000 units annually while that of Plant B is 80,000 units. The annual fixed cost of Plant A is $260,000 per year and the variable cost is $3.20 per unit. The corresponding values for Plant B are $280,000 and $3.90 per unit. At present, Plant A is being operated at 35 per cent of capacity and Plant B is being operated at 40 per cent of capacity.

(a) What are the unit costs of production of Plant A and Plant B?

(b) What is the total cost and the average cost of the total output of both plants?

(c) What would be the total cost to the company and the unit cost if all production were transferred to Plant A?

(d) What would be the total cost to the company and the unit cost if all production were transferred to Plant B?

17. A plant with a capacity of 100,000 units of product per year has constant costs of $225,000 per year and a variable cost per unit of $1.50. There is a standard home market for 50,000 units at $6.50 per unit and a foreign market for 50,000 units at $3.50 per unit.

(a) What profit will result if only the standard home market demand is met?

(b) What profit will result if both the standard home market demand and the foreign market demand are met?

18. A forecast concerning the first 5 years of operation of a proposed, new activity is as follows:

Year	Investment	Depreciation	Operating Cost	Income
1	$200,000	$30,000	$60,000	$ 20,000
2	50,000	50,000	60,000	150,000
3	50,000	60,000	60,000	200,000
4	50,000	70,000	60,000	250,000
5	50,000	80,000	60,000	250,000

(a) Calculate the owner's equity after 5 years.

(b) Calculate the rate of return on the proposed activity.

APPENDICES

SERVICE LIFE PREDICTIONS

In economy problems, patterns of the future depreciation of all manner of assets must be predicted. This is a difficult task. When a machine depreciates through use, a prediction must be made of the extent to which it will be used. If depreciation is caused by the elements, the rate at which deterioration progresses must be established. Even more difficult are the predictions that seek to determine when a machine will become obsolete because of new inventions and new needs, or inadequate owing to unanticipated demand.

Much has been written concerning the service life of equipment. Compilations summarizing the depreciation of many types of equipment in many different situations are available.

Unfortunately such data are only of limited value as a basis for predicting the service life of a particular item of equipment. For the most part, the information that is available consists of tables giving the average life of various types of structures, machines, and so forth. These have been prepared by people of various degrees of competence and ability. In any event, they are largely based on judgments. One difficulty with such tables is that the conditions under which the facilities were used are not sufficiently described to enable application to be made to a particular situation.

Mortality data are very useful for purposes of adjudicating a fair cost for services. Such data may also be very useful in making decisions involving great numbers of units used under similar conditions, such as railroad ties, telephone poles, and electric light bulbs. However, where the future service life of a single unit is a factor in decision, particularly where obsolescence may intervene, mortality data may be of limited use.

Where the service lives of a large number of assets used under similar conditions are known, a number of useful curves can be drawn.

Table A.1. COMPILATION OF THE MORTALITY DATA OF 30,009 WOODEN TELEGRAPH POLES TREATED WITH COAL TAR

Age interval, years (1)	Units retired during age interval, % (2)	Survivors at beginning of age interval, % (3)	Service during age interval, %-years (4)	Remaining service at beginning of age interval, %-years (5)	Expectancy at beginning of age interval, years (6)	Probable life at beginning of age interval, years (7)
0 - ½	0.00	100.00	50.00	1,067.88	10.68	10.68
½- 1½	0.35	100.00	99.82	1,017.88	10.18	10.68
1½- 2½	0.74	99.65	99.28	918.06	9.21	10.71
2½- 3½	1.45	98.91	98.19	818.78	8.28	10.78
3½- 4½	3.19	97.46	95.86	720.59	7.39	10.89
4½- 5½	2.96	94.27	92.79	624.73	6.63	11.13
5½- 6½	5.68	91.31	88.47	531.94	5.83	11.33
6½- 7½	6.11	85.63	82.58	443.47	5.18	11.68
7½- 8½	7.28	79.52	75.88	360.89	4.54	12.04
8½- 9½	9.63	72.24	67.42	285.01	3.95	12.45
9½-10½	10.37	62.61	57.43	217.59	3.48	12.98
10½-11½	10.33	52.24	47.07	160.16	3.07	13.57
11½-12½	9.54	41.91	37.14	113.09	2.70	14.20
12½-13½	9.06	32.37	27.84	75.95	2.34	14.84
13½-14½	7.26	23.31	19.68	48.11	2.06	15.56
14½-15½	6.44	16.05	12.83	28.43	1.77	16.27
15½-16½	3.77	9.61	7.73	15.60	1.62	17.12
16½-17½	3.01	5.84	4.33	7.87	1.35	17.85
17½-18½	1.84	2.83	1.91	3.54	1.25	18.75
18½-19½	0.50	0.99	0.74	1.63	1.65	20.15
19½-20½	0.12	0.49	0.43	0.89	1.82	21.32
20½-21½	0.13	0.37	0.31	0.46	1.24	21.74
21½-22½	0.21	0.24	0.13	0.15	0.63	22.13
22½-23½	0.03	0.03	0.02	0.02	0.67	23.17
23½-24½	0.00	0.00	0.00	0.00	0.00	23.50
Total...	100.00	...	1,067.88	Av. life = 1,067.88 ÷ 100 = 10.68 yrs.		

Mortality data for 30,009 wooden telegraph poles are given in Table A.1.[1] For ease of understanding it may be assumed that all the poles

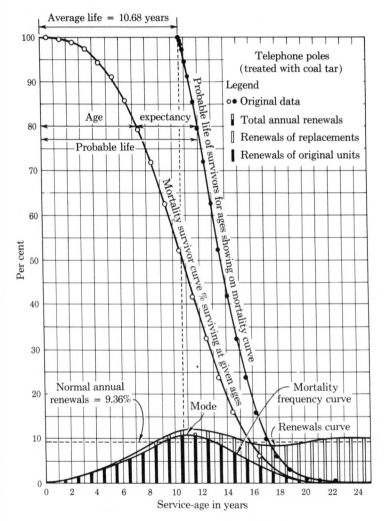

Figure A.1. Mortality curve for 30,009 wood telegraph poles.

[1]Marston, Anson, and Agg, *Engineering Valuation* (New York: McGraw-Hill Book Company, Inc., 1936).

were installed at the same time. On the basis of this supposition, the age interval in Column one will also be the elapsed time since installation. From this data several useful curves may be drawn as is shown in Figure A.1.

Examination of the mortality frequency curve shows that some poles do not survive as long and some poles survive much longer than the average of the group, but that the greatest rate of retirement centers around the average age. In order to maintain service, poles that are retired are immediately replaced. These replacements are subject to the same mortality frequency curve as the original group. Thus after a few years there are renewals of original poles, renewals of renewals, renewals of renewals of renewals, and so forth. A summation of these renewals is given by the renewals curve in Figure A.1.

The mortality survivor curve shows the number of original poles surviving at any service age. This curve is very similar to the survivorship curves for humans which are used in life insurance actuarial work.

The curve showing probable life of survivors is useful in predicting the life of those of the orginal groups that remain in use. Note that the probable life of the group at zero service age is equal to the average life of the group. The curves shown apply only to assets that have the same types of mortality frequency curve and have an average service life of 10.68 years.

To extend the use of this type of data Kurtz[2] has generalized its application by setting up a group of mathematical expressions representative of mortality experience of a large number of items of property. These expressions facilitate mathematical analysis of problems related to mortality. They are particularly valuable for the valuation of property composed of original and renewal items or exclusively of renewal items, such as railroad ties on an old road bed. The Kurtz expressions also greatly facilitate the extension of analyses over periods in the future.

---

[2]Edwin B. Kurtz, *The Science of Valuation and Depreciation* (New York: The Ronald Press, Inc., 1937).

APPENDIX **B**

EQUIVALENT ANNUAL COST
OF AN ASSET

In Chapter 12, the situation was discussed where maintenance cost increased at a constant rate. When this is the case, a general expression for equivalent annual cost may be derived. Let

P = first cost of asset;

L = salvage value of asset at time of retirement;

Q = annual constant portion of operating cost (increases in operating cost are taken into account with g, the next item);

g = rate of increase of annual comparative costs and equal to the sum of the rate of increase in costs due to physical impairment, m', and the rate of increase in comparative costs due to obsolescence, b, that is, $g = m' + b$;

i = interest rate.

If reference is made to Table 12.6 it is clear that if g is substituted for $100 in Column B, then Column G will represent the equivalent annual cost of a series of annual costs as is shown in Column (2), Table B.1.

An expression for the equivalent annual cost of a declining series of the pattern appearing in Column (3) of Table 12.6 was developed in Chapter 5.

$$\text{Equivalent annual cost} \atop \text{of declining series} \Big\} = \frac{1}{i}\left[(P - L)\left(\overset{\text{RP } i\text{-}n}{(\quad\quad)} - \frac{1}{n}\right) + Li\right].$$

Table B.1. INCREASING AND DECREASING SERIES OF PAYMENTS

End of year number (1)	Maintenance plus obsolescence, with a gradient of g (2)	A series declining, with a gradient of g (3)	(2) + (3) (4)
1	0	ng	ng
2	g	$(n-1)g$	ng
. . .	. . .	. . .	. . .
$n-1$	$(n-2)g$	$2g$	ng
n	$(n-1)g$	g	ng

If, in this expression, L is given the value zero and $(P - L)$ the value ng, the expression becomes

$$\frac{ng}{i}\left(\overset{\text{RP } i\text{-}n}{(\quad)} \right) - \frac{1}{n}.$$

This, then, is the equivalent annual cost of the declining series in Column (3), Table B.1. The equivalent annual cost of the series in Column (4), Table B.1, is obviously ng, and the

$$\left. \begin{array}{l} \text{Equivalent annual cost of} \\ \text{increasing series in Column} \\ \text{(2), Table B.1} \end{array} \right\} = ng - \frac{ng}{i}\left(\overset{\text{RP } i\text{-}n}{(\quad)} - \frac{1}{n} \right).$$

Substituting $(\overset{\text{RS } i\text{-}n}{\quad}) + i$ for its equal, $(\overset{\text{RP } i\text{-}n}{\quad})$, results in

$$\frac{g}{i}\left(1 - n(\overset{\text{RS } i\text{-}n}{\quad}) \right).$$

The general expression for equivalent annual cost can now be written for the conditions covered by Table 12.6 and shown in Column I.

Let Q = operating cost, first year;

g = annual increase in operating costs;

P = first cost of asset;

L = salvage cost of asset;

and

equiv. ann. cost, $C = (P - L)(\overset{\text{RP } i\text{-}n}{\quad}) + Li + Q + \frac{g}{i}\left((1 - n(\overset{\text{RS } i\text{-}n}{\quad}) \right).$

This expression is not readily differentiated and solved for n to determine the life of minimum cost. However, for practical purposes a series of useful curves can readily be plotted. First, let $r = g \div (P - L)$, and arrange the equation as follows:

$$C = (Q + Li) + \left[(P - L)(\overset{RP\ i\text{-}n}{}) + \frac{r(P - L)}{i}\left(1 - n(\overset{RS\ i\text{-}n}{}) \right) \right]$$

$$= (Q + Li) + (P - L)\left[(\overset{RP\ i\text{-}n}{}) + \frac{r}{i}\left(1 - n(\overset{RS\ i\text{-}n}{}) \right) \right].$$

A series of curves is next plotted to obtain values of the quantity in the right-hand bracket. One curve will be needed for each value of r desired for each interest rate. A sheet of five or six curves for each interest rate to be considered will be adequate for most purposes.

Values read from the curves are multiplied by $(P - L)$, and the result added to $Q + Li$ to find the total equivalent annual cost, C. The work of this method is simplified if the value of L is 0.

The basing of replacement comparisons, on the assumption that annual comparative costs will rise at a constant rate, appears to have two limitations. First, it seems doubtful that many situations meet the condition that the combined effect of physical impairment and obsolescence increase at a reasonably constant rate. Secondly, the rate of increase in physical impairment and obsolescence is estimated with difficulty. The idea of a rate of increase of cost seems to be a much more difficult concept to use than the concept of an annual cost.

There appears to be little in day to day observation that leads to familiarity with and proficiency in making estimates of rates of increase of comparative costs where this approach would be applicable.

The general effect of obsolescence is to shorten the optimum life of assets subject to replacement. But unless care is exercised in the application of replacement equations, the inclusion of obsolescence may have a reverse effect. This comes about because inclusion of obsolescence as a cost will tend to shorten the optimum life and increase the equivalent annual cost of the asset over its optimum life. This increase in the equivalent annual cost due to including obsolescence makes it more difficult for a possible replacement to "prove in." In many cases this increases the likelihood that the present asset will be continued in use. Unless care is exercised this may happen in turn to succeeding assets, thus increasing the life span in use. The root of the trouble is that the life span on which an asset "proves in" is merely an estimate, which is not used when it is being considered for replacement.

THE MAPI FORMULAS

The MAPI Formulas are replacement formulas, advocated by the Machinery and Allied Products Institute, which maintains offices in Chicago and Washington. These formulas are developed in *Dynamic Equipment Policy*[1] by George Terborgh, Director of Research of MAPI, and in the *MAPI Replacement Manual*.[2]

Sponsored as they are by an organization influential in the manufacture and use of tools in industry, and because of the attention that has been accorded them in the industrial press, the MAPI formulas merit the attention of persons interested in engineering economy.

The MAPI formulas are used to determine whether equipment should be replaced. They take into account capital costs, interest, operating costs, and costs associated with physical impairment and obsolescence.

Terborgh has introduced a few new terms. These will be explained as needed. The term *defender* is used to designate a present asset whose replacement is under consideration. The term *challenger* is an asset under consideration as a replacement for another asset, usually the present defender. The MAPI formulas can be concisely developed and explained on the basis of the tabulations in Table C.1.

In Column B, the P's are the first costs and Q, $Q - b$, $Q - 2b$, etc. are the first year operating costs of a succession of challengers; these

---

[1]George Terborgh, *Dynamic Equipment Policy* (New York: McGraw-Hill Book Company, Inc., 1949).

[2]*MAPI Replacement Manual* (Chicago: Machinery and Allied Products Institute, 1950).

Table C.1. COSTS OF THREE PLANS OF PROVIDING A SERVICE

Year number, A	Costs of available series of challengers, B	Costs of defender, C	Costs of challenger, D
1	$P + Q + 0$	$p + q + 0$	$P + Q + 0$
2	$P + Q - b$	$q + m'_c$	$Q + m'$
3	$P + Q - 2b$	$q + 2m'_c$	$Q + 2m'$
4	$P + Q - 3b$		$Q + 3m'$
5	$P + Q - 4b$		$Q + 4m'$
6	$P + Q - 5b$		$Q + 5m'$
7	$P + Q - 6b$		
8	etc.		

costs are assumed to have become available at one year intervals. The term b is a measure of improvement of an asset and represents a decrease in operating cost or an improvement of income (an income is treated as a negative cost). Column B represents total annual capital and operating costs that would result if a succession of assets were used for one year and then replaced. For simplicity of exposition the salvage value is taken to be zero. The plan of a yearly replacement in Column B takes full advantage of asset improvements as they develop but suffers the disadvantage of high capital costs.

Column C represents the costs associated with continuing to use a defender for three years. The term p represents the salvage value of the defender — the amount that would be received for the defender if it were retired at the beginning of the first year. For simplicity of exposition the defender's future salvage is taken to be zero. The annual costs are represented by q, $q + m'_c$, and $q + 2m'_c$, where m'_c represents costs associated with physical impairment.

Column D represents the costs associated with the acquisition and use of a challenger. Its first cost is represented by P and annual costs by Q, $Q + m'$, $+ Q + 2m'$, etc., of which m' represents costs arising from physical impairment. Again, for simplicity of exposition the asset is assumed to have zero salvage value for any life.

To take into account obsolescence and to simplify comparison of continuing with the defender or installing the defender, a second tabulation is given in Table C.2. Table C.2 is the result of subtracting Q and adding b, $2b$, $3b$, etc., to Columns B, C, and D of Table C.1, year-by-year.

Table C.2. COMPARATIVE COSTS OF THREE PLANS OF PROVIDING A SERVICE

Year number, A	Comparative costs of available series of challengers, B	Comparative costs of defender, C	Comparative costs of challenger, D
1	P	$p + q - Q + 0$	$P + 0$
2	P	$+ q - Q + m'_c + b$	$+ m' + b$
3	P	$+ q - Q + 2m'_c + 2b$	$+ 2m' + 2b$
4	P	$- Q + 2b$	$+ 3m' + 3b$
5	P	$- Q + 2b$	$+ 4m' + 4b$
6	P	$- Q + 2b$	$+ 5m' + 5b$

From the pattern of comparative costs in Column D, the life for minimum comparative cost can be found by the method explained with an example not involving interest in Chapter 12. Where interest is involved, the method explained in Appendix B is applicable if $m' + b$ is replaced by g.

The general expression for cost of the challenger as in Column D, Table C.2 is

$$\text{equiv. ann. cost, } C = (P - L)(\overset{\text{RP } i\text{-}n}{}) + Li + \frac{g}{i}\left(1 - n(\overset{\text{RS } i\text{-}n}{})\right)$$

or

$$C = (P - L)\frac{i(1 + i)^n}{(1 + i)^n - 1} + Li + \frac{g}{i} - \frac{ng}{i}\frac{i}{(1 + i)^n - 1}$$

where L = salvage value of asset on retirement (zero value for conditions in Table C.1). The minimum value of this equation is the *adverse minimum* in Terborgh's terminology.

At this point it is well to mention assumptions which are basic to the MAPI formulas. These are,

1. The future challengers will have the same adverse minimum as the present one.

2. The present challenger will accumulate operating inferiority at a constant rate over its service life.

The condition of the first of these assumptions will be met if the first costs of successive available replacements are equal to P, if the basic annual operating cost of each successive annually available replacement is equal to Q, $Q - b$, $Q - 2b$, $Q - 3b$, etc., and if the annual operating costs of successive available replacements increase at a constant rate of m'. The condition of the assumption can be met in other ways that are not simply represented. For example, year to year variations in the first costs of assets could be compensated for appropriate variations in the other quantities involved.

The conditions of the second assumption are met by the increase of the challenger's comparative operating cost at the constant annual rate of $m' + b = g$ as shown in Column D, Table C.2.

For purposes of illustration assume that the minimum value of the equation for the asset in Column D, Table C.2, occurs for a life of six years. If the original challenger in Column D were retired at the end of six years, it would be replaced by a challenger whose first cost would be P and whose first year operating cost would be $Q - 6b$ and whose operating cost in succeeding years would increase at the rate of m' per year. If Columns B and D, Table C.1, were now extended and if Q were subtracted and $6b$ were added to Columns B and D in Table C.1, the result in Columns B and C of Table C.2 would be a repetition of the pattern of costs shown for years 1 to 6. Thus a life of six years would be the life of the second asset for minimum cost. For the conditions given, replacement at six-year intervals forever would result in minimum equivalent cost.

The adverse minimum of the defender may be determined by using the equation for finding the adverse minimum of the challenger by substituting p for P, l = salvage value at retirement for L and $g' = m' + b$ for g. However, this method is not usually used because if the adverse minimum of a defender has not been reached at the time replacement is being considered, it will be reached shortly. For short periods of time it is simpler to calculate the adverse minimum of a defender on the basis of estimated annual operating costs and losses in salvage value in successive years.

For illustration, assume that the minimum cost of the defender in Column C, Table C.2, occurs for a life of 3 years. Then the equivalent annual cost of the three annual costs of $q - Q$ will be equal to $q - Q$. In Terborgh's terminology $q - Q$ is the *defender's next year's operating inferiority*. Thus the minimum comparative equivalent annual cost of the defender will be the defender's next year's operating inferiority plus the defender's adverse minimum. When this quantity is greater than the challenger's adverse minimum, replacement is indicated. When the defender's cost is rising at the time comparison is made, the defender's adverse minimum will drop out, leaving only the defender's next year's operating inferiority to compare with the defender's adverse minimum.

Because of the difficulty of differentiating the expression

$$C = (P - L)\frac{i(1 + i)^n}{(1 + i)^n - 1} + Li + \frac{g}{i} - \frac{ng}{i}\frac{i}{(1 + i)^n - 1}$$

approximations are used by Terborgh.

The expression for the zero salvage value case is

$$C = \frac{P}{n} + \frac{Pi}{2} + g\frac{(n - 1)}{2} \quad \text{and} \quad \frac{dc}{dn} = -\frac{P}{n^2} + \frac{g}{2} = 0$$

$$n = \sqrt{\frac{2P}{g}}.$$

This value of n results in

$$C_{\min} = \sqrt{2Pg} + \frac{Pi - g}{2} = \text{adverse minimum.}$$

This method of arriving at the adverse minimum requires that the terms P, i, and g be known or estimated. The life, n, need not be known but it may be calculated.

Terborgh advances a second method for determining the adverse minimum which requires a life estimated but eliminates the need for estimating g.

For the zero salvage value case, begin with

$$C = P\frac{i(1 + i)^n}{(1 + i)^n - 1} + \frac{g}{i} - \frac{ng}{i}\frac{i}{(1 + i)^n - 1}.$$

If C is plotted against n as an abscissa, the expression will result in a curve that is concave upward. Thus there are two points on the curve, one of which is on either side of the curve's minimum point for which the ordinates will be equal. Assume that the first point to the right of the axis occurs for an abscissa equal to n and that the second point occurs for an abscissa equal to $n + 1$.

Now the equivalent annual cost of the first n years of the asset's life will be equal to C when $n = n$. Operating costs for the year, n, equal $(n - 1)g$. To continue with the asset through the year $(n + 1)$ will give rise to additional operating costs but to no additional capital costs. The additional operating costs will be equal to ng. Thus ng is the equivalent annual cost of operating during the year $n + 1$. The equivalent annual cost of the first n years can now be set equal to the equivalent annual cost of the year $n + 1$ and

$$C = ng \quad \text{and} \quad g = \frac{C}{n}.$$

This value of g can now be substituted in the above equation to find the value of C for given values of n, P and i, and

$$C = P \frac{i(1 + i)^n}{(1 + i)^n - 1} + \frac{C}{ni} - \frac{nC}{ni} \frac{i}{(1 + i)^n - 1}$$

solving for C results in

$$C_{\min} = \frac{Pni^2}{ni - 1 + \dfrac{1}{(1 + i)^n}}.$$

The method above of arriving at the adverse minimum requires that the terms P, i, and n be known or estimated. The value of g may be calculated if desired. A version of the above expression for taking salvage values into account is given in the *MAPI Replacement Manual*.

Because of the way in which this equation is derived, it does not give a true minimum but only a result that will give equivalent annual costs that are equal for the years, n and $n + 1$, on either side of the minimum. The expression gives values that are a few per cent less than the true minimum, the amount of deviation being most for small values of n. Nearly true minimum values will be obtained if $(n - \frac{1}{2})$ is substituted for all values of n in the above expression.

Persons interested in the replacement problem will find the philosophy, concepts and procedures developed in the two publications which have been quoted both interesting and provocative.

INTEREST TABLES

The computational time required in the solution of engineering economy problems can be reduced by the use of tabular values corresponding to the interest formulas developed in the text. Use of the recommended factor designations during the formulation of the problem simplifies the substitution of the appropriate tabular value. Reduction of the resulting expression to a numerical answer may be accomplished by hand, by a slide rule, or by a desk calculator.

Individual tabular values are given to a number of decimal places sufficient for most practical applications. Since the end result of an engineering economy study is based on estimated quantities and will be used in decision making, the analysis does not need to be accurate to a great many decimal places. In order to develop results with a degree of accuracy beyond that which may be obtained by the use of tabular values it will be necessary to directly use the formulas and employ logarithmic operations. Of course, the formulas may be used where their direct application will be more convenient than the use of tabular values.

If the magnitude of the problem requires the use of an electronic digital computer, the continuous compounding formulas lend themselves more readily to programming than do the annual compounding expressions. The burdensome portions of the formulas, involving powers of e, are easily reduced by the use of standard subroutines.

	Single Payment		Equal-Payment Series			
	Compound-amount factor	Present-worth factor	Compound-amount factor	Sinking-fund factor	Present-worth factor	Capital-recovery factor
n	SP i-n ( )	PS i-n ( )	SR i-n ( )	RS i-n ( )	PR i-n ( )	RP i-n ( )
1	1.020	0.98039	1.000	1.00000	0.98039	1.02000
2	1.040	0.96117	2.020	0.49505	1.94156	0.51505
3	1.061	0.94232	3.060	0.32675	2.88388	0.34675
4	1.082	0.92385	4.122	0.24262	3.80773	0.26262
5	1.104	0.90573	5.204	0.19216	4.71346	0.21216
6	1.126	0.88797	6.308	0.15853	5.60143	0.17853
7	1.149	0.87056	7.434	0.13451	6.47199	0.15451
8	1.172	0.85349	8.583	0.11651	7.32548	0.13651
9	1.195	0.83676	9.755	0.10252	8.16224	0.12252
10	1.219	0.82035	10.950	0.09133	8.98258	0.11133
11	1.243	0.80426	12.169	0.08218	9.78685	0.10218
12	1.268	0.78849	13.412	0.07456	10.57534	0.09456
13	1.294	0.77303	14.680	0.06812	11.34837	0.08812
14	1.319	0.75788	15.974	0.06260	12.10625	0.08260
15	1.346	0.74301	17.293	0.05783	12.84926	0.07783
16	1.373	0.72845	18.639	0.05365	13.57771	0.07365
17	1.400	0.71416	20.012	0.04997	14.29187	0.06997
18	1.428	0.70016	21.412	0.04670	14.99203	0.06670
19	1.457	0.68643	22.841	0.04378	15.67846	0.06378
20	1.486	0.67297	24.297	0.04116	16.35143	0.06116
21	1.516	0.65978	25.783	0.03878	17.01121	0.05878
22	1.546	0.64684	27.299	0.03663	17.65805	0.05663
23	1.577	0.63416	28.845	0.03467	18.29220	0.05467
24	1.608	0.62172	30.422	0.03287	18.91392	0.05287
25	1.641	0.60953	32.030	0.03122	19.52346	0.05122
26	1.673	0.59758	33.671	0.02970	20.12104	0.04970
27	1.707	0.58586	35.344	0.02829	20.70690	0.04829
28	1.741	0.57437	37.051	0.02699	21.28127	0.04699
29	1.776	0.56311	38.792	0.02578	21.84438	0.04578
30	1.811	0.55207	40.568	0.02465	22.39646	0.04465
35	2.000	0.50003	49.994	0.02000	24.99862	0.04000
40	2.208	0.45289	60.402	0.01656	27.35548	0.03656
45	2.438	0.41020	71.893	0.01391	29.49016	0.03391
50	2.692	0.37153	84.579	0.01182	31.42361	0.03182
55	2.972	0.33650	98.587	0.01014	33.17479	0.03014
60	3.281	0.30478	114.052	0.00877	34.76088	0.02877
70	4.000	0.25003	149.978	0.00667	37.49862	0.02667
80	4.875	0.20511	193.772	0.00516	39.74451	0.02516
90	5.943	0.16826	247.157	0.00405	41.58693	0.02405
100	7.245	0.13803	312.232	0.00320	43.09835	0.02320

Table D.2. 3% INTEREST FACTORS FOR ANNUAL COMPOUNDING INTEREST

	Single Payment		Equal-Payment Series			
n	Compound-amount factor	Present-worth factor	Compound-amount factor	Sinking-fund factor	Present-worth factor	Capital-recovery factor
	SP *i-n* ( )	PS *i-n* ( )	SR *i-n* ( )	RS *i-n* ( )	PR *i-n* ( )	RP *i-n* ( )
1	1.030	0.97087	1.000	1.00000	0.97087	1.03000
2	1.061	0.94260	2.030	0.49261	1.91347	0.52261
3	1.093	0.91514	3.091	0.32353	2.82861	0.35353
4	1.126	0.88849	4.184	0.23903	3.71710	0.26903
5	1.159	0.86261	5.309	0.18835	4.57971	0.21835
6	1.194	0.83748	6.468	0.15460	5.41719	0.18460
7	1.230	0.81309	7.662	0.13051	6.23028	0.16051
8	1.267	0.78941	8.892	0.11246	7.01969	0.14246
9	1.305	0.76642	10.159	0.09843	7.78611	0.12843
10	1.344	0.74409	11.464	0.08723	8.53020	0.11723
11	1.384	0.72242	12.808	0.07808	9.25263	0.10808
12	1.426	0.70138	14.192	0.07046	9.95401	0.10046
13	1.469	0.68095	15.618	0.06403	10.63496	0.09403
14	1.513	0.66112	17.086	0.05853	11.29608	0.08853
15	1.558	0.64186	18.599	0.05377	11.93794	0.08377
16	1.605	0.62317	20.157	0.04961	12.56111	0.07961
17	1.653	0.60502	21.762	0.04595	13.16612	0.07595
18	1.702	0.58739	23.414	0.04271	13.75352	0.07271
19	1.754	0.57029	25.117	0.03981	14.32380	0.06981
20	1.806	0.55368	26.870	0.03722	14.87748	0.06722
21	1.860	0.53755	28.677	0.03487	15.41503	0.06487
22	1.916	0.52189	30.537	0.03275	15.93692	0.06275
23	1.974	0.50669	32.453	0.03081	16.44361	0.06081
24	2.033	0.49193	34.426	0.02905	16.93555	0.05905
25	2.094	0.47761	36.459	0.02743	17.41315	0.05743
26	2.157	0.46369	38.553	0.02594	17.87685	0.05594
27	2.221	0.45019	40.710	0.02456	18.32704	0.05456
28	2.288	0.43708	42.931	0.02329	18.76411	0.05329
29	2.357	0.42435	45.219	0.02211	19.18846	0.05211
30	2.427	0.41199	47.575	0.02102	19.60045	0.05102
35	2.814	0.35538	60.462	0.01654	21.48722	0.04654
40	3.262	0.30656	75.401	0.01326	23.11478	0.04326
45	3.782	0.26444	92.720	0.01079	24.51872	0.04079
50	4.384	0.22811	112.797	0.00887	25.72977	0.03887
55	5.082	0.19677	136.072	0.00735	26.77443	0.03735
60	5.892	0.16973	163.054	0.00613	27.67557	0.03613
70	7.918	0.12630	230.594	0.00434	29.12342	0.03434
80	10.641	0.09398	321.363	0.00311	30.20077	0.03311
90	14.300	0.06993	443.349	0.00226	31.00241	0.03226
100	19.219	0.05203	607.288	0.00165	31.59891	0.03165

Table D.3. 4% INTEREST FACTORS FOR ANNUAL COMPOUNDING INTEREST

n	Single Payment		Equal-Payment Series			
	Compound-amount factor	Present-worth factor	Compound-amount factor	Sinking-fund factor	Present-worth factor	Capital-recovery factor
	SP *i-n* ( )	PS *i-n* ( )	SR *i-n* ( )	RS *i-n* ( )	PR *i-n* ( )	RP *i-n* ( )
1	1.040	0.96154	1.000	1.00000	0.96154	1.04000
2	1.082	0.92456	2.040	0.49020	1.88609	0.53020
3	1.125	0.88900	3.122	0.32035	2.77509	0.36035
4	1.170	0.85480	4.246	0.23549	3.62990	0.27549
5	1.217	0.82193	5.416	0.18463	4.45182	0.22463
6	1.265	0.79031	6.633	0.15076	5.24214	0.19076
7	1.316	0.75992	7.898	0.12661	6.00205	0.16661
8	1.369	0.73069	9.214	0.10853	6.73275	0.14853
9	1.423	0.70259	10.583	0.09449	7.43533	0.13449
10	1.480	0.67556	12.006	0.08329	8.11090	0.12329
11	1.539	0.64958	13.486	0.07415	8.76048	0.11415
12	1.601	0.62460	15.026	0.06655	9.38507	0.10655
13	1.665	0.60057	16.627	0.06014	9.98565	0.10014
14	1.732	0.57748	18.292	0.05467	10.56312	0.09467
15	1.801	0.55526	20.024	0.04994	11.11839	0.08994
16	1.873	0.53391	21.825	0.04582	11.65230	0.08582
17	1.948	0.51337	23.698	0.04220	12.16567	0.08220
18	2.026	0.49363	25.645	0.03899	12.65930	0.07899
19	2.107	0.47464	27.671	0.03614	13.13394	0.07614
20	2.191	0.45639	29.778	0.03358	13.59033	0.07358
21	2.279	0.43883	31.969	0.03128	14.02916	0.07128
22	2.370	0.42196	34.248	0.02920	14.45112	0.06920
23	2.465	0.40573	36.618	0.02731	14.85684	0.06731
24	2.563	0.39012	39.083	0.02559	15.24696	0.06559
25	2.666	0.37512	41.646	0.02401	15.62208	0.06401
26	2.772	0.36069	44.312	0.02257	15.98277	0.06257
27	2.883	0.34682	47.084	0.02124	16.32959	0.06124
28	2.999	0.33348	49.968	0.02001	16.66306	0.06001
29	3.119	0.32065	52.966	0.01888	16.98372	0.05888
30	3.243	0.30832	56.085	0.01783	17.29203	0.05783
35	3.946	0.25342	73.652	0.01358	18.66461	0.05358
40	4.801	0.20829	95.026	0.01052	19.79277	0.05052
45	5.841	0.17120	121.029	0.00826	20.72004	0.04826
50	7.107	0.14071	152.667	0.00655	21.48218	0.04655
55	8.646	0.11566	191.159	0.00523	22.10861	0.04523
60	10.520	0.09506	237.991	0.00420	22.62349	0.04420
70	15.572	0.06422	364.291	0.00275	23.39452	0.04275
80	23.050	0.04338	551.245	0.00181	23.91539	0.04181
90	34.119	0.02931	827.984	0.00121	24.26728	0.04121
100	50.505	0.01980	1237.624	0.00081	24.50500	0.04081

Table D.4. 5% INTEREST FACTORS FOR ANNUAL COMPOUNDING INTEREST

n	Single Payment		Equal-Payment Series			
	Compound-amount factor	Present-worth factor	Compound-amount factor	Sinking-fund factor	Present-worth factor	Capital-recovery factor
	SP i-n ( )	PS i-n ( )	SR i-n ( )	RS i-n ( )	PR i-n ( )	RP i-n ( )
1	1.050	0.95238	1.000	1.00000	0.95238	1.05000
2	1.103	0.90703	2.050	0.48780	1.85941	0.53780
3	1.158	0.86384	3.153	0.31721	2.72325	0.36721
4	1.216	0.82270	4.310	0.23201	3.54595	0.28201
5	1.276	0.78353	5.526	0.18097	4.32948	0.23097
6	1.340	0.74622	6.802	0.14702	5.07569	0.19702
7	1.407	0.71068	8.142	0.12282	5.78637	0.17282
8	1.477	0.67684	9.549	0.10742	6.46321	0.15472
9	1.551	0.64461	11.027	0.09069	7.10782	0.14069
10	1.629	0.61391	12.578	0.07950	7.72174	0.12950
11	1.710	0.58468	14.207	0.07039	8.30641	0.12039
12	1.796	0.55684	15.917	0.06283	8.86325	0.11283
13	1.886	0.53032	17.713	0.05646	9.39357	0.10646
14	1.980	0.50507	19.599	0.05102	9.89864	0.10102
15	2.079	0.48102	21.579	0.04634	10.37966	0.09634
16	2.183	0.45811	23.657	0.04227	10.83777	0.09227
17	2.292	0.43630	25.840	0.03870	11.27407	0.08870
18	2.407	0.41552	28.132	0.03555	11.68959	0.08555
19	2.527	0.39573	30.539	0.03275	12.08532	0.08275
20	2.653	0.37689	33.066	0.03024	12.46221	0.08024
21	2.786	0.35894	35.719	0.02800	12.82115	0.07800
22	2.925	0.34185	38.505	0.02597	13.16300	0.07597
23	3.072	0.32557	41.430	0.02414	13.48857	0.07414
24	3.225	0.31007	44.502	0.02247	13.79864	0.07247
25	3.386	0.29530	47.727	0.02095	14.09394	0.07095
26	3.556	0.28124	51.113	0.01956	14.37519	0.06956
27	3.733	0.26785	54.669	0.01829	14.64303	0.06829
28	3.920	0.25509	58.403	0.01712	14.89813	0.06712
29	4.116	0.24295	62.323	0.01605	15.14107	0.06605
30	4.322	0.23138	66.439	0.01505	15.37245	0.06505
35	5.516	0.18129	90.320	0.01107	16.37419	0.06107
40	7.040	0.14205	120.800	0.00828	17.15909	0.05828
45	8.985	0.11130	159.700	0.00626	17.77407	0.05626
50	11.467	0.08720	209.348	0.00478	18.25593	0.05478
55	14.636	0.06833	272.713	0.00367	18.63347	0.05367
60	18.679	0.05354	353.584	0.00283	18.92929	0.05283
70	30.426	0.03287	588.529	0.00170	19.34268	0.05170
80	49.561	0.02018	971.229	0.00103	19.59646	0.05103
90	80.730	0.01239	1594.608	0.00063	19.75226	0.05063
100	131.501	0.00760	2610.026	0.00038	19.84791	0.05038

Table D.5. 6% INTEREST FACTORS FOR ANNUAL COMPOUNDING INTEREST

	Single Payment		Equal-Payment Series			
	Compound-amount factor	Present-worth factor	Compound-amount factor	Sinking-fund factor	Present-worth factor	Capital-recovery factor
n	SP i-n ( )	PS i-n ( )	SR i-n ( )	RS i-n ( )	PR i-n ( )	RP i-n ( )
1	1.060	0.94340	1.000	1.00000	0.94340	1.06000
2	1.124	0.89000	2.060	0.48544	1.83339	0.54544
3	1.191	0.83962	3.184	0.31411	2.67301	0.37411
4	1.262	0.79209	4.375	0.22859	3.46510	0.28859
5	1.338	0.74726	5.637	0.17740	4.21236	0.23740
6	1.419	0.70496	6.975	0.14336	4.91732	0.20336
7	1.504	0.66506	8.394	0.11914	5.58238	0.17914
8	1.594	0.62741	9.897	0.10104	6.20979	0.16104
9	1.689	0.59190	11.491	0.08702	6.80169	0.14702
10	1.791	0.55839	13.181	0.07587	7.36009	0.13587
11	1.898	0.52679	14.972	0.06679	7.88687	0.12679
12	2.012	0.49697	16.870	0.05928	8.38384	0.11928
13	2.133	0.46884	18.882	0.05296	8.85268	0.11296
14	2.261	0.44230	21.015	0.04758	9.29498	0.10758
15	2.397	0.41727	23.276	0.04296	9.71225	0.10296
16	2.540	0.39365	25.673	0.03895	10.10590	0.09895
17	2.693	0.37136	28.213	0.03544	10.47726	0.09544
18	2.854	0.35034	30.906	0.03236	10.82760	0.09236
19	3.026	0.33051	33.760	0.02962	11.15812	0.08962
20	3.207	0.31180	36.786	0.02718	11.46992	0.08718
21	3.400	0.29416	39.993	0.02500	11.76408	0.08500
22	3.604	0.27751	43.392	0.02305	12.04158	0.08305
23	3.820	0.26180	46.996	0.02128	12.30338	0.08128
24	4.049	0.24698	50.816	0.01968	12.55036	0.07968
25	4.292	0.23300	54.865	0.01823	12.78336	0.07823
26	4.549	0.21981	59.156	0.01690	13.00317	0.07690
27	4.822	0.20737	63.706	0.01570	13.21053	0.07570
28	5.112	0.19563	68.528	0.01459	13.40616	0.07459
29	5.418	0.18456	73.640	0.01358	13.59072	0.07358
30	5.743	0.17411	79.058	0.01265	13.76483	0.07265
35	7.686	0.13011	111.435	0.00897	14.49825	0.06897
40	10.286	0.09722	154.762	0.00646	15.04630	0.06646
45	13.765	0.07265	212.744	0.00470	15.45583	0.06470
50	18.420	0.05429	290.336	0.00344	15.76186	0.06344
55	24.650	0.04057	394.172	0.00254	15.99054	0.06254
60	32.988	0.03031	533.128	0.00188	16.16143	0.06188
70	59.076	0.01693	967.932	0.00103	16.38454	0.06103
80	105.796	0.00945	1746.600	0.00057	16.50913	0.06057
90	189.465	0.00528	3141.075	0.00032	16.57870	0.06032
100	339.302	0.00295	5638.369	0.00018	16.61755	0.06018

Table D.6. 7% INTEREST FACTORS FOR ANNUAL COMPOUNDING INTEREST

	Single Payment		Equal-Payment Series			
n	Compound-amount factor	Present-worth factor	Compound-amount factor	Sinking-fund factor	Present-worth factor	Capital-recovery factor
	SP i-n ( )	PS i-n ( )	SR i-n ( )	RS i-n ( )	PR i-n ( )	RP i-n ( )
1	1.070	0.93458	1.000	1.00000	0.93458	1.07000
2	1.145	0.87344	2.070	0.48309	1.80802	0.55309
3	1.225	0.81630	3.215	0.31105	2.62432	0.38105
4	1.311	0.76290	4.440	0.22523	3.38721	0.29523
5	1.403	0.71299	5.751	0.17389	4.10020	0.24389
6	1.501	0.66634	7.153	0.13980	4.76654	0.20980
7	1.606	0.62275	8.654	0.11555	5.38929	0.18555
8	1.718	0.58201	10.260	0.09747	5.97130	0.16747
9	1.838	0.54393	11.978	0.08349	6.51523	0.15349
10	1.967	0.50835	13.816	0.07238	7.02358	0.14238
11	2.105	0.47509	15.784	0.06336	7.49867	0.13336
12	2.252	0.44401	17.888	0.05590	7.94269	0.12590
13	2.410	0.41496	20.141	0.04965	8.35765	0.11965
14	2.579	0.38782	22.550	0.04434	8.74547	0.11434
15	2.759	0.36245	25.129	0.03979	9.10791	0.10979
16	2.952	0.33873	27.888	0.03586	9.44665	0.10586
17	3.159	0.31657	30.840	0.03243	9.76322	0.10243
18	3.380	0.29586	33.999	0.02941	10.05909	0.09941
19	3.617	0.27651	37.379	0.02675	10.33559	0.09675
20	3.870	0.25842	40.995	0.02439	10.59401	0.09439
21	4.141	0.24151	44.865	0.02229	10.83553	0.09229
22	4.430	0.22571	49.006	0.02041	11.06124	0.09041
23	4.741	0.21095	53.436	0.01871	11.27219	0.08871
24	5.072	0.19715	58.177	0.01719	11.46933	0.08719
25	5.427	0.18425	63.249	0.01581	11.65358	0.08581
26	5.807	0.17220	68.676	0.01456	11.82578	0.08456
27	6.214	0.16093	74.484	0.01343	11.98671	0.08343
28	6.649	0.15040	80.698	0.01239	12.13711	0.08239
29	7.114	0.14056	87.347	0.01145	12.27767	0.08145
30	7.612	0.13137	94.461	0.01059	12.40904	0.08059
35	10.677	0.09366	138.237	0.00723	12.94767	0.07723
40	14.974	0.06678	199.635	0.00501	13.33171	0.07501
45	21.002	0.04761	285.749	0.00350	13.60552	0.07350
50	29.457	0.03395	406.529	0.00246	13.80075	0.07246
55	41.315	0.02420	575.929	0.00174	13.93994	0.07174
60	57.946	0.01726	813.520	0.00123	14.03918	0.07123
70	113.989	0.00877	1614.134	0.00062	14.16039	0.07062
80	224.234	0.00446	3189.062	0.00031	14.22201	0.07031
90	441.103	0.00227	6287.185	0.00016	14.25333	0.07016
100	867.716	0.00115	12381.661	0.00008	14.26925	0.07008

	Single Payment		Equal-Payment Series			
n	Compound-amount factor	Present-worth factor	Compound-amount factor	Sinking-fund factor	Present-worth factor	Capital-recovery factor
	SP i-n ( )	PS i-n ( )	SR i-n ( )	RS i-n ( )	PR i-n ( )	RP i-n ( )
1	1.080	0.92593	1.000	1.00000	0.92593	1.08000
2	1.166	0.85734	2.080	0.48077	1.78326	0.56077
3	1.260	0.79383	3.246	0.30803	2.57710	0.38803
4	1.360	0.73503	4.506	0.22192	3.31213	0.30192
5	1.469	0.68058	5.867	0.17046	3.99271	0.25046
6	1.587	0.63017	7.336	0.13632	4.62288	0.21632
7	1.714	0.58349	8.923	0.11207	5.20637	0.19207
8	1.851	0.54027	10.637	0.09401	5.74664	0.17401
9	1.999	0.50025	12.488	0.08008	6.24689	0.16008
10	2.159	0.46319	14.487	0.06903	6.71008	0.14903
11	2.332	0.42888	16.645	0.06008	7.13896	0.14008
12	2.518	0.39711	18.977	0.05270	7.53608	0.13270
13	2.720	0.36770	21.495	0.04652	7.90378	0.12652
14	2.937	0.34046	24.215	0.04130	8.24424	0.12130
15	3.172	0.31524	27.152	0.03683	8.55948	0.11683
16	3.426	0.29189	30.324	0.03298	8.85137	0.11298
17	3.700	0.27027	33.750	0.02963	9.12164	0.10963
18	3.996	0.25025	37.450	0.02670	9.37189	0.10670
19	4.316	0.23171	41.446	0.02413	9.60360	0.10413
20	4.661	0.21455	45.762	0.02185	9.81815	0.10185
21	5.034	0.19866	50.423	0.01983	10.01680	0.09983
22	5.437	0.18394	55.457	0.01803	10.20074	0.09803
23	5.871	0.17032	60.893	0.01642	10.37106	0.09642
24	6.341	0.15770	66.765	0.01498	10.52876	0.09498
25	6.848	0.14602	73.106	0.01368	10.67478	0.09368
26	7.396	0.13520	79.954	0.01251	10.80998	0.09251
27	7.988	0.12519	87.351	0.01145	10.93516	0.09145
28	8.627	0.11591	95.339	0.01049	11.05108	0.09049
29	9.317	0.10733	103.966	0.00962	11.15841	0.08962
30	10.063	0.09938	113.283	0.00883	11.25778	0.08883
35	14.785	0.06763	172.317	0.00580	11.65457	0.08580
40	21.725	0.04603	259.057	0.00386	11.92461	0.08386
45	31.920	0.03133	386.506	0.00259	12.10840	0.08259
50	46.902	0.02132	573.770	0.00174	12.23348	0.08174
55	68.914	0.01451	848.923	0.00118	12.31861	0.08118
60	101.257	0.00988	1253.213	0.00080	12.37655	0.08080
70	218.606	0.00457	2720.080	0.00037	12.44282	0.08037
80	471.955	0.00212	5886.935	0.00017	12.47351	0.08017
90	1018.915	0.00098	12723.937	0.00008	12.48773	0.08008
100	2199.761	0.00045	27484.515	0.00004	12.49432	0.08004

Table D.8. 9% INTEREST FACTORS FOR ANNUAL COMPOUNDING INTEREST

	Single Payment		Equal-Payment Series			
	Compound-amount factor	Present-worth factor	Compound-amount factor	Sinking-fund factor	Present-worth factor	Capital-recovery factor
n	SP i-n ( )	PS i-n ( )	SR i-n ( )	RS i-n ( )	PR i-n ( )	RP i-n ( )
1	1.090	0.91743	1.000	1.00000	0.91743	1.09000
2	1.188	0.84168	2.090	0.47847	1.75911	0.56847
3	1.295	0.77218	3.278	0.30505	2.53129	0.39505
4	1.412	0.70843	4.573	0.21867	3.23972	0.30867
5	1.539	0.64993	5.985	0.16709	3.88965	0.25709
6	1.677	0.59627	7.523	0.13292	4.48592	0.22292
7	1.828	0.54703	9.200	0.10869	5.03295	0.19869
8	1.993	0.50187	11.028	0.09067	5.53482	0.18067
9	2.172	0.46043	13.021	0.07680	5.99525	0.16680
10	2.367	0.42241	15.193	0.06582	6.41766	0.15582
11	2.580	0.38753	17.560	0.05695	6.80519	0.14695
12	2.813	0.35553	20.141	0.04965	7.16072	0.13965
13	3.066	0.32618	22.953	0.04357	7.48690	0.13357
14	3.342	0.29925	26.019	0.03843	7.78615	0.12843
15	3.642	0.27454	29.361	0.03406	8.06069	0.12406
16	3.970	0.25187	33.003	0.03030	8.31256	0.12030
17	4.328	0.23107	36.974	0.02705	8.54363	0.11705
18	4.717	0.21199	41.301	0.02421	8.75562	0.11421
19	5.142	0.19449	46.018	0.02173	8.95011	0.11173
20	5.604	0.17843	51.160	0.01955	9.12855	0.10955
21	6.109	0.16370	56.765	0.01762	9.29224	0.10762
22	6.659	0.15018	62.873	0.01590	9.44243	0.10590
23	7.258	0.13778	69.532	0.01438	9.58021	0.10438
24	7.911	0.12640	76.790	0.01302	9.70661	0.10302
25	8.623	0.11597	84.701	0.01181	9.82258	0.10181
26	9.399	0.10639	93.324	0.01072	9.92897	0.10072
27	10.245	0.09761	102.723	0.00973	10.02658	0.09973
28	11.167	0.08955	112.968	0.00885	10.11613	0.09885
29	12.172	0.08215	124.135	0.00806	10.19828	0.09806
30	13.268	0.07537	136.308	0.00734	10.27365	0.09734
35	20.414	0.04899	215.711	0.00464	10.56682	0.09464
40	31.409	0.03184	337.882	0.00296	10.75736	0.09296
45	48.327	0.02069	525.859	0.00190	10.88120	0.09190
50	74.358	0.01345	815.084	0.00123	10.96168	0.09123
55	114.408	0.00874	1260.092	0.00079	11.01399	0.09079
60	176.031	0.00568	1944.792	0.00051	11.04799	0.09051
70	416.730	0.00240	4619.223	0.00022	11.08445	0.09022
80	986.552	0.00101	10950.573	0.00009	11.09985	0.09009
90	2335.526	0.00043	25939.182	0.00004	11.10635	0.09004
100	5529.041	0.00018	61422.674	0.00002	11.10910	0.09002

Table D.9. 10% INTEREST FACTORS FOR ANNUAL COMPOUNDING INTEREST

	Single Payment		Equal-Payment Series			
	Compound-amount factor	Present-worth factor	Compound-amount factor	Sinking-fund factor	Present-worth factor	Capital-recovery factor
n	SP i-n ( )	PS i-n ( )	SR i-n ( )	RS i-n ( )	PR i-n ( )	RP i-n ( )
1	1.100	0.90909	1.000	1.00000	0.90909	1.10000
2	1.210	0.82645	2.100	0.47619	1.73554	0.57619
3	1.331	0.75131	3.310	0.30211	2.48685	0.40211
4	1.464	0.68301	4.641	0.21547	3.16987	0.31547
5	1.611	0.62092	6.105	0.16380	3.79079	0.26380
6	1.772	0.56447	7.716	0.12961	4.35526	0.22961
7	1.949	0.51316	9.487	0.10541	4.86842	0.20541
8	2.144	0.46651	11.436	0.08744	5.33493	0.18744
9	2.358	0.42410	13.579	0.07364	5.75902	0.17364
10	2.594	0.38554	15.937	0.06275	6.14457	0.16275
11	2.853	0.35049	18.531	0.05396	6.49506	0.15396
12	3.138	0.31863	21.384	0.04676	6.81369	0.14676
13	3.452	0.28966	24.523	0.04078	7.10336	0.14078
14	3.797	0.26333	27.975	0.03575	7.36669	0.13575
15	4.177	0.23939	31.772	0.03147	7.60608	0.13147
16	4.595	0.21763	35.950	0.02782	7.82371	0.12782
17	5.054	0.19784	40.545	0.02466	8.02155	0.12466
18	5.560	0.17986	45.599	0.02193	8.20141	0.12193
19	6.116	0.16351	51.159	0.01955	8.36492	0.11955
20	6.727	0.14864	57.275	0.01746	8.51356	0.11746
21	7.400	0.13513	64.002	0.01562	8.64869	0.11562
22	8.140	0.12285	71.403	0.01401	8.77154	0.11401
23	8.954	0.11168	79.543	0.01257	8.88322	0.11257
24	9.850	0.10153	88.497	0.01130	8.98474	0.11130
25	10.835	0.09230	98.347	0.01017	9.07704	0.11017
26	11.918	0.08391	109.182	0.00916	9.16095	0.10916
27	13.110	0.07628	121.100	0.00826	9.23722	0.10826
28	14.421	0.06934	134.210	0.00745	9.30657	0.10745
29	15.863	0.06304	148.631	0.00673	9.36961	0.10673
30	17.449	0.05731	164.494	0.00608	9.42691	0.10608
35	28.102	0.03558	271.024	0.00369	9.64416	0.10369
40	45.259	0.02209	442.593	0.00226	9.77905	0.10226
45	72.890	0.01372	718.905	0.00139	9.86281	0.10139
50	117.391	0.00852	1163.908	0.00086	9.91481	0.10086
55	189.059	0.00529	1880.591	0.00053	9.94711	0.10053
60	304.482	0.00328	3034.816	0.00033	9.96716	0.10033
70	789.747	0.00127	7887.469	0.00013	9.98734	0.10013
80	2048.400	0.00049	20474.000	0.00005	9.99512	0.10005
90	5313.022	0.00019	53120.222	0.00002	9.99812	0.10002
100	13780.611	0.00007	137796.110	0.00001	9.99927	0.10001

Table D.10. EFFECTIVE INTEREST RATES CORRESPONDING TO NOMINAL RATE φ

φ	Semi-annually $\left(1+\dfrac{\varphi}{2}\right)^2 - 1$	Quarterly $\left(1+\dfrac{\varphi}{4}\right)^4 - 1$	Monthly $\left(1+\dfrac{\varphi}{12}\right)^{12} - 1$	Weekly $\left(1+\dfrac{\varphi}{52}\right)^{52} - 1$	Daily $\left(1+\dfrac{\varphi}{365}\right)^{365} - 1$	Continuously $\left(1+\dfrac{\varphi}{\infty}\right)^{\infty} - 1$
1	1.0025	1.0038	1.0046	1.0049	1.0050	1.0050
2	2.0100	2.0151	2.0184	2.0197	2.0200	2.0201
3	3.0225	3.0339	3.0416	3.0444	3.0451	3.0455
4	4.0400	4.0604	4.0741	4.0793	4.0805	4.0811
5	5.0625	5.0945	5.1161	5.1244	5.1261	5.1271
6	6.0900	6.1364	6.1678	6.1797	6.1799	6.1837
7	7.1225	7.1859	7.2290	7.2455	7.2469	7.2508
8	8.1600	8.2432	8.2999	8.3217	8.3246	8.3287
9	9.2025	9.3083	9.3807	9.4085	9.4132	9.4174
10	10.2500	10.3813	10.4713	10.5060	10.5126	10.5171
11	11.3025	11.4621	11.5718	11.6144	11.6231	11.6278
12	12.3600	12.5509	12.6825	12.7336	12.7447	12.7497
13	13.4225	13.6476	13.8032	13.8644	13.8775	13.8828
14	14.4900	14.7523	14.9341	15.0057	15.0217	15.0274
15	15.5625	15.8650	16.0755	16.1582	16.1773	16.1834
16	16.6400	16.9859	17.2270	17.3221	17.3446	17.3511
17	17.7225	18.1148	18.3891	18.4974	18.5235	18.5305
18	18.8100	19.2517	19.5618	19.6843	19.7142	19.7217
19	19.9025	20.3971	20.7451	20.8828	20.9169	20.9250
20	21.0000	21.5506	21.9390	22.0931	22.1316	22.1403
21	22.1025	22.7124	23.1439	23.3153	23.3584	23.3678
22	23.2100	23.8825	24.3596	24.5494	24.5976	24.6077
23	24.3225	25.0609	25.5863	25.7957	25.8492	25.8600
24	25.4400	26.2477	26.8242	27.0542	27.1133	27.1249
25	26.5625	27.4429	28.0731	28.3250	28.3901	28.4025
26	27.6900	28.6466	29.3333	29.6090	29.6796	29.6930
27	28.8225	29.8588	30.6050	30.9049	30.9821	30.9964
28	29.9600	31.0796	31.8880	32.2135	32.2976	32.3130
29	31.1025	32.3089	33.1826	33.5350	33.6264	33.6428
30	32.2500	33.5469	34.4889	34.8693	34.9684	34.9859
31	33.4025	34.7936	35.8068	36.2168	36.3238	36.3425
32	34.5600	36.0489	37.1366	37.5775	37.6928	37.7128
33	35.7225	37.3130	38.4784	38.9515	39.0756	39.0968
34	36.8900	38.5859	39.8321	40.3389	40.4722	40.4948
35	38.0625	39.8676	41.1979	41.7399	41.8827	41.9068

	Single Payment		Equal-Payment Series			
n	Compound-amount factor	Present-worth factor	Compound-amount factor	Sinking-fund factor	Present-worth factor	Capital-recovery factor
	SP φ-n ( )	PS φ-n ( )	SR φ-n ( )	RS φ-n ( )	PR φ-n ( )	RP φ-n ( )
1	1.020	0.98020	1.000	1.00000	0.98020	1.02020
2	1.041	0.96079	2.020	0.49500	1.94099	0.51520
3	1.062	0.94176	3.061	0.32669	2.88276	0.34689
4	1.083	0.92312	4.123	0.24255	3.80588	0.26275
5	1.105	0.90484	5.206	0.19208	4.71071	0.21228
6	1.127	0.88692	6.311	0.15845	5.59764	0.17865
7	1.150	0.86936	7.439	0.13443	6.46700	0.15463
8	1.174	0.85214	8.589	0.11643	7.31914	0.13663
9	1.197	0.83527	9.763	0.10243	8.15442	0.12263
10	1.221	0.81873	10.960	0.09124	8.97315	0.11144
11	1.246	0.80252	12.181	0.08209	9.77567	0.10229
12	1.271	0.78663	13.427	0.07448	10.56230	0.09468
13	1.297	0.77105	14.699	0.06803	11.33335	0.08824
14	1.323	0.75578	15.995	0.06252	12.08914	0.08272
15	1.350	0.74082	17.319	0.05774	12.82996	0.07794
16	1.377	0.72615	18.668	0.05357	13.55611	0.07377
17	1.405	0.71177	20.046	0.04989	14.26788	0.07009
18	1.433	0.69768	21.451	0.04662	14.96556	0.06682
19	1.462	0.68386	22.884	0.04370	15.64942	0.06390
20	1.492	0.67032	24.346	0.04107	16.31974	0.06128
21	1.522	0.65705	25.838	0.03870	16.97679	0.05890
22	1.553	0.64404	27.360	0.03655	17.62082	0.05675
23	1.584	0.63128	28.913	0.03459	18.25211	0.05479
24	1.616	0.61878	30.497	0.03279	18.87089	0.05299
25	1.649	0.60653	32.113	0.03114	19.47743	0.05134
26	1.682	0.59452	33.762	0.02962	20.07195	0.04982
27	1.716	0.58275	35.444	0.02821	20.65470	0.04842
28	1.751	0.57121	37.160	0.02691	21.22591	0.04711
29	1.786	0.55990	38.910	0.02570	21.78581	0.04590
30	1.822	0.54881	40.696	0.02457	22.33462	0.04477
35	2.014	0.49659	50.183	0.01993	24.91992	0.04013
40	2.226	0.44933	60.666	0.01648	27.25919	0.03668
45	2.460	0.40657	72.253	0.01384	29.37585	0.03404
50	2.718	0.36788	85.058	0.01176	31.29108	0.03196
55	3.004	0.33287	99.210	0.01008	33.02406	0.03028
60	3.320	0.30119	114.850	0.00871	34.59212	0.02891
70	4.055	0.24660	151.238	0.00661	37.29478	0.02681
80	4.953	0.20190	195.682	0.00511	39.50753	0.02531
90	6.050	0.16530	249.966	0.00400	41.31918	0.02420
100	7.389	0.13534	316.270	0.00316	42.80243	0.02336

Table D.12. 3% INTEREST FACTORS FOR CONTINUOUS COMPOUNDING INTEREST

n	Single Payment		Equal-Payment Series			
	Compound-amount factor	Present-worth factor	Compound-amount factor	Sinking-fund factor	Present-worth factor	Capital-recovery factor
	SP φ-n ( )	PS φ-n ( )	SR φ-n ( )	RS φ-n ( )	PR φ-n ( )	RP φ-n ( )
1	1.030	0.97045	1.000	1.00000	0.97045	1.03045
2	1.062	0.94176	2.030	0.49250	1.91221	0.52295
3	1.094	0.91393	3.092	0.32338	2.82614	0.35384
4	1.127	0.88692	4.186	0.23886	3.71307	0.26932
5	1.162	0.86071	5.314	0.18818	4.57377	0.21864
6	1.197	0.83527	6.476	0.15442	5.40905	0.18488
7	1.234	0.81058	7.673	0.13033	6.21963	0.16078
8	1.271	0.78663	8.907	0.11228	7.00626	0.14273
9	1.310	0.76338	10.178	0.09825	7.76964	0.12871
10	1.350	0.74082	11.488	0.08705	8.51046	0.11750
11	1.391	0.71892	12.838	0.07790	9.22938	0.10835
12	1.433	0.69768	14.229	0.07028	9.92706	0.10073
13	1.477	0.67706	15.662	0.06385	10.60412	0.09430
14	1.522	0.65705	17.139	0.05835	11.26117	0.08880
15	1.568	0.63763	18.661	0.05359	11.89879	0.08404
16	1.616	0.61878	20.229	0.04943	12.51758	0.07989
17	1.665	0.60050	21.845	0.04578	13.11808	0.07623
18	1.716	0.58275	23.511	0.04253	13.70082	0.07299
19	1.768	0.56553	25.227	0.03964	14.26635	0.07010
20	1.822	0.54881	26.995	0.03704	14.81516	0.06750
21	1.878	0.53259	28.817	0.03470	15.34775	0.06516
22	1.935	0.51685	30.695	0.03258	15.86461	0.06303
23	1.994	0.50158	32.630	0.03065	16.36618	0.06110
24	2.054	0.48675	34.623	0.02888	16.85294	0.05934
25	2.117	0.47237	36.678	0.02726	17.32530	0.05772
26	2.181	0.45841	38.795	0.02578	17.78371	0.05623
27	2.248	0.44486	40.976	0.02440	18.22857	0.05486
28	2.316	0.43171	43.224	0.02314	18.66028	0.05359
29	2.387	0.41895	45.540	0.02196	19.07923	0.05241
30	2.460	0.40657	47.927	0.02086	19.48580	0.05132
35	2.858	0.34994	60.998	0.01639	21.34536	0.04685
40	3.320	0.30119	76.183	0.01313	22.94590	0.04358
45	3.857	0.25924	93.826	0.01066	24.32349	0.04111
50	4.482	0.22313	114.324	0.00875	25.50920	0.03920
55	5.207	0.19205	138.140	0.00724	26.52974	0.03769
60	6.050	0.16530	165.810	0.00603	27.40814	0.03649
70	8.166	0.12246	235.307	0.00425	28.81491	0.03470
80	11.023	0.09072	329.120	0.00304	29.85707	0.03349
90	14.880	0.06721	455.753	0.00219	30.62912	0.03265
100	20.086	0.04979	626.690	0.00160	31.20107	0.03205

	Single Payment		Equal-Payment Series			
n	Compound-amount factor	Present-worth factor	Compound-amount factor	Sinking-fund factor	Present-worth factor	Capital-recovery factor
	SP φ-n ( )	PS φ-n ( )	SR φ-n ( )	RS φ-n ( )	PR φ-n ( )	RP φ-n ( )
1	1.041	0.96079	1.000	1.00000	0.96079	1.04081
2	1.083	0.92312	2.041	0.49000	1.88391	0.53081
3	1.127	0.88692	3.124	0.32009	2.77083	0.36090
4	1.174	0.85214	4.252	0.23521	3.62297	0.27602
5	1.221	0.81873	5.425	0.18433	4.44170	0.22514
6	1.271	0.78663	6.647	0.15046	5.22832	0.19127
7	1.323	0.75578	7.918	0.12630	5.98411	0.16711
8	1.377	0.72615	9.241	0.10821	6.71026	0.14903
9	1.433	0.69768	10.618	0.09418	7.40793	0.13499
10	1.492	0.67032	12.051	0.08298	8.07825	0.12379
11	1.553	0.64404	13.543	0.07384	8.72229	0.11465
12	1.616	0.61878	15.096	0.06624	9.34107	0.10705
13	1.682	0.59452	16.712	0.05984	9.93559	0.10065
14	1.751	0.57121	18.394	0.05437	10.50680	0.09518
15	1.822	0 54881	20.145	0.04964	11.05561	0.09045
16	1.896	0.52729	21.967	0.04552	11.58290	0.08633
17	1.974	0.50662	23.863	0.04191	12.08952	0.08272
18	2.054	0.48675	25.837	0.03870	12.57627	0.07951
19	2.138	0.46767	27.892	0.03585	13.04394	0.07666
20	2.226	0.44933	30.030	0.03330	13.49327	0.07411
21	2.316	0.43171	32.255	0.03100	13.92498	0.07181
22	2.411	0.41478	34.572	0.02893	14.33976	0.06974
23	2.509	0.39852	36.983	0.02704	14.73828	0.06785
24	2.612	0.38289	39.492	0.02532	15.12117	0.06613
25	2.718	0.36788	42.104	0.02375	15.48905	0.06456
26	2.829	0.35345	44.822	0.02231	15.84251	0.06312
27	2.945	0.33960	47.651	0.02099	16.18210	0.06180
28	3.065	0.32628	50.596	0.01976	16.50838	0.06058
29	3.190	0.31349	53.661	0.01864	16.82187	0.05945
30	3.320	0.30119	56.851	0.01759	17.12306	0.05840
35	4.055	0.24660	74.863	0.01336	18.46087	0.05417
40	4.953	0.20190	96.862	0.01032	19.55618	0.05113
45	6.050	0.16530	123.733	0.00808	20.45295	0.04889
50	7.389	0.13534	156.553	0.00639	21.18715	0.04720
55	9.025	0.11080	196.639	0.00509	21.78827	0.04590
60	11.023	0.09072	245.601	0.00407	22.28043	0.04488
70	16.445	0.06081	378.445	0.00264	23.01327	0.04345
80	24.533	0.04076	576.625	0.00173	23.50451	0.04255
90	36.598	0.02732	872.275	0.00115	23.83380	0.04196
100	54.598	0.01832	1313.333	0.00076	24.05452	0.04157

Table D.14. 5% INTEREST FACTORS FOR CONTINUOUS COMPOUNDING INTEREST

	Single Payment		Equal-Payment Series			
n	Compound-amount factor	Present-worth factor	Compound-amount factor	Sinking-fund factor	Present-worth factor	Capital-recovery factor
	SP φ-n ( )	PS φ-n ( )	SR φ-n ( )	RS φ-n ( )	·PR φ-n ( )	RP φ-n ( )
1	1.051	0.95123	1.000	1.00000	0.95123	1.05127
2	1.105	0.90484	2.051	0.48750	1.85607	0.53877
3	1.162	0.86071	3.156	0.31681	2.71677	0.36808
4	1.221	0.81873	4.318	0.23157	3.53551	0.28284
5	1.284	0.77880	5.540	0.18052	4.31431	0.23179
6	1.350	0.74082	6.824	0.14655	5.05512	0.19782
7	1.419	0.70469	8.174	0.12235	5.75981	0.17362
8	1.492	0.67032	9.593	0.10425	6.43013	0.15552
9	1.568	0.63763	11.084	0.09022	7.06776	0.14149
10	1.649	0.60653	12.653	0.07903	7.67429	0.13031
11	1.733	0.57695	14.301	0.06992	8.25124	0.12119
12	1.822	0.54881	16.035	0.06236	8.80005	0.11364
13	1.916	0.52205	17.857	0.05600	9.32210	0.10727
14	2.014	0.49659	19.772	0.05058	9.81868	0.10185
15	2.117	0.47237	21.786	0.04590	10.29105	0.09717
16	2.226	0.44933	23.903	0.04184	10.74038	0.09311
17	2.340	0.42741	26.129	0.03827	11.16779	0.08954
18	2.460	0.40657	28.468	0.03513	11.57436	0.08640
19	2.586	0.38674	30.928	0.03233	11.96110	0.08360
20	2.718	0.36788	33.514	0.02984	12.32898	0.08111
21	2.858	0.34994	36.232	0.02760	12.67892	0.07887
22	3.004	0.33287	39.090	0.02558	13.01179	0.07685
23	3.158	0.31664	42.094	0.02376	13.32843	0.07503
24	3.320	0.30119	45.252	0.02210	13.62962	0.07337
25	3.490	0.28650	48.572	0.02059	13.91613	0.07186
26	3.669	0.27253	52.062	0.01921	14.18866	0.07048
27	3.857	0.25924	55.732	0.01794	14.44790	0.06921
28	4.055	0.24660	59.589	0.01678	14.69450	0.06805
29	4.263	0.23457	63.644	0.01571	14.92907	0.06698
30	4.482	0.22313	67.907	0.01473	15.15220	0.06600
35	5.755	0.17377	92.735	0.01078	16.11485	0.06205
40	7.389	0.13534	124.613	0.00802	16.86456	0.05930
45	9.488	0.10540	165.546	0.00604	17.44844	0.05731
50	12.182	0.08208	218.105	0.00458	17.90316	0.05586
55	15.643	0.06393	285.592	0.00350	18.25731	0.05477
60	20.086	0.04979	372.247	0.00269	18.53311	0.05396
70	33.115	0.03020	626.385	0.00160	18.91519	0.05287
80	54.598	0.01832	1045.387	0.00096	19.14693	0.05223
90	90.017	0.01111	1736.205	0.00058	19.28749	0.05185
100	148.413	0.00674	2875.171	0.00035	19.37275	0.05162

	Single Payment		Equal-Payment Series			
n	Compound-amount factor	Present-worth factor	Compound-amount factor	Sinking-fund factor	Present-worth factor	Capital-recovery factor
	SP φ-n ( )	PS φ-n ( )	SR φ-n ( )	RS φ-n ( )	PR φ-n ( )	RP φ-n ( )
1	1.062	0.94176	1.000	1.00000	0.94176	1.06184
2	1.127	0.88692	2.062	0.48500	1.82869	0.54684
3	1.197	0.83527	3.189	0.31354	2.66396	0.37538
4	1.271	0.78663	4.387	0.22797	3.45059	0.28971
5	1.350	0.74082	5.658	0.17675	4.19140	0.23858
6	1.433	0.69768	7.008	0.14278	4.88908	0.20454
7	1.522	0.65705	8.441	0.11847	5.54613	0.18031
8	1.616	0.61878	9.963	0.10037	6.16491	0.16221
9	1.716	0.58275	11.579	0.08636	6.74766	0.14820
10	1.822	0.54881	13.295	0.07522	7.29647	0.13705
11	1.935	0.51685	15.117	0.06615	7.81332	0.12799
12	2.054	0.48675	17.052	0.05864	8.30008	0.12048
13	2.181	0.45841	19.106	0.05234	8.75848	0.11418
14	2.316	0.43171	21.288	0.04698	9.19019	0.10881
15	2.460	0.40657	23.604	0.04237	9.59676	0.10420
16	2.612	0.38289	26.064	0.03837	9.97966	0.10020
17	2.773	0.36059	28.676	0.03487	10.34025	0.09671
18	2.945	0.33960	31.449	0.03180	10.67985	0.09363
19	3.127	0.31982	34.393	0.02908	10.99967	0.09091
20	3.320	0.30119	37.520	0.02665	11.30086	0.08849
21	3.525	0.28365	40.840	0.02449	11.58452	0.08632
22	3.743	0.26714	44.366	0.02254	11.85165	0.08438
23	3.975	0.25158	48.109	0.02079	12.10323	0.08262
24	4.221	0.23693	52.084	0.01920	12.34016	0.08104
25	4.482	0.22313	56.305	0.01776	12.56329	0.07960
26	4.759	0.21014	60.786	0.01645	12.77343	0.07829
27	5.053	0.19790	65.545	0.01526	12.97132	0.07709
28	5.366	0.18637	70.598	0.01416	13.15770	0.07600
29	5.697	0.17552	75.964	0.01316	13.33322	0.07500
30	6.050	0.16530	81.661	0.01225	13.49852	0.07408
35	8.166	0.12246	115.889	0.00863	14.19135	0.07047
40	11.023	0.09072	162.092	0.00617	14.70462	0.06801
45	14.880	0.06721	224.459	0.00446	15.08485	0.06629
50	20.086	0.04979	308.645	0.00324	15.36654	0.06508
55	27.113	0.03688	422.285	0.00237	15.57522	0.06420
60	36.598	0.02732	575.683	0.00174	15.72981	0.06357
70	66.686	0.01500	1062.258	0.00094	15.92917	0.06278
80	121.510	0.00823	1948.856	0.00051	16.03859	0.06235
90	221.406	0.00452	3564.342	0.00028	16.09864	0.06212
100	403.429	0.00248	6507.949	0.00015	16.13159	0.06199

Table D.16. 7% INTEREST FACTORS FOR CONTINUOUS COMPOUNDING INTEREST

n	Single Payment		Equal-Payment Series			
	Compound-amount factor	Present-worth factor	Compound-amount factor	Sinking-fund factor	Present-worth factor	Capital-recovery factor
	SP φ-n ( )	PS φ-n ( )	SR φ-n ( )	RS φ-n ( )	PR φ-n ( )	RP φ-n ( )
1	1.073	0.93239	1.000	1.00000	0.93239	1.07251
2	1.150	0.86936	2.073	0.48251	1.80175	0.55502
3	1.234	0.81058	3.223	0.31029	2.61234	0.38280
4	1.323	0.75578	4.456	0.22439	3.36812	0.29690
5	1.419	0.70469	5.780	0.17302	4.07281	0.24553
6	1.522	0.65705	7.199	0.13891	4.72985	0.21142
7	1.632	0.61263	8.721	0.11467	5.34248	0.18718
8	1.751	0.57121	10.353	0.09659	5.91369	0.16910
9	1.878	0.53259	12.104	0.08262	6.44628	0.15513
10	2.014	0.49659	13.981	0.07152	6.94287	0.14403
11	2.160	0.46301	15.995	0.06252	7.40588	0.13503
12	2.316	0.43171	18.155	0.05508	7.83759	0.12759
13	2.484	0.40252	20.471	0.04885	8.24011	0.12136
14	2.664	0.37531	22.955	0.04356	8.61542	0.11607
15	2.858	0.34994	25.620	0.03903	8.96536	0.11154
16	3.065	0.32628	28.478	0.03512	9.29164	0.10762
17	3.287	0.30422	31.542	0.03170	9.59586	0.10421
18	3.525	0.28365	34.829	0.02871	9.87952	0.10122
19	3.781	0.26448	38.355	0.02607	10.14399	0.09858
20	4.055	0.24660	42.136	0.02373	10.39059	0.09624
21	4.349	0.22993	46.191	0.02165	10.62052	0.09416
22	4.665	0.21438	50.540	0.01979	10.83490	0.09229
23	5.003	0.19989	55.205	0.01811	11.03478	0.09062
24	5.366	0.18637	60.208	0.01661	11.22116	0.08912
25	5.755	0.17377	65.573	0.01525	11.39493	0.08776
26	6.172	0.16203	71.328	0.01402	11.55696	0.08653
27	6.619	0.15107	77.500	0.01290	11.70803	0.08541
28	7.099	0.14086	84.119	0.01189	11.84889	0.08440
29	7.614	0.13134	91.218	0.01096	11.98022	0.08347
30	8.166	0.12246	98.833	0.01012	12.10268	0.08263
35	11.588	0.08629	146.030	0.00685	12.60142	0.07936
40	16.445	0.06081	213.006	0.00469	12.95288	0.07720
45	23.336	0.04285	308.049	0.00325	13.20055	0.07575
50	33.115	0.03020	442.922	0.00226	13.37507	0.07477
55	46.993	0.02128	634.315	0.00158	13.49806	0.07408
60	66.686	0.01500	905.916	0.00110	13.58473	0.07361
70	134.290	0.00745	1838.272	0.00054	13.68884	0.07305
80	270.426	0.00370	3715.806	0.00027	13.74054	0.07278
90	544.572	0.00184	7496.696	0.00013	13.76622	0.07264
100	1096.633	0.00091	15110.473	0.00007	13.77897	0.07257

	Single Payment		Equal-Payment Series			
	Compound-amount factor	Present-worth factor	Compound-amount factor	Sinking-fund factor	Present-worth factor	Capital-recovery factor
n	SP φ-n ( )	PS φ-n ( )	SR φ-n ( )	RS φ-n ( )	PR φ-n ( )	RP φ-n ( )
1	1.083	0.92312	1.000	1.00000	0.92312	1.08329
2	1.174	0.85214	2.083	0.48001	1.77526	0.56330
3	1.271	0.78663	3.257	0.30705	2.56189	0.39034
4	1.377	0.72615	4.528	0.22085	3.28804	0.30413
5	1.492	0.67032	5.905	0.16934	3.95836	0.25263
6	1.616	0.61878	7.397	0.13519	4.57714	0.21848
7	1.751	0.57121	9.013	0.11095	5.14835	0.19424
8	1.896	0.52729	10.764	0.09290	5.67564	0.17619
9	2.054	0.48675	12.660	0.07899	6.16239	0.16227
10	2.226	0.44933	14.715	0.06796	6.61172	0.15125
11	2.411	0.41478	16.940	0.05903	7.02650	0.14232
12	2.612	0.38289	19.351	0.05168	7.40940	0.13496
13	2.829	0.35345	21.963	0.04553	7.76285	0.12882
14	3.065	0.32628	24.792	0.04034	8.08913	0.12362
15	3.320	0.30119	27.857	0.03590	8.39032	0.11918
16	3.597	0.27804	31.177	0.03207	8.66836	0.11536
17	3.896	0.25666	34.774	0.02876	8.92502	0.11204
18	4.221	0.23693	38.670	0.02586	9.16195	0.10915
19	4.572	0.21871	42.890	0.02332	9.38066	0.10660
20	4.953	0.20190	47.463	0.02107	9.58256	0.10436
21	5.366	0.18637	52.416	0.01908	9.76893	0.10237
22	5.812	0.17204	57.781	0.01731	9.94098	0.10059
23	6.297	0.15882	63.594	0.01572	10.09979	0.09901
24	6.821	0.14661	69.890	0.01431	10.24640	0.09760
25	7.389	0.13534	76.711	0.01304	10.38174	0.09632
26	8.004	0.12493	84.100	0.01189	10.50667	0.09518
27	8.671	0.11533	92.105	0.01086	10.62199	0.09414
28	9.393	0.10646	100.776	0.00992	10.72845	0.09321
29	10.176	0.09827	110.169	0.00908	10.82672	0.09236
30	11.023	0.09072	120.345	0.00831	10.91744	0.09160
35	16.445	0.06081	185.439	0.00539	11.27654	0.08868
40	24.533	0.04076	282.547	0.00354	11.51724	0.08683
45	36.598	0.02732	427.416	0.00234	11.67859	0.08563
50	54.598	0.01832	643.535	0.00155	11.78675	0.08484
55	81.451	0.01228	965.946	0.00104	11.85925	0.08432
60	121.510	0.00823	1446.928	0.00069	11.90785	0.08398
70	270.426	0.00370	3234.912	0.00031	11.96226	0.08360
80	601.845	0.00166	7214.143	0.00014	11.98671	0.08343
90	1339.431	0.00075	16070.085	0.00006	11.99770	0.08335
100	2980.958	0.00034	35779.346	0.00003	12.00263	0.08332

Table D.18. 9% INTEREST FACTORS FOR CONTINUOUS COMPOUNDING INTEREST

	Single Payment		Equal-Payment Series			
	Compound-amount factor	Present-worth factor	Compound-amount factor	Sinking-fund factor	Present-worth factor	Capital-recovery factor
n	SP φ-n ( )	PS φ-n ( )	SR φ-n ( )	RS φ-n ( )	PR φ-n ( )	RP φ-n ( )
1	1.094	0.91393	1.000	1.00000	0.91393	1.09417
2	1.197	0.83527	2.094	0.47752	1.74920	0.57169
3	1.310	0.76338	3.291	0.30382	2.51258	0.39800
4	1.433	0.69768	4.601	0.21733	3.21026	0.31150
5	1.568	0.63763	6.035	0.16571	3.84788	0.25988
6	1.716	0.58275	7.603	0.13153	4.43063	0.22570
7	1.878	0.53259	9.319	0.10731	4.96322	0.20148
8	2.054	0.48675	11.197	0.08931	5.44998	0.18349
9	2.248	0.44486	13.251	0.07547	5.89483	0.16964
10	2.460	0.40657	15.499	0.06452	6.30140	0.15869
11	2.691	0.37158	17.959	0.05568	6.67298	0.14986
12	2.945	0.33960	20.650	0.04843	7.01258	0.14260
13	3.222	0.31037	23.594	0.04238	7.32294	0.13656
14	3.525	0.28365	26.816	0.03729	7.60660	0.13146
15	3.857	0.25924	30.342	0.03296	7.86584	0.12713
16	4.221	0.23693	34.199	0.02924	8.10277	0.12341
17	4.618	0.21654	38.420	0.02603	8.31930	0.12020
18	5.053	0.19790	43.038	0.02324	8.51720	0.11741
19	5.529	0.18087	48.091	0.02079	8.69807	0.11497
20	6.050	0.16530	53.620	0.01865	8.86336	0.11282
21	6.619	0.15107	59.670	0.01676	9.01444	0.11093
22	7.243	0.13807	66.289	0.01509	9.15251	0.10926
23	7.925	0.12619	73.532	0.01360	9.27869	0.10777
24	8.671	0.11533	81.457	0.01228	9.39402	0.10645
25	9.488	0.10540	90.128	0.01110	9.49942	0.10527
26	10.381	0.09633	99.616	0.01004	9.59574	0.10421
27	11.359	0.08804	109.997	0.00909	9.68378	0.10327
28	12.429	0.08046	121.356	0.00824	9.76424	0.10241
29	13.599	0.07353	133.784	0.00747	9.83777	0.10165
30	14.880	0.06721	147.383	0.00679	9.90498	0.10096
35	23.336	0.04285	237.178	0.00422	10.16358	0.09839
40	36.598	0.02732	378.004	0.00265	10.32847	0.09682
45	57.397	0.01742	598.863	0.00167	10.43361	0.09584
50	90.017	0.01111	945.238	0.00106	10.50065	0.09523
55	141.175	0.00708	1488.463	0.00067	10.54339	0.09485
60	221.406	0.00452	2340.409	0.00043	10.57065	0.09460
70	544.572	0.00184	5771.977	0.00017	10.59911	0.09435
80	1339.431	0.00075	14212.272	0.00007	10.61068	0.09424
90	3294.468	0.00030	34972.047	0.00003	10.61538	0.09420
100	8103.084	0.00012	86032.855	0.00001	10.61730	0.09419

	Single Payment		Equal-Payment Series			
n	Compound-amount factor	Present-worth factor	Compound-amount factor	Sinking-fund factor	Present-worth factor	Capital-recovery factor
	SP φ-n ( )	PS φ-n ( )	SR φ-n ( )	RS φ-n ( )	PR φ-n ( )	RP φ-n ( )
1	1.105	0.90484	1.000	1.00000	0.90484	1.10517
2	1.221	0.81873	2.105	0.47502	1.72357	0.58019
3	1.350	0.74082	3.327	0.30061	2.46439	0.40578
4	1.492	0.67032	4.676	0.21384	3.13471	0.31901
5	1.649	0.60653	6.168	0.16212	3.74124	0.26729
6	1.822	0.54881	7.817	0.12793	4.29005	0.23310
7	2.014	0.49659	9.639	0.10374	4.78663	0.20892
8	2.226	0.44933	11.653	0.08582	5.23596	0.19099
9	2.460	0.40657	13.878	0.07205	5.64253	0.17723
10	2.718	0.36788	16.338	0.06121	6.01041	0.16638
11	3.004	0.33287	19.056	0.05248	6.34328	0.15765
12	3.320	0.30119	22.060	0.04533	6.64448	0.15050
13	3.669	0.27253	25.381	0.03940	6.91701	0.14457
14	4.055	0.24660	29.050	0.03442	7.16361	0.13959
15	4.482	0.22313	33.105	0.03021	7.38674	0.13538
16	4.953	0.20190	37.587	0.02661	7.58863	0.13178
17	5.474	0.18268	42.540	0.02351	7.77132	0.12868
18	6.050	0.16530	48.014	0.02083	7.93662	0.12600
19	6.686	0.14957	54.063	0.01850	8.08619	0.12367
20	7.389	0.13534	60.749	0.01646	8.22152	0.12163
21	8.166	0.12246	68.138	0.01468	8.34398	0.11985
22	9.025	0.11080	76.305	0.01311	8.45478	0.11828
23	9.974	0.10026	85.330	0.01172	8.55504	0.11689
24	11.023	0.09072	95.304	0.01049	8.64576	0.11566
25	12.182	0.08208	106.327	0.00940	8.72784	0.11458
26	13.464	0.07427	118.509	0.00844	8.80211	0.11361
27	14.880	0.06721	131.973	0.00758	8.86932	0.11275
28	16.445	0.06081	146.853	0.00681	8.93013	0.11198
29	18.174	0.05502	163.297	0.00612	8.98515	0.11129
30	20.086	0.04979	181.472	0.00551	9.03494	0.11068
35	33.115	0.03020	305.364	0.00327	9.22121	0.10845
40	54.598	0.01832	509.629	0.00196	9.33418	0.10713
45	90.017	0.01111	846.405	0.00118	9.40271	0.10635
50	148.413	0.00674	1401.653	0.00071	9.44427	0.10588
55	244.692	0.00409	2317.104	0.00043	9.46947	0.10560
60	403.429	0.00248	3826.427	0.00026	9.48476	0.10543
70	1096.633	0.00091	10417.645	0.00010	9.49966	0.10527
80	2980.958	0.00034	28334.434	0.00004	9.50514	0.10521
90	8103.084	0.00012	77037.316	0.00001	9.50716	0.10518
100	22026.466	0.00005	209425.470	0.00000	9.50790	0.10518

Table D.20. FUNDS-FLOW CONVERSION FACTOR

φ	$\dfrac{e\varphi - 1}{\varphi}$ FFC φ ( )
1	1.005020
2	1.010065
3	1.015150
4	1.020270
5	1.025422
6	1.030608
7	1.035831
8	1.041088
9	1.046381
10	1.051709
11	1.057073
12	1.062474
13	1.067910
14	1.073384
15	1.078894
16	1.084443
17	1.090028
18	1.095652
19	1.101313
20	1.107014
21	1.112752
22	1.118530
23	1.124347
24	1.130204
25	1.136101
26	1.142038
27	1.148016
28	1.154035
29	1.160094
30	1.166196
31	1.172339
32	1.178524
33	1.184751
34	1.191022
35	1.197335
36	1.203692
37	1.210093
38	1.216538
39	1.223027
40	1.229561

Table D.21. GRADIENT CONVERSION FACTORS FOR ANNUAL COMPOUNDING INTEREST

$$\frac{1}{i} - \frac{n}{i} \left(\text{RS } i\text{-}n \right)$$

n	GCF 1%-n ( )	GCF 2%-n ( )	GCF 3%-n ( )	GCF 4%-n ( )	GCF 5%-n ( )
1	0.000000	0.000000	0.000000	0.000000	0.000000
2	0.497520	0.495050	0.492611	0.490197	0.487805
3	0.993370	0.986800	0.980297	0.973860	0.967487
4	1.487540	1.475274	1.463058	1.451002	1.439050
5	1.980200	1.960400	1.940910	1.921611	1.902523
6	2.471060	2.442250	2.413850	2.385714	2.357902
7	2.960270	2.920826	2.881856	2.843320	2.805225
8	3.447760	3.396086	3.344976	3.294437	3.244509
9	3.933710	3.868061	3.803188	3.739082	3.675786
10	4.417910	4.336732	4.256508	4.177269	4.099087
11	4.900480	4.802130	4.704946	4.609016	4.514445
12	5.381440	5.264243	5.148507	5.034351	4.921903
13	5.860750	5.723067	5.587209	5.453292	5.321503
14	6.338360	6.178613	6.021051	5.865864	5.713289
15	6.814300	6.630892	6.450052	6.272090	6.097314
16	7.288630	7.079899	6.874225	6.672004	6.473630
17	7.761300	7.525634	7.293578	7.065631	6.842293
18	8.232330	7.968104	7.708128	7.453006	7.203361
19	8.701650	8.407325	8.117887	7.834160	7.556897
20	9.169360	8.843283	8.522873	8.209129	7.902966
21	9.635410	9.275990	8.923102	8.577948	8.241634
22	10.099800	9.705462	9.318588	8.940657	8.572977
23	10.562570	10.131684	9.709353	9.297296	8.897063
24	11.023660	10.554681	10.095412	9.647904	9.213967
25	11.483120	10.974453	10.476784	9.992526	9.523772
26	11.940920	11.391000	10.853492	10.331204	9.826554
27	12.397080	11.804335	11.225555	10.663987	10.122396
28	12.851590	12.214460	11.592993	10.990921	10.411384
29	13.304450	12.621386	11.955827	11.312050	10.693602
30	13.755660	13.025118	12.314085	11.627428	10.969139
31	14.205240	13.425662	12.667784	11.937104	11.238086
32	14.653180	13.823029	13.016950	12.241130	11.500533
33	15.099460	14.217224	13.361610	12.539559	11.756572
34	15.544110	14.608256	13.701785	12.832447	12.006298
35	15.987110	14.996133	14.037502	13.119846	12.249806
36	16.428490	15.380864	14.368789	13.401812	12.487191
37	16.868210	15.762460	14.695672	13.678404	12.718553
38	17.306310	16.140925	15.018177	13.949679	12.943987
39	17.742780	16.516268	15.336335	14.215697	13.163594
40	18.177610	16.888503	15.650171	14.476514	13.377472

Table D.22. GRADIENT CONVERSION FACTORS FOR ANNUAL COMPOUNDING INTEREST

$$\frac{1}{i} - \frac{n}{i} \left(\quad \overset{RS\ i\text{-}n}{} \quad \right)$$

n	GCF 6%-n ( )	GCF 7%-n ( )	GCF 8%-n ( )	GCF 9%-n ( )	GCF 10%-n ( )
1	0.000000	0.000000	0.000000	0.000000	0.000000
2	0.485437	0.483092	0.480770	0.478469	0.476191
3	0.961176	0.954929	0.948744	0.942620	0.936556
4	1.427230	1.415536	1.403958	1.392504	1.381168
5	1.883634	1.864950	1.846473	1.828196	1.810126
6	2.330403	2.303216	2.276346	2.249792	2.223558
7	2.767582	2.730393	2.693666	2.657404	2.621616
8	3.195208	3.146542	3.098524	3.051166	3.004479
9	3.613332	3.551740	3.491033	3.431231	3.372352
10	4.022007	3.946072	3.871314	3.797768	3.725461
11	4.421295	4.329629	4.239503	4.150965	4.064054
12	4.811261	4.702517	4.595748	4.491023	4.388402
13	5.191977	5.064843	4.940207	4.818163	4.698792
14	5.563521	5.416726	5.273050	5.132618	4.995529
15	5.925976	5.758294	5.594460	5.434631	5.278933
16	6.279428	6.089680	5.904625	5.724461	5.549341
17	6.623972	6.411024	6.203745	6.002376	5.807097
18	6.959704	6.722473	6.492029	6.268653	6.052560
19	7.286726	7.024182	6.769688	6.523580	6.286095
20	7.605147	7.316307	7.036948	6.767450	6.508075
21	7.915074	7.599014	7.294034	7.000563	6.718878
22	8.216624	7.872471	7.541182	7.223224	6.918886
23	8.509914	8.136853	7.778627	7.435742	7.108483
24	8.795065	8.392335	8.006611	7.638429	7.288054
25	9.072201	8.639101	8.225382	7.831597	7.457982
26	9.341449	8.877332	8.435184	8.015563	7.618650
27	9.602942	9.107216	8.636268	8.190640	7.770437
28	9.856809	9.328943	8.828883	8.357141	7.913717
29	10.103186	9.542701	9.013281	8.515378	8.048859
30	10.342210	9.748684	9.189713	8.665661	8.176226
31	10.574019	9.947084	9.358428	8.808294	8.296174
32	10.798753	10.138096	9.519675	8.943579	8.409051
33	11.016552	10.321912	9.673702	9.071812	8.515196
34	11.227559	10.498727	9.820753	9.193286	8.614940
35	11.431916	10.668734	9.961072	9.308286	8.708604
36	11.629766	10.832127	10.094897	9.417091	8.796497
37	11.821253	10.989095	10.222464	9.519976	8.878922
38	12.006521	11.139829	10.344006	9.617206	8.956169
39	12.185714	11.284518	10.459750	9.709040	9.028517
40	12.358976	11.423349	10.569920	9.795730	9.096235

Table D.23. GRADIENT CONVERSION FACTORS FOR CONTINUOUS COMPOUNDING INTEREST

n	$\dfrac{1}{e^{\varphi} - 1} - \dfrac{n}{e^{n\varphi} - 1}$				
	GCF 1%-n ( )	GCF 2%-n ( )	GCF 3%-n ( )	GCF 4%-n ( )	GCF 5%-n ( )
1	0.000000	0.000000	0.000000	0.000000	0.000000
2	0.496978	0.495129	0.492512	0.489995	0.487498
3	0.992898	0.986729	0.980045	0.973334	0.966675
4	1.487237	1.475119	1.462558	1.450011	1.437547
5	1.979682	1.960097	1.940051	1.920044	1.900106
6	2.470436	2.441797	2.412590	2.383428	2.354390
7	2.959702	2.920125	2.880131	2.840196	2.800413
8	3.447217	3.395151	3.342684	3.290349	3.238207
9	3.933033	3.866846	3.800277	3.733898	3.667800
10	4.417172	4.335217	4.252910	4.170870	4.089225
11	4.899719	4.800255	4.700582	4.601279	4.502522
12	5.380572	5.261986	5.143310	5.025151	4.907735
13	5.859725	5.720417	5.581104	5.442508	5.304908
14	6.337228	6.175522	6.013973	5.853374	5.694091
15	6.813053	6.627325	6.441926	6.257779	6.075338
16	7.287281	7.075828	6.864980	6.655754	6.448706
17	7.759765	7.521024	7.283149	7.047327	6.814254
18	8.230670	7.962926	7.696447	7.432535	7.172046
19	8.699856	8.401542	8.104887	7.811411	7.522148
20	9.167413	8.836869	8.508485	8.183993	7.864631
21	9.633293	9.268920	8.907262	8.550320	8.199567
22	10.097488	9.697687	9.301230	8.910430	8.527031
23	10.560059	10.123193	9.690412	9.264368	8.847101
24	11.020951	10.545431	10.074826	9.612176	9.159859
25	11.480211	10.964414	10.454491	9.953900	9.465387
26	11.937812	11.380146	10.829429	10.289586	9.763772
27	12.393730	11.792631	11.199659	10.619282	10.055100
28	12.848023	12.201877	11.565206	10.943038	10.339463
29	13.300658	12.607893	11.926089	11.260905	10.616951
30	13.751628	13.010688	12.282337	11.572935	10.887658
31	14.200951	13.410264	12.633970	11.879181	11.151680
32	14.648635	13.806637	12.981015	12.179698	11.409114
33	15.094644	14.199805	13.323496	12.474542	11.660058
34	15.539027	14.589783	13.661438	12.763770	11.904613
35	15.981743	14.976579	13.994872	13.047439	12.142877
36	16.422830	15.360199	14.323822	13.325609	12.374955
37	16.862266	15.740654	14.648317	13.598339	12.600948
38	17.300062	16.117951	14.968385	13.865690	12.820960
39	17.736210	16.492104	15.284056	14.127724	13.035096
40	18.170717	16.863115	15.595359	14.384503	13.243460

n	$\dfrac{1}{e^\varphi - 1} - \dfrac{n}{e^{n\varphi} - 1}$				
	GCF 6%-n ( )	GCF 7%-n ( )	GCF 8%-n ( )	GCF 9%-n ( )	GCF 10%-n ( )
1	0.000000	0.000000	0.000000	0.000000	0.000000
2	0.485023	0.482504	0.480008	0.477515	0.475024
3	0.960039	0.953370	0.946717	0.940078	0.933445
4	1.425086	1.412617	1.400177	1.387755	1.375354
5	1.880199	1.860291	1.840438	1.820627	1.800863
6	2.325399	2.296445	2.267578	2.238801	2.210118
7	2.760730	2.721133	2.681690	2.642406	2.603296
8	3.186234	3.134433	3.082880	3.031594	2.980603
9	3.601967	3.536426	3.471270	3.406538	3.342273
10	4.007986	3.927205	3.846999	3.767431	3.688566
11	4.404359	4.306874	4.210218	4.114484	4.019766
12	4.791157	4.675545	4.561091	4.447926	4.336180
13	5.168458	5.033339	4.899796	4.768004	4.638136
14	5.536347	5.380388	5.226522	5.074979	4.925982
15	5.894912	5.716830	5.541470	5.369128	5.200079
16	6.244251	6.042812	5.844852	5.650738	5.460807
17	6.584463	6.358489	6.136888	5.920110	5.708557
18	6.915655	6.664020	6.417807	6.177553	5.943728
19	7.237936	6.959575	6.687848	6.423386	6.166730
20	7.551423	7.245327	6.947254	6.657936	6.377980
21	7.856235	7.521455	7.196278	6.881534	6.577897
22	8.152495	7.788144	7.435173	7.094517	6.766905
23	8.440330	8.045582	7.664202	7.297224	6.945426
24	8.719873	8.293962	7.883629	7.489998	7.113882
25	8.991256	8.533481	8.093720	7.673182	7.272696
26	9.254616	8.764337	8.294746	7.847119	7.422282
27	9.510095	8.986733	8.486975	8.012150	7.563051
28	9.757833	9.200873	8.670680	8.168614	7.695407
29	9.997976	9.406962	8.846131	8.316848	7.819748
30	10.230670	9.605207	9.013598	8.457183	7.936462
31	10.456062	9.795815	9.173351	8.589948	8.045928
32	10.674302	9.978993	9.325655	8.715463	8.148513
33	10.885541	10.154949	9.470776	8.834045	8.244577
34	11.089929	10.323891	9.608973	8.946002	8.334466
35	11.287619	10.486023	9.740504	9.051636	8.418515
36	11.478763	10.641551	9.865623	9.151240	8.497047
37	11.663514	10.790677	9.984579	9.245102	8.570373
38	11.842023	10.933603	10.097617	9.333497	8.638791
39	12.014444	11.070529	10.204975	9.416695	8.702589
40	12.180927	11.201649	10.306887	9.494957	8.762039

APPENDIX **E**

SELECTED REFERENCES

Barish, N. N., *Economic Analysis* (New York: McGraw-Hill Book Company, Inc., 1962).

Barnard, Chester I., *The Functions of the Executive* (Cambridge, Mass.: Harvard University Press, 1938).

Barnes, Ralph M., *Motion and Time Study* (New York: John Wiley & Sons, Inc., 1953).

Bowman, E. H. and R. B. Fetter, *Analysis for Production Management* (Homewood, Ill.: Richard D. Irwin, Inc., 1961).

Buffa, E. S., *Modern Production Management* (New York: John Wiley & Sons, Inc., 1961).

Buffa, E. S., *Models for Production and Operations Management* (New York: John Wiley & Sons, Inc., 1963).

Bullinger, C. E., *Engineering Economy* (New York: McGraw-Hill Book Company, Inc., 1958).

Churchman, C. W., R. L. Ackoff, and E. L. Arnoff, *Introduction to Operations Research* (New York: John Wiley & Sons, Inc., 1957).

Coppock, J. D., *Economics of the Business Firm* (New York: McGraw-Hill Book Company, Inc., 1959).

Dean, J., *Managerial Economics* (Englewood Cliffs, N. J.: Prentice-Hall, Inc., 1951).

DeGarmo, E. P., *Engineering Economy* (New York: The Macmillan Company, 1960).

Eidmann, Frank L., *Economic Control of Engineering and Manufacturing* (New York: McGraw-Hill Book Company, Inc., 1931).

Grant, E. L., *Basic Accounting and Cost Accounting* (New York: McGraw-Hill Book Company, Inc., 1956).

Grant, E. L. and W. G. Ireson, *Principles of Engineering Economy* (New York: The Ronald Press Company, 1960).

Ireson, W. G. and E. L. Grant, *Handbook of Industrial Engineering and Management* (Englewood Cliffs, N. J.: Prentice-Hall, Inc., 1955).

Kurtz, Edwin B., *The Science of Valuation and Depreciation* (New York: The Ronald Press Company, Inc., 1937).

Marston, Anson, and Thomas R. Agg, *Engineering Valuation* (New York: McGraw-Hill Book Company, Inc., 1936).

Marston, A., R. Winfrey, and J. C. Hempstead, *Engineering Valuation and Depreciation* (New York: McGraw-Hill Book Company, Inc., 1953).

Maynard, H. B., *Industrial Engineering Handbook* (New York: McGraw-Hill Book Company, Inc., 1956).

Miller, D. W. and M. K. Starr, *Executive Decisions and Operations Research* (Englewood Cliffs, N. J.: Prentice-Hall, Inc., 1960).

Morris, W. T., *Engineering Economy* (Homewood, Ill.: Richard D. Irwin, Inc., 1960).

Peters, M. S., *Plant Design and Economics for Chemical Engineers* (New York: McGraw-Hill Book Company, Inc., 1958).

Sasieni, M., A. Yaspan, and L. Friedman, *Operations Research: Methods and Problems* (New York: John Wiley & Sons, Inc., 1959).

Schweyer, H. E., *Process Engineering Economics* (New York: McGraw-Hill Book Company, Inc., 1955).

Simon, H. A., *Administrative Behavior* (New York: The Macmillan Company, 1957).

Specthrie, S. W., *Industrial Accounting* (Englewood Cliffs, N. J.: Prentice-Hall, Inc., 1959).

Spencer, M. H. and L. Siegelman, *Managerial Economics* (Homewood, Ill.: Richard D. Irwin, Inc., 1959).

Terborgh, G., *Business Investment Policy* (Washington, D. C.: Machinery and Allied Products Institute, 1958).

Terborgh, G., *Dynamic Equipment Policy* (New York: McGraw-Hill Book Company, Inc., 1949).

Tucker, H. and M. C. Leager, *Highway Economics* (Scranton, Pa.: International Textbook Company, 1942).

Tyler, C. and C. H. Winter, Jr., *Chemical Engineering Economics* (New York: McGraw-Hill Book Company, Inc., 1959).

INDEX